THE OLD FARMER'S ALMANAC

CALCULATED ON A NEW AND IMPROVED PLAN FOR THE YEAR OF OUR LORD

Being Leap Year and (until July 1) 156th year of Canadian Confederation

FITTED FOR OTTAWA, WITH SPECIAL CORRECTIONS
AND CALCULATIONS TO ANSWER FOR ALL THE CANADIAN PROVINCES.

Containing, besides the large number of Astronomical Calculations and
the Farmer's Calendar for every month in the year, a variety of
NEW, USEFUL, & ENTERTAINING MATTER.

ESTABLISHED IN 1792
BY ROBERT B. THOMAS (1766–1846)

Rest not! Life is sweeping by,
Go and dare before you die;
Something mighty and sublime
Leave behind to conquer time.

–Johann Wolfgang von Goethe, German writer (1749–1832)

Cover design registered
U.S. Trademark Office

Copyright © 2023 by Yankee Publishing Incorporated,
A 100% Employee-Owned Company

ISSN 0078-4516

Library of Congress
Card No. 56-29681

Cover illustration by Steven Noble • Original wood engraving (above) by Randy Miller

The Old Farmer's Almanac • Almanac.ca
P.O. Box 520, Dublin, NH 03444 • 603-563-8111

CONTENTS

12 16 20

2024 TRENDS
Facts to Ponder and Forecasts to Watch For   6

192

30

VERY *LUCKY* 13

Hello, friends! Since its start in 1792, this Almanac has had only 13 editors. This is about to change, as yours truly, number 13, steps aside after nearly 23 years.

Our founder and first editor, Robert B. Thomas (depicted on the cover), stated in his first edition that his mission (and hence that of every ensuing editor) was to be "useful, with a pleasant degree of humor." I will leave you to judge whether my contributions have been practical and amusing, but we all must acknowledge that this oldest continuously published North American periodical owes its longevity also to a considerable degree of luck—as do I.

One of my first assignments was to read every edition. In so doing, I saw how each of my predecessors had made his mark. I learned, for example, that in 1938—for reasons known only to himself—Roger Scaife, aka number 10, replaced the full weather forecasts with weather "averages." He needed no small amount of luck for the publication to survive his unintended impact, as sales of copies dropped precipitously.

I thought that I had a good idea in 2005, when I transposed the weather forecasts (usually in the back) with the Calendar Pages (always up front). For giving the predictions prominence, I expected a windfall of reader appreciation. Instead, I raised a windstorm of criticism, such as: "The Almanac is a calendar; weather should never supplant the calendar! Don't you know your job?!" Luckily, circulation held steady and I endured the tempest.

Another idea that could have sunk me was eliminating the tide times and heights in 2018. Your requests to reinstate the data showed me once again how much you care about this annual—and that again I had been pushing my luck.

Fortune has thus favored me even from the beginning. In the moments between being offered this job and accepting it, I was told that if I had any fear about being number 13, arrangements could be made for someone to sit in for a while so that I could start as number 14 without qualm or trepidation. Luckily for me—and, I hope, for you—I declined that proposition. Thank you for your abiding loyalty, trust, enthusiasm, and generosity. Join me in a cheer to the years!

–J. S., June 2023

However, it is by our works and not our words that we would be judged. These, we hope, will sustain us in the humble though proud station we have so long held in the name of

Your obedient servant,

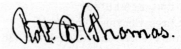

2024 TRENDS

ON THE FARM

Increased demand for farmland in high-growth areas of the U.S. is pricing farmers and ranchers off the land. They are struggling to find comparable acreage to lease to maintain the viability of their operations.

–Gary Joiner, spokesperson, Texas Farm Bureau

FARMERS NEED WORKERS

■ Labor shortages on the farm have become the biggest challenge in the industry. Strategically becoming an employer of choice has become increasingly important for farmers hoping to attract, hire, and keep the best employees.

–Sara Mann, Ph.D., professor, University of Guelph

BUZZWORD
Grow-cers: grocery stores that sell produce from on-site indoor farms

CUSTOMER CONNECTIONS

■ Farmers' on-farm shops are inviting other local producers to sell their meat and produce.

■ Farmers are growing flowers and creating wedding arrangements, offering "you pick" options, or hosting you-pick-and-arrange events.

–Caitlyn Lamm, spokesperson, Iowa Farm Bureau Federation

FARMERS' CHALLENGES

■ Being an agricultural producer is particularly stressful these days, given the high input

FOLLOW US:

costs and interest rates, the diseases that affect animals or plants, unpredictable weather events, and ongoing labor shortages.

–Cameron Newbigging, spokesperson, Agriculture and Agri-Food Canada

STRENGTH IN NUMBERS

Farmers are teaming up to navigate challenges:

■ Egg farmers are forming co-ops.

■ Volunteers are being trained to provide social and emotional support to farmers they know.

TECH TAKEOVERS

The use of drones in agriculture is expanding rapidly.
–Ty Higgins, spokesperson, Ohio Farm Bureau

Farm drones . . .
■ plant cover crops

■ apply herbicides when soil is too wet for conventional machinery

■ drop cover crop seeds into corn and

BY THE NUMBERS

$485: average cost to rent a chicken coop and two egg-laying hens for 6 months

$35,000: annual labor cost per acre for California strawberry growers

5,500: tons of unsold grocery store food (e.g., bruised fruit, stale bread) used as chicken feed in the U.S., 2022

soybean fields prior to harvest (giving them more time to grow)

Farm robots . . .
■ use lasers to eliminate weeds without disturbing soil
■ pick ripe strawberries
■ apply fertilizer

FORWARD THINKERS . . .

■ use precision agriculture, with sensors and data analysis to optimize production and reduce costs

■ farm vertically in controlled indoor environments near urban centers for year-round crop production

■ raise fish, crustaceans, and mollusks in indoor aquaculture systems
–Daniel Levine, director, The Avant-Guide Institute

"FARMERS" EVERYWHERE

■ Farmers are demonstrating apple cidering, beekeeping, and maple sugaring to library patrons.

■ People are loaning their yards to students, who grow food there and then donate it to the community and/or to schools for use in cooking classes.

(continued)

IN THE GARDEN

Due to long wait lists, there is pressure on local governments to expand their community garden programs.

–Kathy Jentz, co-author, The Urban Garden *(Cool Springs Press, 2022)*

TOP GARDENING PROJECTS

1. creating vegetable gardens
2. planting flowering shrubs
3. growing new varieties of edibles
4. planting fruit trees
5. adding container gardens

–Axiom 2023 Gardening Outlook Survey

COMING TO OUR SENSES

■ Gardeners want a wider array of sensory experiences, with plants that invite the sniffing and scrunching of aromatic leaves or soft textures. Lilac, lavender, and anise hyssop are making a comeback.

–Cheney Creamer, chair, Canadian Horticultural Therapy Association

BUZZWORD
Yard-sharing: landowners allow growers to use their property in exchange for free or discounted produce

MORE NATIVE PLANTS

Renewing native ecosystems has become a big priority in both home gardens and public green spaces.

■ *At home:* We're planting blends of native wildflower seeds.

■ *In public areas:* Gardens are being planted with native plants that provide flowers, fruit, and seeds as food for pollinators.

–Cheney Creamer

(continued)

FOLLOW US:

LEADER
IN LAND & LIFESTYLE
PROPERTIES

United Country is the leading country and lifestyle real estate company specializing in land, farms, ranches, horse property, certified organic properties, country homes, recreational land and some of the best properties in lifestyle real estate.

Browse through our catalog or visit our website to find properties nationwide and let United Country Real Estate help you

Find Your Freedom.

'PONDEROSA' LEMON

INDOOR EXOTICS

Gardeners are growing fruiting, rare, and tropical plants indoors in containers for visual interest and as conversation starters. Top picks . . .

- in hanging baskets, 'Cipo' sweet orange
- fruit-bearing 'Ponderosa' lemon tree
- 3-foot-tall, fruit-bearing 'Super Dwarf Cavendish' banana
- flowering ginger plants

–Randy Schultz, founder, HomeGardenandHomestead.com

LEAFY STANDOUTS

- Gardeners are planting with contrasting colors to make plants more visible in a sea of green.

–Chad Davis, director of Conservatories and Horticulture Design, Longwood Gardens

BEST CHOICES

- 'Blue Chiffon' rose of Sharon, 'Ghost' fern, 'Nightrider' hybrid Asiatic lily, Ocean Sunset series 'Orange Glow' ice plant

–Jung Seed Company

'GHOST' FERN

- ColorBloom series gerbera, 'Jupiter White' exacum, Hula series spreading begonia, AngelDance series angelonia, 'Big Blue' salvia, Solarscape series impatiens

–Ball Horticultural Company

BY THE NUMBERS

35% of gardeners have in-ground plots.

9% garden from balconies.

6% have indoor gardens.

–Axiom 2023 Gardening Outlook Survey

NEW VEGGIE VARIETIES

- 'Amish Gold' slicer tomato, 'Dragonfly' hybrid pepper, 'Kai Kai' hybrid winter squash, 'Tricked You' hybrid jalapeño

–Jung Seed Company

- 'Mochi' hybrid cherry tomato, 'Glow Stix Sunrise Mix' carrots, 'Bottle Rocket' cayenne pepper, Salanova series 'Red Tango' lettuce

–Johnny's Selected Seeds

'DRAGONFLY' PEPPER

EASY DOES IT

Robots are making garden chores easier by:

- locating and eliminating broadleaf weeds
- mowing the lawn

PEOPLE ARE TALKING ABOUT . . .

- ornamental and edible plants in the same containers

–Kathy Jentz

(continued)

■ embracing a "live and let live" philosophy toward native insects
–C. L. Fornari, founder, Gardenlady.com

IN LIEU OF LAWNS

There is a move away from turf-grass lawns toward more sustainable landscape choices.

■ *in dry climates:* succulents

■ *in wet climates:* clover or moss
–Kathy Jentz

LANTANA

ZINNIA

HELPING NATURE

■ *To feed butterflies:* We're dedicating space in home gardens to grow monarchs' food sources.
–Andrew Bunting, V.P. of horticulture, Pennsylvania Horticultural Society

■ *On behalf of bees:* We're choosing bee-friendly blooms: coneflowers, pentas, salvias, and zinnias.
–Dave Forehand, V.P. of gardens, Dallas Arboretum and Botanical Garden

WE'RE BUDGET-MINDED

■ Cost-conscious grocery shoppers are:
1. buying store brands
2. spending less on nonfood items
3. going to restaurants less frequently
4. avoiding costly items (meat, seafood, sweets)
5. comparison-shopping
–Gardner Food & Agricultural Policy Survey, 2022

EDIBLE ASSISTS

■ People are looking to up their home cooking game in easy ways. High-quality salts, oils, spices, meal starters, and condiments offer

(continued)

GOOD EATS

Food producers will find new ways to "upcycle"—using stale bread for croutons, brewing beer from surplus grains, and making vegetable broths from scraps.
–Sylvain Charlebois, Ph.D., Agri-Food Analytics Lab, Dalhousie University

assistance—with everything from cold-pressed almond oil to finishing salts.

–Jonathan Deutsch, Ph.D., director, Drexel Food Lab, Drexel University

"EASY DOES IT" INGREDIENTS

■ Consumers want to make meal prep easy but exciting.

–Denise Purcell, V.P., resource development, Specialty Food Association

We're using . . .

■ grain bowls as side dishes

■ dried pulled pork in entrées or soups

■ seafood boil ingredients (shrimp, crab legs, lobster, corn on the cob, sauce) sold frozen in a bag

■ flavor bases/seasonings for sauces, stews, and soups

FLAVORS WE'RE CRAVING . . .

■ globally inspired condiments, sauces, oils, and seasonings: Mexican salsa macha, West African shito sauce, Indian achaar

■ cocktails made with whey

■ chile peppers to flavor cheeses, beverages, and honey
–Denise Purcell

PEOPLE ARE TALKING ABOUT . . .

■ choosing animal-based meat over pricier plant-based alternatives

■ freeze-dried eggs and alternatives that are soy- or bean-based
–Katherine Basbaum, dietician, UVA Health

■ learning from butchers how to break down an entire side of pork or beef and/or how to make sausage

BY THE NUMBERS

$16.19: average U.S. monthly fee for an interest-bearing checking account

$9,658: average U.S. balance required to avoid a monthly fee

54%: percentage of Americans who pay credit card bills in full each month

1.3%: percentage of Americans with a perfect 850 credit score

714: average credit score (scores range from 300 to 850)

$133: average cost of a shopping trip when parents shop solo

$179: average cost of a shopping trip when parents shop with kids

42%: percentage of workers who say that they're underpaid when they're actually being paid above market scale

MONEY MATTERS

After dramatic changes in interest rates, inflation, and market volatility, this year will be about balancing our budgets and mindful spending.

–Lisa Hannam, executive editor, MoneySense

WALLETS, WATCH OUT!

■ People who drank a complimentary cup of caffeinated coffee before shopping spent more and bought more items than those who had chosen decaf or water.

FINANCIAL RELATIONSHIPS

■ 43% of Americans in relationships say that their significant other doesn't know everything about their spending.
–Edelman Financial Engines

BUZZWORDS
Nesting renters: people who upgrade their living spaces despite not owning them

■ $29,878 is the minimum salary that makes someone "date-able."

■ 27% of people talked about salaries only after marriage.
–Western & Southern survey, 2022

(continued)

15

AROUND THE HOUSE

Folks will lean toward "editing" their homes to ensure that the items in them are things they love, have meaning, and serve a specific function.

–Jenny Marrs, host of HGTV's "Fixer to Fabulous"

R$_X$: RELAX

■ People are using plants and natural materials and adding spa bathrooms and retreat spaces for exercise and meditation.
–2023 Trends Outlook Report, American Society of Interior Designers

ARCHITECTURAL ROBOTICS

■ Beds will rise to reveal couches and tables underneath.

■ Walls with an entertainment center on one side and storage/shelving on the other will glide on a track, creating or concealing space.

WANTS AND NEEDS

■ car-charging stations

■ pantry space

■ outdoor kitchens
–Matt Tinder, director, The American Institute of Architects

WA-A-A-Y DOWNSIZING

■ Living small—in 1,200 square feet or less—is gaining ground.
–Fifi O'Neill, author, Small Homes, Big Appeal *(CICO Books, 2023)*

BY THE NUMBERS

79% of homeowners would rather renovate their current home than move to a different one.

16% of couples consider separating during home improvements.

$14,163: average amount spent on repairs or upgrades before putting a house on the market

$3,771: average value that a deep cleaning adds to a selling price

76% of people would buy a house that's ugly on the outside but perfect on the inside.

13% of Gen Zers consider home a physical space.

48% of Gen Zers describe home as a feeling that can be created wherever they go.

80% of young adults in the U.S. live less than 100 miles from where they grew up.

(continued)

FOLLOW US:

Reflections of the Past
Sustainability for the Future

NICE TOUCHES

- skylights and periscopes

- compost bins set into kitchen counters

- furniture with space to grow seedlings

–Sheila Kennedy, FAIA, professor of architecture, Massachusetts Institute of Technology

SOLAR WITH STYLE

- solar roofing that looks like shingles, in black or terra-cotta

- solar shingles integrated within a roof (not on top of it)

FRESH IDEAS

- photo frames that charge phones

- gas fireplaces suspended from ceilings

- "scent styling": fragrances for rooms

- chairs with bookshelves and reading lights

–The Future of Home Interiors 2030, WGSN

CULTURE

People are infusing nature into every aspect of daily life.

–Mary Guzowski, professor, School of Architecture, University of Minnesota

PEOPLE ARE TALKING ABOUT . . .

- the Human Library, which offers people "on loan" to talk about specific topics, in the interest of civic engagement

- paper maps hung as artwork

- "sleep streamers" who video themselves while asleep and allow others to watch and/or trigger lights or sounds to wake them

- cars that play classical music when the driver is tense

WHAT WORKERS WANT

- knowledge of the range of salaries for all positions in a company (aka "pay transparency")

- cards, prepaid by the employer, for meals or groceries (to encourage healthier eating and workers eating together) or *(continued)*

Prevagen®
Improves Memory*[1]

#1 PHARMACIST RECOMMENDED
MEMORY SUPPORT BRAND

Prevagen® is America's best-selling brain support supplement[‡] and has been clinically shown to help with mild memory loss associated with aging.*[1]

Prevagen is available at stores nationwide.

Walgreens   **CVS/pharmacy**   **RITE AID**   **Walmart**

to use in ordering meals through an app (to support local restaurants)

■ 4-day workweeks

■ "financial wellness" programs to help with retirement planning, budgeting, debt management, and investment advice

ALL IN A DAY

■ **3:00 P.M.:** time of day when most people feel the least energetic

■ **4:** number of extra hours that Americans say that they would need to finish their daily to-do list

■ **5:** average number of things that people have on their to-do list on any given day
–survey by OnePoll on behalf of Dave's Killer Bread

ON THE ROAD

■ 11.2 million U.S. households own an RV.

■ 400,000 RV owners live in their RVs full-time.

■ There are 1.6 million RV campsites in the U.S.

OUR ANIMAL FRIENDS

Tech is helping us to read the signals of our pets so that we can react quickly to protect their health and well-being.
–Christine Carrière, CEO, Pets Canada

BUZZWORD
Petflation: spending more money on your pets now than in previous years

PET COSTS

■ Gen Zers, Millennials, and baby boomers are spending more than ever to keep their pet healthy, happy, and living longer.
–Phillip M. Cooper, president, Pet Industry Expert

(continued)

FOLLOW US:

FIREWOOD ALERT!

You have the power to protect forests and trees!

BUY IT WHERE YOU BURN IT.

Invasive pests like the emerald ash borer can hitchhike in your firewood. You can prevent the spread of these damaging insects and diseases by following these firewood tips:

▶ Buy locally harvested firewood at or near your destination.

▶ Buy certified heat-treated firewood, if available.

▶ Gather firewood on site where permitted.

What might be in your firewood?

SPONGY MOTH is a devastating pest of oaks and other trees. Moths lay tan patches of eggs on firewood, campers, vehicles, patio furniture — anything outside! When these items are moved to new areas, this pest gets a free ride.

SPOTTED LANTERNFLY sucks sap from dozens of tree and plant species. This pest loves tree-of-heaven but will feed on black walnut, white oak, sycamore, and grape. Like the spongy moth, this pest lays clusters of eggs on just about any dry surface, from landscaping stone to firewood!

ASIAN LONGHORNED BEETLE will tunnel through, and destroy, over 20 species of trees — especially maple trees. The larvae of this beetle bore into tree branches and trunks, making it an easy pest to accidentally transport in firewood.

EMERALD ASH BORER — the infamous killer of ash trees — is found in forests and city trees across much of the eastern and central United States. This insect is notoriously good at hitching rides in infested firewood, which is how most new infestations start — like the patch of trees now infested near Portland, Oregon. Don't give this tree-killing bug a ride to a new forest, or a new state.

DONTMOVE FIREWOOD.org

This graphic is for illustrative purposes only. Many of these pests will only infest certain types of trees, making it very unlikely for a single log to contain all species as shown.

Visit dontmovefirewood.org for more information.

- $1,320 is the amount projected to be spent annually, per U.S. pet, by 2025.

- 26% of Canadian pet owners will spend more on pet foods touting extra health benefits.

- $525, on average, is spent on veterinarian bills each year.

THE DATA ON DOGS

- *Fact:* Dogs can detect stress from their owner's scent.

- *Being studied:* Do dogs affect our health by changing our brain activity?

PEOPLE ARE TALKING ABOUT . . .

- robotic laser systems that ID poop to be scooped

- homeowners renting their yards by the hour for dogs that need space to run around

BY THE NUMBERS

60% of pet owners forgo gym memberships and exercise with their animals.

42% of pet owners won't stay in a hotel that doesn't allow pets.

$10,000 per year, on average, is paid by pet retailers to cats and dogs to try out new toys.

35% of Canadian pet owners allow pets to sleep in their beds.

15% of Americans own five or more pets.

- doggy doors that open remotely when owners aren't home

SERVICES WITH A SMILE

- Retailers are adding pet clinics.

- Drugstores are selling pet medications.

- Pet specialty stores are offering grooming, boarding, vet care, and dog training.
  –Phillip M. Cooper

PET-FRIENDLY MUST-HAVES

- abstract art shelving for cats to climb

- dog-washing stations in mudrooms

- pullout drawers for food bowls

- dog caves under staircases

PETS ARE EATING . . .

- *fresh food* that's home-delivered already cooked or from refrigerators in pet aisles

- *insect- and plant-based proteins* to help heart, joint, dental, and digestive health or mental well-being

- *supplements:* probiotics for behavioral improvements; turmeric, pumpkin, and collagen for treats
  –Phillip M. Cooper

- *freeze-dried food* "that's easy to use and will remain stable for long periods"
  –Phillip M. Cooper

(continued on page 26)

FOLLOW US:

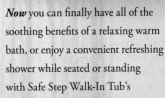

23

Choose Life
Grow Young with HGH

From the landmark book Grow Young with HGH comes the most powerful, over-the-counter health supplement in the history of man. Human growth hormone was first discovered in 1920 and has long been thought by the medical community to be necessary only to stimulate the body to full adult size and therefore unnecessary past the age of 20. Recent studies, however, have overturned this notion completely, discovering instead that the natural decline of Human Growth Hormone (HGH), from ages 21 to 61 (the average age at which there is only a trace left in the body) and is the main reason why the body ages and fails to regenerate itself to its 25 year-old biological age.

Like a picked flower cut from the source, we gradually wilt physically and mentally and become vulnerable to a host of degenerative diseases, that we simply weren't susceptible to in our early adult years.

Modern medical science now regards aging as a disease that is treatable and preventable and that "aging", the disease, is actually a compilation of various diseases and pathologies, from everything, like a rise in blood glucose and pressure to diabetes, skin wrinkling and so on. All of these aging symptoms can be stopped and rolled back by maintaining Growth Hormone levels in the blood at the same levels HGH existed in the blood when we were 25 years old.

There is a receptor site in almost every

cell in the human body for HGH, so its regenerative and healing effects are very comprehensive.

Growth Hormone, first synthesized in 1985 under the Reagan Orphan drug act, to treat dwarfism, was quickly recognized to stop aging in its tracks and reverse it to a remarkable degree. Since then, only the lucky and the rich have had access to it at the cost of $10,000 US per year.

The next big breakthrough was to come in 1997 when a group of doctors and scientists, developed an all-natural source product which would cause your own natural HGH to be released again and do all the remarkable things it did for you in your 20's. Now available to every adult for about the price of a coffee and donut a day.

GHR is now available in America, just in time for the aging Baby Boomers and everyone else from age 30 to 90 who doesn't want to age rapidly but would rather stay young, beautiful and healthy all of the time.

The new HGH releasers are winning converts from the synthetic HGH users as well, since GHR is just as effective, is oral instead of self-injectable and is very affordable.

GHR is a natural releaser, has no known side effects, unlike the synthetic version and has no known drug interactions. Progressive doctors admit that this is the direction medicine is seeking to go, to get the body to heal itself instead of employing drugs. GHR is truly a revolutionary paradigm shift in medicine and, like any modern leap frog advance, many others will be left in the dust holding their limited, or useless drugs and remedies.

It is now thought that HGH is so comprehensive in its healing and regenerative powers that it is today, where the computer industry was twenty years ago, that it will displace so many prescription and non-prescription drugs and health remedies that it is staggering to think of.

The president of BIE Health Products stated in a recent interview, "I've been waiting for these products since the 70's. We knew they would come, if only we could stay healthy and live long enough to see them! If you want to stay on top of your game, physically and mentally as you age, this product is a boon, especially for the highly skilled professionals who have made large investments in their education, and experience. Also with the failure of Congress to honor our seniors with pharmaceutical coverage policy, it's more important than ever to take pro-active steps to safeguard your health. Continued use of GHR will make a radical difference in your health, HGH is particularly helpful to the elderly who, given a choice, would rather stay independent in their own home, strong, healthy and alert enough to manage their own affairs, exercise and stay involved in their communities. Frank, age 85, walks two miles a day, plays golf, belongs to a dance club for seniors, had a girl friend again and doesn't need Viagra, passed his driver's test and is hardly ever home when we call - GHR delivers."

HGH is known to relieve symptoms of Asthma, Angina, Chronic Fatigue, Constipation, Lower back pain and Sciatica, Cataracts and Macular Degeneration, Menopause, Fibromyalgia, Regular and Diabetic Neuropathy, Hepatitis, helps Kidney Dialysis and Heart and Stroke recovery.

For more information or to order call
877-849-4777
www.biehealth.ca

These statements have not been evaluated by the FDA. Copyright © 2000. Code OFA.

(continued from page 22)

YOUR HEALTH OUTLOOK

The mental health field is actively looking at video games to treat diseases in lieu of medication.

–Eric Alan Gantwerker, M.D., associate professor, Donald and Barbara Zucker School of Medicine at Hofstra/Northwell

SECRETS TO GOOD SLUMBER

- Schedule a "worry session" before going to sleep.

- "Savor": Review a good experience from the day in detail before drifting off.

BY THE NUMBERS

7.9 hours: mean sleep duration for Canadian adults

6:54 A.M.: wake-up time of the average Canadian

7:31 A.M.: wake-up time of the average American

29 pounds: average amount of weight Americans want to lose

R$_X$: A PLANT

Researchers have found that people . . .

- feel more peaceful after being near a tall plant for 15 minutes

- feel calmer and have sharper focus and better memory when near indoor plants

- react most positively to plants with dense foliage, bright green leaves, and rounded contours

COMING SOON

- wearables that track our exposure to sunlight

- carbon-absorbing paint made from demolished concrete

- apps that tell us where to get exposure to phytoncides (airborne chemicals given off by plants to protect themselves)

PEOPLE ARE TALKING ABOUT . . .

- "incidental" exercise—walking faster on the way to work, running up a flight of stairs, getting off the bus one stop early, squatting while waiting in line

(continued)

FOLLOW US:

FASHION

People are personalizing clothing with embroidery, patches, and yarn mending and by painting or dyeing fabric.

–Leslie H. Simpson, Ph.D., associate professor and coordinator, Fashion Design Program, Stevenson University

SWAP SHOPPERS

Thrifty fashion fanatics are swapping outfits . . .

■ with each other

■ at branded retail clothing stores

■ at ticketed meetups held at parks, coffee shops, or wineries (for savings and to hear the stories behind the clothing)

BUZZWORDS
Two-mile clothing: comfortable clothes that are appropriate for work both at home and in the office
–WGSN

READY FOR ANYTHING

■ Clothing will suit fluid lifestyles that include different workplaces (onsite or at-home), exercise preferences, and outdoor activities.

■ Blazers will be waist-cinchable with bungee cords and toggles, for relaxed or fitted looks.

■ Trousers will be cinched at the ankle.

■ Tailored pants will have elasticized waistbands.

FOLLOW US:

■ Shirts will have removable sleeves and/or collars.

–Anika Kozlowski, fashion design assistant professor, Toronto Metropolitan University

THE LOOKS FOR WOMEN

■ suits and pants in dark denim

■ oversize trousers, jackets, and boyfriend shirts

■ wrap and slip dresses (layered with turtlenecks and slacks in cold weather)

–Lynn Boorady, professor and department head, Department of Design, Housing, and Merchandising, Oklahoma State University

THE LOOKS FOR MEN

■ *classics with a twist:* denim tuxedos; green loafers; chambray shirts paired with

track pants; khakis, loose-fitting and cropped

■ *minimalist:* blazers with no pockets, collars, or buttons

■ *casual:* business pants with drawstrings

FASHION CENTS

■ Consumers now think of the resale market value of items that they purchase.

–Lynn Boorady

PEOPLE ARE TALKING ABOUT . . .

■ *in summer:* jackets and vests, with fans

BY THE NUMBERS

25% of apparel and footwear shoppers are loyal to specific brands.

$2,086: what average U.S. consumers spend on apparel annually

$991: what average U.S. consumers spend on shoes per year

66% of clothing or shoe purchasers read up to 25 reviews before doing so.

$268: average value of never-worn outfits in closets

6% of adults have worn everything in their closet at least once.

76% of Canadians value feeling comfortable over looking stylish.

■ *in winter:* battery-powered, machine-washable, heated layers

■ stylish clothing for the wheelchair-bound (easy to get on/off while sitting)

–Leslie H. Simpson

■ lanyard-style, crossbody pouches to carry phones ■

BOUQUETS
FROM BLOOMS AND
BRANCHES

THE INGREDIENTS FOR YEAR-ROUND FLORAL ARRANGEMENTS MAY BE RIGHT AT YOUR FINGERTIPS.

BY LYNN COULTER

The next time that you desire an arrangement for your desk- or tabletop, browse your backyard, farmers' market, or vegetable plot. We've got a hunch that you can find plenty of natural materials to make beautiful, inexpensive arrangements within walking distance of your home—if you are willing to share cuttings and are prepared to ask permission. Here are some ideas.

FIND FLOWERS

Most bouquets start with flowers, of course, so aim to use the annuals, perennials, and bulbs already growing in your beds and borders. Nell Foster, an Arizona-based seasoned landscaper and environmental horticulturist who owns Joy Us Garden (Joyusgarden.com), likes to snip blossoms from alstroemerias, dahlias, hydrangeas, and zinnias because they last a long time after cutting. Foster also picks wildflowers such as bachelor buttons, black-eyed Susans, goldenrod, and wild yarrow. (Harvest only from your own property, unless you have clear consent from the property owner, and never take plants that are threatened or endangered.)

Be a little bit choosy. Some cut wildflowers, such as Queen Anne's lace, don't last long. "I've found that the thinner and more delicate the stem, like that of a California poppy or wild toadflax, the faster they wilt," reports Foster.

To prolong your flowers, recut the stems when you get home and put them into water right away. "Clear soda can be added for a bit of sugar, which flowers enjoy. I just usually change the water every few days to keep it fresh," Foster notes.

(continued)

AN AUTUMN DISPLAY
OF ARTICHOKES,
TOMATOES,
AND RASPBERRIES
BLENDED
WITH BORAGE,
CALENDULA, AND
ROSEMARY

MIX IN FRUIT AND VEGGIES

The farmers' market or even grocery store produce section can be a source for seasonal arrangements. Granny Smith apples, artichokes, brussels sprout stalks, purple eggplants, grape clusters, oranges, and pomegranates can add color and texture to arrangements.

"Stick fruit on wooden skewers, heavy-gauge wire, or wire saved from old silk flowers and have them coming up out of the bouquet," suggests Sara Jenkins-Sutton, who co-owns Topiarius Urban Garden and Floral Design (Topiarius .com) in Chicago. "Add asparagus stalks, leafy greens, herbs, and lettuce for beautiful, lush arrangements."

One mistake that beginners make, says Jenkins-Sutton, is not using enough materials, resulting in arrangements that look thin. "A few stems can be an elegant look. But it's more fun if you use a lot of one thing or maybe a couple of things. Go as full as you possibly can."

(continued)

CONTAIN YOURSELF

Store-bought or leftover florist vases will hold your home-made bouquets adequately, but try thinking beyond the glass. In autumn, Jenkins-Sutton gets creative with pumpkins from her vegetable patch: "Use a drill bit to make vase holes the size that you want and then insert your stems," she advises.

Other "patchwork" planter ideas can incorporate melons, pumpkins, or winter squashes that have been hollowed out. Set a glass jar inside to hold your cuttings and slip a plate or saucer under your veggie-vase to protect your tabletop. Good choices for harvesttime arrangements are chrysanthemums and trailing sweet autumn clematis.

For something completely different, Jenkins-Sutton puts lemons, limes, and pears into glass cylinders and then fills them with water and cut flowers. The fruit "act like a floral frog," she says, to hold the stems in place.

(continued)

AN EARLY WINTER DISPLAY OF DAHLIAS, ZINNIAS, IVY, AND HYDRANGEAS IN A PUMPKIN VASE

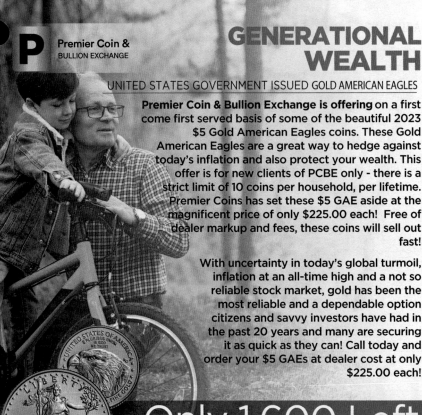

DAFFODILS AND PUSSY WILLOWS GUARANTEE A CHEERY SPRING BOUQUET.

BRANCH OUT

Different sizes of branches, stems, and twigs can anchor a display and make great backbones for informal arrangements, Foster observes.

Curly willow branches provide fascination in their natural brown and green state. Or, for a lively effect, spray paint them—try gold for the holidays. Similarly, fuzzy pussy willows add texture and a degree of fun.

In spring, cut branches from magnolias, spirea, viburnums, and witch hazels or flowering stems from apple,

cherry, peach, and pear trees for your arrangement. Nicholas Staddon, a plantsman who has been working with breeders and plant explorers for more than 25 years, trims branches from forsythias, lilacs, and quince to force.

Autumn options abound. "Red- and yellow-twig dogwoods have stems that range from amber to red and drop-dead fall color," he notes. Also, look for dried hydrangea blooms to bring indoors, along with seedpods; stems studded with rose hips; or cuttings of bear grass,

lily grass, and steel grass. "Many grasses produce magnificent plumes or flower heads," comments Staddon, who spritzes his flower heads with hair spray to help to keep the seeds from dropping. "Good choices are calamagrostis, sometimes called 'reed grass,' and miscanthus," he says.

To add sparkle in winter, coat branches, cones, and nuts with spray adhesive and sprinkle with glitter. At Christmastime, Staddon brings the hair spray back out to add shine to holly berries.

(continued)

Photo: Friedrich Strauss/GAP Photos

DiTarando
Animal Art/Garden Elements

Roger's sculpture covers the gamut from fine art to whimsy, including functional garden elements, weathervanes, birdbaths, gates, fountains, and more. Given the sculptures' unique eclectic qualities, they work in sophisticated to comfortable environments.

www.ditarando.com • 860.614.2704

FORAGE FOR FUN

Use your imagination to identify other materials for your bouquets. Hot peppers add rainbows of color, while herbs such as dill and rosemary provide fragrance as well as texture. Foster drapes graceful vines of honeysuckle and wild sweet pea for a sense of movement. For trailing accents, cut cucumber vines or yellow-blossom squash vines. (Just remember: You're sacrificing some of your harvest when you cut from vegetable plants.)

Foliage that turns to a brilliant color in autumn is yet another option. Snip from maples, serviceberries, sumac, sweet gums, and other trees and shrubs.

If you can't find everything that you want in your own woods or yard, "walk around the neighborhood with your pruners and basket," Staddon suggests. "Knock on your neighbors' doors, ask if you can take cuttings, and give them your biggest, brightest smile." Share a bouquet of the cuttings later, and you may never have to ask again. ∎

Lynn Coulter is an Atlanta-based freelance writer and the author of *Gardening with Heirloom Seeds* (UNC Press, 2006).

SUMMER FLOWERS AND HERBS MINGLE TO MAKE A FRAGRANT AND TEXTURAL BOUQUET.

WHETHER FOR BREADS OR BRAGGING
RIGHTS, YOU'LL GET A RISE OUT
OF GROWING GRAINS. BY SARA PITZER

GO THE WITH GRAIN

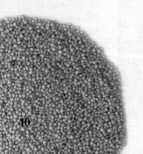

**NEXT TO THOROUGH
PREPARATION OF
THE SOIL, THE MOST
IMPORTANT
THING IN SECURING
A GOOD CROP IS
THE PROPER SELECTION
AND PREPARATION
OF THE SEED.**
–FACTS FOR FARMERS, 1870

AMARANTH

QUINOA

BARLEY

GRAINS TO GROW

AMARANTH AND QUINOA

Amaranth does best in warm climates; quinoa, in cool regions. Both are large, broadleaf, native American plants high in protein and other nutrients, easy to grow, and useful as grains or vegetables.

BARLEY

Barley is a fast-maturing grain that thrives in cool weather, does well in alkaline soil, and contains more soluble fiber than do oats.

BUCKWHEAT

Buckwheat improves soil as you grow it. The seeds grind into a strongly flavored flour.

(continued)

G rains are among the easiest plants to grow in home gardens, but before you drop that first seed into the ground, consider these questions:
- How much grain do you want or need to harvest: enough to make bread for a year, or are you experimenting with a new crop?
- Do you have the proper conditions: sun from dawn to dusk, an inch or so of rain or irrigation per week, and well-draining, moderately fertile soil?
- Can you buy equipment jointly with other growers or borrow or rent what you'll need (e.g., seed cleaners, seed hullers, winnowers, flour mills)?
- Will you have the time, energy, equipment, and muscle to harvest, thresh, winnow, and hull the grain?
- Do you have storage space that is dry and free of insects and rodents and where the temperature is consistent and no higher than 70°F?

HOW MUCH TO GROW

Start small. Growing grains is easy. Threshing, winnowing, and hulling them takes raw, brute energy. As a beginner, it's likely that you'll lose a lot of grain in these final steps. Consider a trial area in the first year so that you can learn how the grain behaves, what its cultivation problems are, how long it takes you to handle it, and how it is affected by varying climate conditions.

You'll get a decent yield and less grief from a modest plot of reasonable size—say, a 100-square-foot planting. A 10x10- or 20x5-foot bed fits nicely in a typical backyard and is manageable for planting and harvesting. Your

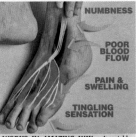

BUCKWHEAT

CORN

MILLET

CORN
The taste of home-grown cornmeal is delightful. To harvest corn as a grain, let a few ears go past their prime, then use your hand to twist the dried corn off the ears.

MILLET
Millet thrives in hot, dry climates. The seeds are encased in thin hulls; to remove them, rub a handful of grain between your palms.

OATS
Oats, a cool-climate crop, are easy to grow yet hard to hull. If you grow old-style oats to eat, find a method of hulling before you sow or else plant a hull-less oat strain. *(continued)*

first harvest of wheat may give you 4 pounds of grain, which will grind into 14 cups of flour—enough for three or four loaves of bread. As you gain experience, this same plot could yield as much as 26 pounds of grain or about 90 cups of flour—and enough bread for half a year.

However, even when you can't harvest what you plant, your efforts won't be wasted. Most small grains make a fine cover crop that not only cuts down on weeds and reduces erosion while it is growing but also produces a nutritious green manure that enriches the soil after you till the plants under.

PREPARING THE SOIL
It takes no more work to prepare the soil for grains than it does to get it ready for any other garden plant. Most grains thrive in loose, well-draining, moderately fertile soil in a spot that receives full sun all day. To ensure that your crops get a good start, test your soil.

SOWING STYLES
Grains are sown in narrow or wide rows or solid blocks. Because some grains are tall, run your rows north–south so that each plant in the row receives an equal amount of sun.

Narrow rows are the traditional planting pattern but not the most productive.

Wide rows are a great way for a first-time grain grower to start. With this method, you create 3- to

RICE **RYE** **WHEAT**

RICE
Rice requires wet soil and a long, hot growing season. It's perfect for those low spots in your yard that never dry. Rice can also be grown in pots.

RYE
Rye is almost immune to failure. In addition to being frost-hardy and growable in poor soil, it's also a good cover crop.

WHEAT
This cool-season crop is easy to grow, harvest, thresh, store, and grind in small amounts. In most regions, it is planted in fall and harvested the following spring.

4-foot-wide beds that are about 18 inches apart. The width depends on how far in you can reach to weed from both sides of the bed and the amount of space that the plants need while they grow.

When you plant in wide rows, you never have to walk on the bed to weed and the soil in the rows stays loose—perfect for root growth. You'll save money on amendments because you need to work only the soil in the planted rows. A wide row accommodates two or more rows of grain, depending on the spacing that the plants require.

Some crops, such as wheat and especially corn, can be grown in a solid block pattern. Essentially, this is a mini-field in which you broadcast the seeds evenly over the planting area.

Measure and mark out the rows with twine and stakes, then build up their height a few inches by scooping soil from the path onto the beds. Spread amendments over the rows and till them in. Finally, shape the rows so that the top is flat and level and the sides flare slightly at the bottom. Apply a thick layer of mulch on the path between beds or grow a cover crop such as clover to keep mud and weeds at bay and help to feed the soil for next year's garden.

Sow by digging trenches with your hoe, sprinkling in some seeds, and covering them. Alternatively, lightly scatter or broadcast seeds by hand across the rows. After the seeds are sown, work them into the soil with a rake. How deep to rake them in depends on the grain. Depths can range from ½ to 2½ inches. *(continued)*

EXPERIENCE THE *Miracle*

gdefy®

PATENTED VERSOSHOCK®
SHOCK ABSORPTION TECHNOLOGY

"After suffering with extreme foot pain for months, I can finally walk again with no pain. **They are truly miracle shoes!**" – Carol D.

See more miracle testimonials at gdefy.com

Enjoy the benefits of exercise without harmful impact on your joints!

✓ Renewed Energy
✓ Maximum Protection
✓ Improved Posture
✓ Relieve Pain

60-DAY "TRY DEFY" MONEY-BACK GUARANTEE!

MIGHTY WALK $155 MED/WIDE/X-WIDE AVAILABLE
This product is not intended to treat, cure or prevent any disease.

Women

TB9024FUB
Blue/Beige

TB9024FWI
White/Pink

TB9024FLW
Black/White

Men

TB9024MRW
Red/White/Blue

TB9024MUO
Blue/Orange

TB9024MGU
Gray/Blue

$30 OFF orders of $150 or more
Promo Code PN2ART2
Expires December 31, 2024
FREE SHIPPING, EXCHANGES & RETURNS

800-429-0039 · www.gdefy.com

Plus Free Corrective Fit Orthotics
for plantar fasciitis, stability & support!

SOW

GROW

HARVEST

SEED-STARTERS

- Locate garden seed companies that offer grains in small quantities or search online for "cover crop seeds" and "grain seeds." It will be easier to find unnamed varieties than named cultivars.

- Save seeds from each year's harvest to plant in the next year. (Check for any restrictions on saving your variety first.) Choose the plumpest seeds or those from the most productive plant (or earliest or most pest-free), and you'll one day be planting your own "improved" variety.

In order to get a good stand of plants, seeds and soil must be in contact. To ensure this, make a pass over the planting area with a lawn roller. No roller? Put down a plank and walk on it for the same result.

HARVESTING A SMALL PLOT

To harvest a small plot (up to 150 square feet), break the heads off the stems. Drop them into a bucket as you work, then spread them out to dry for several days before threshing. Alternatively, you could cut the grain with pruners, leaving a 12-inch stem; bundle a few stems; and hang the harvest to dry, as you would to dry herbs and flowers.

A sickle is a traditional tool that is well suited to small spaces and easy for a novice to use. Cutting with a sickle is a matter of grab-and-cut, grab-and-cut. For example, if you're right-handed, you would hold the stalks of grain in your left hand and swing the sickle with your right to cut at ground level. Kneel or crouch as you harvest so that you won't tire too quickly. Lay the cut grain in windrows (small piles along the row), with all of the heads pointed in the same direction. Let the grain dry for several days before threshing. For larger plots, try harvesting with a blade trimmer.

Although just basic guidelines, these are enough to get you started. And sow it goes! ∎

Excerpted and adapted from *Homegrown Whole Grains* (Storey Publishing, 2009) by Sara Pitzer and used with permission.

When it's built by *hand,*
It's connected to the *Heart.*

For three generations, the builders, blacksmiths and craftsmen at Country Carpenters have put their hands and their hearts into designing and building the finest New England Style buildings available. Hand-selected materials, hand-forged hardware, all hand-built and hand-finished by real people. You can feel the difference in your heart.

NEW ENGLAND STYLE
Country Carpenters INC.
POST & BEAM BUILDINGS

COUNTRY BARNS, CARRIAGE HOUSES, POOL & GARDEN SHEDS, CABINS

—————— *Visit our models on display! We ship nationwide!* ——————

326 Gilead Street, Hebron, CT 06248 • 860.228.2276 • countrycarpenters.com

*Farmers across the continent
are keeping it local—economically
and environmentally.*

Farming Today

GOOD RAIN FARM
Camas, Washington

Stinging nettles, viewed as a noxious, invasive weed, are usually yanked out of yards or fields, but at Good Rain Farm, they're grown as a crop. "Stinging nettles are an Indigenous First Food, a staple of my people's diet for thousands of years," says farmer Michelle Week, who educates customers about her produce via recipes, blogs, and newsletters.

Week, who founded the farm in 2018, is of Sinixt (pronounced "sin-EYEKST") ancestry. Good Rain Farm (or x̌ast sx̣ʷit, pronounced "hast SQUEE-ett," in the traditional language of the Sinixt, aka Arrow Lakes Peoples) is a 3-acre operation located on the rainy, foggy, west side of the Cascade Mountains.

The farm offers an internship program to train beginning farmers. "We grow over 100 varieties of plants that require a lot of hands-on care in a small space," reports Week, "and we could not do this detailed farm work without a lot of well-trained field workers."

Good Rain Farm has moved four times. "Finding farmland to rent is very difficult, and finding land to purchase for farming is nearly impossible, especially close to Portland, where our members mostly live," comments Week.

The farm serves 150 families through a seasonal community-supported agriculture (CSA) program. Customers receive Indigenous First Foods of the region such as rose hips, salmonberries (a cousin of black- and raspberries), wood sorrel, currants, camas root (a bulb), acorns, Oregon stonecrop (sedum), and wapato (a tuber). The farm also sells produce wholesale to local businesses, restaurants, and schools.

"I am really in the business of telling Indigenous Food stories," notes Week. "In this way, I am fighting the erasure and extinction of my people, of my language, and of my ancestral foods." Week proudly adds that about half of the CSA members receive low- or no-cost shares: "Poverty does not lessen people's desire and need for fresh, sustainably grown produce." ■ *(continued)*

for Tomorrow

BY KAREN DAVIDSON AND
STACEY KUSTERBECK

"I AM REALLY IN
THE BUSINESS OF
TELLING INDIGENOUS
FOOD STORIES."

51

"THERE ARE NO SHORTCUTS IN FARMING. IF YOU WANT TO DO IT WELL, THEN YOU NEED TO STRIVE FOR EXCELLENCE."

GOLDEN RETREAT VINEYARD
Summerland, British Columbia

If it's true that 10,000 hours of intensive practice are required to master complex skills, then David Kozuki would be a good example of this axiom. He was a medical researcher and a jazz pianist before becoming a wine-grape grower at age 36.

It was in his great-grandparents' apple orchard in Summerland that he found his true mission: growing grapes. With inherited responsibility for the property, he transformed it from an orchard into a 20-acre vineyard, which was incorporated as a business in 2007—but Kozuki's personal transformation was not yet complete. "I was a new farmer who had never driven a tractor," he recalls. "And since I had no farming experience, my crew wouldn't even allow me to do any handwork for several weeks."

Since this ominous start, Kozuki has proven adept at tending the vineyards by undertaking such chores as pruning dormant vines to maintain canopy architecture while thinning shoots to bring the vines into vegetative and fruiting balance.

His acumen proved critical in 2022, when unseasonable winter temperatures plummeted to –30°C (–22°F) and caused bud damage. "Prescriptive pruning decisions were assigned based on the degree of severity of the bud damage," he explains. "Selective thinning after bud break was a two-part decision: Identify whether the primary bud was viable, and if it were not, choose the most fruitful secondary buds."

This painstaking attention to detail was rewarded. A near-perfect growing season followed, with harvest yields off by only 10 percent from 5-year averages —a result known to be respected by his fellow growers in the Okanagan Valley. "I put into play that marriage of the structural rightness of science with the free-flowing swing of jazz," he concludes. "There are no shortcuts in farming. If you want to do it well, then you need to strive for excellence." ■ *(continued)*

GEMPERLE ORCHARDS
Turlock, California

Blooming cover crops of mustard and clover are planted between rows of almond trees on the 135 acres that make up Gemperle Orchards. "There are a million great reasons to do cover crops. But then, there is the other argument—that you are putting in more plants that will need more water," says grower Christine Gemperle, who manages the orchard with her brother, Erich.

Still, the cover crops allow water to penetrate the ground more deeply and their organic matter helps the soil to hold on to the water, so on balance, it's a net gain.

This is but one example of the complexities of the almond orchard, which produces over 300,000 pounds of almonds annually. "There are different tradeoffs with every decision," Gemperle points out—and many, if not most, of these involve water.

Gemperle grew up watching her father grow almonds and returned to the farm after earning a biology degree. The scientific expertise has value. "Farmers need to have some knowledge of engineering, biology, finance, business, chemistry—your hands are in so many pies at the same time," she says.

She and her brother host researchers on their property to study tree growth and water usage. In the summer of 2022, they measured water evaporation in the orchards; in time, this data will reveal exactly how much water is used. "To be on the edge of this emerging research, firsthand, is really important because these are all of the questions that growers need the answers to," reports Gemperle. The research will allow them to more precisely apply water and use less overall.

Scientists also study pollinators, another family interest. Her father was a beekeeper, with an understanding of the close connection between pollinators and almond-growing. Says Gemperle: "Almond growers have always had symbiotic relations with beekeepers. Our crops depend 100 percent on healthy bee populations." ■ *(continued)*

"TO BE ON THE EDGE OF THIS EMERGING RESEARCH, FIRSTHAND, IS REALLY IMPORTANT."

Photo: Gemperle Orchards

COMING SOON!

Our new product is sure to get your cold chickens clucking.

Sign up for product updates and early bird savings at **CaframoBrands.com**, or call us at **1-800-567-3556**.

by **Caframo**®

"WE WANT TO CREATE A HIGH-FUNCTIONING SOIL SO THAT WE CAN WEATHER DRY SPELLS."

UPLAND ORGANICS
Wood Mountain, Saskatchewan

K*eep a living root in the soil as long as possible.* This is one of the soil principles of married couple Allison Squires and Cody Straza, who are stewarding the 4,500 acres that make up their Upland Organics mixed cattle and organic grain farm. Since purchasing the land in 2010, they have been unearthing the secrets of soil microbial life. "It made us sad when we learned that the smell of freshly worked earth is actually organic matter oxidizing [releasing carbon]. Our aim is to keep carbon in the soil," says Squires.

This discovery led them to till-in their crops of lentils, flax, durum wheat, and Khorasan wheat only once a year. Disturbing the soil as little as possible also preserves moisture that can be as little as 1.25 inches per year. "We want to create a high-functioning soil so that we can weather dry spells," Squires reports.

To keep the soil in place, they plant cover crops such as oats, millet, yellow blossom clover, and nitrogen-fixing peas. "Cover crops can do anything, one thing at a time," notes Straza. "Once we identify the issue, such as nitrogen-building, weed suppression, grazing, or organic matter–building, we pick a few plants that will be keystone players."

To the surprise of these organic growers, livestock are the last building block. To utilize their burgeoning cover crops in 2018, they experimented with a neighbor's cows at a higher-than-normal number per acre. The cattle ended up grazing the top third of the cover crop and then trampling the rest before they could be rotated into the next block of forage. The resultant cow manure, however, paid off by returning organic matter to the soil. This convinced them to buy 300 cows of their own. They conclude: "Our method is a multilayer ecosystem that we now consider a whole-farm approach to sequestering carbon in the soil." ■ *(continued)*

JANIE'S FARM AND MILL
Ashkum, Illinois

About a decade ago, Harold Wilken watched as yet another semi-truck loaded with tons of organic wheat pulled away from his 3,300-acre farm bound for a feed mill in upstate New York. Suddenly, Wilken had an epiphany: "Why am I shipping my grain 700 miles away to feed chickens, when there are so many people nearby who eat bread?"

Finding a way to sell direct to these consumers called for major changes to Janie's Farm's operations—as well as collaborations with bakers, distributors, and even scientists. "A lot of things came together at the same time," Wilken recalls. He bought a nearby abandoned building, converted it into a large stone mill, and asked University of Illinois researchers for help in identifying the best grain to mill (the verdict: hard red winter wheat).

In the first production year, customers could choose from five high-quality, whole grain, organic flours. "People tried our flour, and word of mouth got out," Wilken reports.

Today, the mill offers 45 flours and grains, ships up to 100 orders direct-to-consumer daily, and sells about 450,000 pounds of flour annually. Wilken notes that most wholesale orders are delivered by him, as "it's important for me to develop these relationships, instead of just having a driver drop it off."

Recently, a visibly relieved bagel baker came out to meet the delivery truck, admitting that he'd been putting out a mediocre product after running out of high-protein bread flour from Janie's Mill. "Hearing that gives me real satisfaction in knowing that we're doing the right thing," Wilken observes.

The only downside of the close ties with customers is some weight gain, acknowledges Wilken: "All the bakers think the best way to thank the farmer is with a loaf of bread." ■ *(continued)*

"WHY AM I SHIPPING MY GRAIN 700 MILES AWAY TO FEED CHICKENS, WHEN THERE ARE SO MANY PEOPLE NEARBY WHO EAT BREAD?"

59

"WE DECIDED THAT THIS SYSTEM WOULD ALLOW THE COWS TO HAVE A GOOD LIFE."

CROVALLEY HOLSTEINS
Hastings, Ontario

Robots are keeping many Canadian dairy farms in the family. This is the case for Cynthia and John Crowley as well as the fifth generation of their family, sons Justin and Ryan. In 2016, the Crowleys decided to build a freestall barn that could house 110 Holstein cows and an automated milking system. The system's undercarriage has a robotic arm with suction cups that automatically detect where to attach to each udder's four teats. Each cow wears a neckband transponder with a unique electronic number, leaving her free to feed, rest, socialize, and be milked as desired. With these choices, she may decide to be milked up to five times per day—in which case, upon entering the milking crate, she is rewarded with sweetened haylage, the most tender early stage of the hay crop.

Swoosh—and the sensors record liters of milk produced per day, butterfat percentage, and more. All of these statistics can be viewed from the comfort of the office. In the past, dairy husbandry involved physical observation. Now it's more cerebral, requiring the review of daily data and patterns. For example, a cow's electronic collar tracks her behavior, such as distance walked per day. If a cow is restless, she's likely in heat and should be bred to produce next year's calf.

There's still hands-on care. For example, Cynthia feeds the calves. Newborns are closely monitored for two feedings of colostrum (immunity-boosting milk from the mother). There are other chores, but by adopting a robotic system, the family has released more time for analysis of overall herd production. "We decided that this system would not only allow the cows to have a good life but also enable us to have a more flexible, less labor-intensive one, too," says Cynthia, adding: "I don't milk cows anymore." ■

Canadian profiles are by **Karen Davidson**, editor of *The Grower*, a leading Canadian horticultural magazine, and frequent contributor to the Almanac.
U.S. profiles are by **Stacey Kusterbeck**, a regular contributor to the Almanac.

WE ALL FLIP FOR
PANCAKES!

BY SARAH PERREAULT

Flapjacks, griddle cakes, hotcakes, buckwheats, johnnycakes, flannel cakes. No matter what you call them, these are all generally the same thing—pancakes—and people have been loving them for centuries!

Although the 5th century B.C. Greek poets Cratinus and Magnes were the first to actually document "warm cakes" made from flour, honey, olive oil, and milk, there is evidence pointing to pancakes having been eaten much earlier. The 5,300-year-old remains of "Ötzi the Iceman," discovered perfectly preserved in a glacier on the Austrian-Italian border in 1991, revealed remnants in his stomach of an unleavened bread made of einkorn wheat. Tiny particles of charcoal attached to the sample indicated that the pancake-like food had been cooked next to a fire or on a hot rock.

Pope Gregory I (c. 540–604) inadvertently popularized pancakes among the masses. He decreed that Christians had to abstain from eating meat and animal products such as milk, butter, and eggs during Lent, the 40 days (not including Sundays) leading up to Easter on the Christian calendar that begin with Ash Wednesday. The faithful purged their households of the unwanted ingredients by making and consuming pancakes, doughnuts, and other pastries on Shrove Tuesday, the day before the fasting period.

The English have long celebrated the humble pancake. A pancake race in Olney, Buckinghamshire, dates from 1445. Legend has it originating with a woman who was cooking pancakes in advance of an

Photos: t_kimura/Getty Images; opposite, LauriPatterson/Getty Images

FUN FACTS

■ The pancake tortoise is named for the shape of its shell, which is flatter yet more flexible than that of a typical tortoise. This flexibility allows the agile tortoise to climb into small crevices to escape predators rather than retreat into its shell.

■ On February 8, 2016, in Rufford, England, James Haywood and Dave Nicholls set a record by stacking 213 pancakes to a height of 3 feet 4 inches.

■ Pancake ice can be found in both fresh and salt water. It sometimes forms when water that is beginning to freeze is disturbed by wind or waves. As each small piece of ice bumps into others, sharp angles around its edge are worn down to form a ridge or rim—giving it the appearance of a pancake.

WEARING AN APRON AND HEADSCARF, OLNEY RACERS FLIP A PANCAKE IN A SKILLET AT THE START AND FINISH OF A RACE.

imminent Shrove Tuesday church service. When she heard the church bells ring, she rushed out the door to attend the service—still wearing her headscarf and apron and with pancake-laden skillet in hand. (Headscarves were mandatory attire for women in church in those days.) In her honor and spirit, today's racers must wear an apron and headscarf and run with a skillet containing a pancake to be flipped at the start of the 415-yard race and then

again at the finish line. The event has inspired runners from afar: In 1950, members of the Junior Chamber of Commerce in Liberal, Kansas, challenged Olney's residents to a friendly competition that has been going on ever since in their respective communities.

The Jewish holiday of Chanukah is also a time for partaking in pancakes. During this 8-day celebration, Jewish cultures eat latkes, or potato pancakes fried in oil. Oil plays a symbolic

role in the festivities: After a revolt by Jews in the 2nd century B.C. that reclaimed the Temple of Jerusalem, it is said that the victors could find only a vessel with enough oil to keep the Temple menorah lit for just 1 day—yet miraculously it lasted for 8 days.

Hungry? Make some pancakes, even if it isn't Shrove Tuesday (Feb. 13 this year). Try out the following recipes or have fun by creating your own!

Photos: Steve Parsons/PA Images/Getty Images; opposite, Yelena Yemchuk/Getty Images

BLUEBERRY BUTTERMILK PANCAKES

1½ cups all-purpose flour
1¼ teaspoons baking soda
½ teaspoon salt
2 cups buttermilk

1 teaspoon vanilla extract
1 egg, separated
1 cup blueberries

In a bowl, combine flour, baking soda, and salt. Make a well in the center of the dry ingredients and into it put the buttermilk, vanilla, and egg yolk. Stir until barely combined.

In a separate chilled bowl, beat egg white until stiff, then fold into batter.

Using a ¼ cup measure, drop batter onto a hot, greased griddle or skillet. Sprinkle a few blueberries over each pancake and cook for 3 to 5 minutes, or until bubbles form. Flip pancakes and cook the other side for an additional 2 to 3 minutes. Serve warm. **Makes 4 servings.**

(continued)

LATKES

4 large russet potatoes,
  peeled and grated
1 onion, grated
1 egg, lightly beaten
2 tablespoons all-purpose flour
1 teaspoon kosher or sea salt,
  plus extra for seasoning
½ teaspoon baking powder
2 tablespoons vegetable oil,
  plus more as needed
freshly ground black pepper,
  to taste
sour cream, applesauce, or fresh
  dill, for topping

Place potatoes and onions in a sieve or kitchen towel and squeeze out any excess water.

In a bowl, combine grated mixture, egg, flour, salt, and baking powder.

Warm oil in a large, heavy skillet over medium heat. Drop batter into skillet one heaping spoonful at a time (don't crowd the pan). Flatten gently; don't push potatoes too hard into oil. Fry in batches, adding more oil, if necessary, for 4 minutes per side, or until golden brown. Drain on paper towels and season well with salt and pepper.

Serve immediately with preferred toppings on the side.

Makes 12 servings. ■

Sarah Perreault, food editor of *The Old Farmer's Almanac*, prefers pumpkin pancakes to all other breakfast griddle goodies.

2023 RECIPE CONTEST WINNERS

We asked you for your best recipes using ginger,
and we received many delicious dishes. Sincere thanks
to all of you who took the time to submit recipes!

Styling and photography: Samantha Jones/Vaughan Communications

FIRST PRIZE: $300
**GINGER GREMOLATA
BAKED SALMON**
(recipe on page 200)

SECOND PRIZE: $200
**THAI GINGER
MEATBALL SALAD**
(recipe on page 200)

(continued)

THIRD PRIZE: $100
**GINGER PEACH CRISP
WITH GINGER-INFUSED
WHIPPED CREAM**
(recipe on page 200)

ENTER THE 2024 RECIPE CONTEST: FAVORITE HOLIDAY DISH
Got a scary Halloween treat, super side dish for
Thanksgiving, festive New Year's punch, or other holiday favorite?
Send it in and it could win! See contest rules on page 251.

HONORABLE MENTION
GINGER SWIRL BUNS
(recipe on page 201)

(continued on page 200)

Alaska
NORTH
AMERICA
Greenland
Labrador
Atlantic
Ocean
Pacific
Ocean
California
Gulf Stream
Canary
N. Equatorial
N. Equatorial
Equatorial
S. Equatorial
SOUTH
AMERICA
Atlantic
Ocean
Pacific
Ocean
Humboldt
S. Pacific
Brazil

CURRENT EVENTS

Why the oceans hold a key to our future climate

E arth is a complex system in which a mosaic of parts—oceans, land, and atmosphere—interact to create and sustain life as we know it. Any changes to one part of this system can have cascading impacts on other parts. As the average global temperature steadily increases due to greenhouse gas emissions, ocean currents are shifting. The changes are so consequential that new observations, often with specialized equipment, make headlines. For example, one current, the Atlantic Meridional Overturning Circulation (AMOC), was first measured in the 1950s. In the '90s, observations suggested that it might have been weakening, or slowing. It is now the subject of intense focus because a weak AMOC could be dire for life on Earth.

WHAT IS AN OCEAN CURRENT?

Just as the trade winds and jet streams move air in our atmosphere, currents move the ocean waters. Ocean currents do not have banks like rivers do, but they are particularly strong around the edges of the ocean basins where the continents and seafloor topography direct (and redirect) their flow. The largest currents have names—for example, the Gulf Stream (the part of the AMOC that flows from the Gulf of Mexico northward along the east coast of North America) and the Humboldt

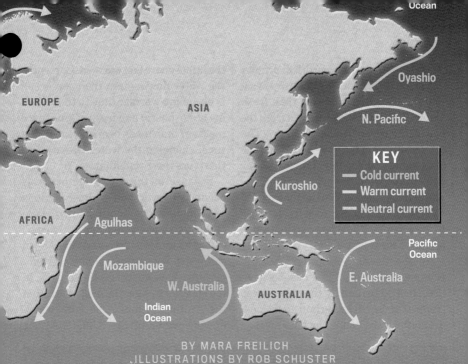

EUROPE

ASIA

AFRICA

AUSTRALIA

Oyashio

N. Pacific

Kuroshio

Agulhas

Mozambique

W. Australia

E. Australia

Indian
Ocean

Pacific
Ocean

Ocean

KEY
— Cold current
— Warm current
— Neutral current

BY MARA FREILICH
ILLUSTRATIONS BY ROB SCHUSTER

Current (which flows northward along the west coast of South America)—which signify their importance to life on the continents.

Ocean currents transport enormous amounts of water. The Gulf Stream moves from 30 to 150 million cubic meters per second, depending on location. In contrast, all of Earth's rivers input 1.2 million cubic meters per second of freshwater flow into the oceans.

The AMOC carries heat—in the form of warm water—northward. The water releases heat that warms the atmosphere and affects atmospheric pressure and wind patterns. As the water cools, it becomes denser. Eventually, in the far north Atlantic, the dense, cold water sinks, forming subsurface currents that turn southward. In the deep ocean, this cold water spreads through all of the ocean basins.

But not all ocean currents flow predictably. Many move in swirling, chaotic patterns, variously merging and separating. Together, the currents connect all of the ocean basins in a global system known as the "ocean conveyer belt." The belt carries water both downward into the depths of the ocean interior and upward toward the sea surface. The deepest, densest cold waters in the Pacific Ocean may have last been in contact with the atmosphere hundreds of years ago!

HOW ARE CURRENTS FORMED?

Ocean currents are generated by multiple forces. One of these is wind, which pushes water, creating surface currents. However, ocean currents move more slowly than wind. The fastest ocean currents travel at speeds only slightly greater than 5 miles per hour. Below the surface, variations in the density of

73

seawater also generate and drive currents.

One factor in seawater density is salinity. Salt water is denser than fresh water. When water evaporates from the ocean, the ocean becomes saltier. (The temperatures of both the ocean and the atmosphere affect how quickly water evaporates from the ocean.) Rain, rivers, and melting ice, like the thawing ice caps in Greenland, restore fresh water to the ocean—although these exchanges are not necessarily equal.

Another factor in ocean density is the water temperature. The oceans have absorbed 90 percent of the excess heat trapped on Earth by carbon emissions, dramatically reducing the amount that the atmosphere has warmed. Currently, the water flowing into the deep ocean is becoming warmer (due to the warming atmosphere) and fresher (due to ice melting) than it has been in a very long time, changing the water density and therefore the circulation.

Because of these two factors, this ocean conveyor belt—whose actions are complicated—is also known as the "thermohaline circulation" ("thermo" refers to temperature and "haline" to saltiness). Sometimes salinity and temperature have counteracting effects. In the cold North Atlantic, meltwater from the Arctic can make the northward-flowing water of the AMOC fresher

EDDIES AND CURRENTS

Ocean currents transport heat, making the east coast of North America warmer than the west coast at the same latitude. These currents have consistent patterns, but move in variable swirling paths called eddies and meanders. The Gulf Stream takes a meandering path as it transports warm water from south to north. Warm water is red and cold water is green and blue in the image below.

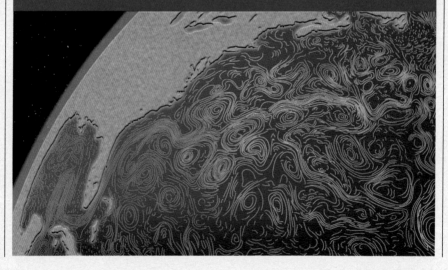

Graphic adapted from NASA

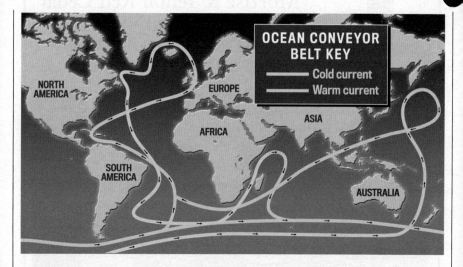

and therefore lighter, thus preventing it from sinking to depth even though it is cold. Some scientists think that such an effect is one possible cause of a slowing AMOC.

WHY ARE OCEAN CURRENTS IMPORTANT?

Water has been found to be especially effective at redistributing and storing heat. Ocean water can absorb more heat than air in the atmosphere can without significantly increasing in temperature. The amount of energy required to warm a cubic foot of ocean by 1 degree C is nearly 5,000 times what is needed to warm a cubic foot of air by the same amount. During the summer, when the air is warmer than the ocean, the ocean absorbs heat. During the winter, when the air is cool, the ocean slowly releases heat back to the atmosphere. By doing so, the ocean has a moderating effect on the climate of nearby land. This is why, along the U.S. East Coast and

parts of Atlantic Canada in winter, the heat-radiating Atlantic Ocean can turn snowstorms into rainstorms.

Similarly, myriad ocean currents—from the southward-flowing Labrador Current in the Atlantic Ocean to the California and Alaska Currents off the West Coast in the Pacific—impact local and global weather by altering the temperature and moisture content of the atmosphere. As atmospheric winds travel over the ocean, they pick up—or lose—heat and moisture. The ocean has a moderating effect on temperatures over land when warm, moisture-laden (or cool, dry) ocean winds blow over it.

CATCHING THE WAVES

Scientists study the movement of ocean currents via arrays of moorings that contain instruments designed to measure seawater's speed, temperature, salinity, and other properties (e.g., nutrients and oxygen). This information, combined with satellite observations of the ocean

GROW YOUR BEST GARDENS EVER!

The Old Farmer's Almanac Gardener's Handbooks are loaded with advice and inspiration to guarantee success for any gardener.

ON SALE NOW!

COMING IN APRIL 2024!

VEGETABLE GARDENER'S HANDBOOK
Sow, grow, and harvest delicious fresh food!

FLOWER GARDENER'S HANDBOOK
Surround yourself with gorgeous color all season!

CONTAINER GARDENER'S HANDBOOK
Learn how to grow almost anything in containers!

EACH HANDBOOK INCLUDES:

- practical advice for everything from soil to seedlings to storing the harvest
- inspirational ideas for creative enjoyment
- tips for easy plant and pot maintenance
- pest and disease prevention and care
- tables and charts for easy reference
- humorous anecdotes and advice from fellow gardeners
- pages for notes and record-keeping
- and too much more to mention!

COLLECT THEM ALL! GET YOUR COPIES TODAY!

GO TO ALMANAC.COM/SHOP OR AMAZON

77

surface, has shown that ocean currents are variable, not steady. Some current patterns vary by tens of years ("decadal" variability is a common measure); the El Niño Southern Oscillation (ENSO) in the Pacific is one example of this. The Atlantic Multidecadal Oscillation (AMO), linked to the AMOC, is another. As our observational record gets longer, scientists can detect suggestions of variations in the strengths of the ocean currents and their properties. Such changes could have a significant impact on our climate and weather for a long time.

Far below the sea surface, ocean water is insulated from the rapidly changing atmosphere, and its temperature and salinity change very slowly. Nevertheless, conditions in the deep ocean are still often determined by conditions at the sea surface. Water whose temperature and salinity have changed during a storm in one time and place at the surface will re-emerge in a different location, carried there by the ocean currents. Polar melting or changes in storminess in one year affect global weather and climate years—even centuries—later because of ocean circulation.

Even small variations in the temperature, strength, and positions of ocean currents can have important impacts on weather. For example, if the Gulf Stream slowed its transport

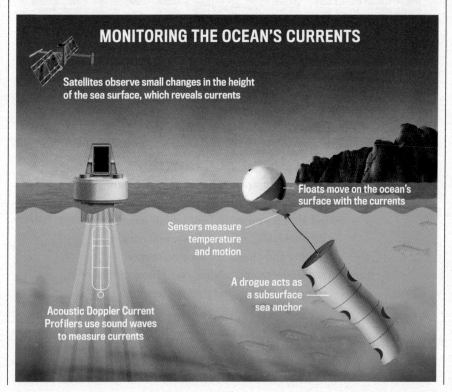

MONITORING THE OCEAN'S CURRENTS

Satellites observe small changes in the height of the sea surface, which reveals currents

Floats move on the ocean's surface with the currents

Sensors measure temperature and motion

A drogue acts as a subsurface sea anchor

Acoustic Doppler Current Profilers use sound waves to measure currents

Graphic adapted from NOAA

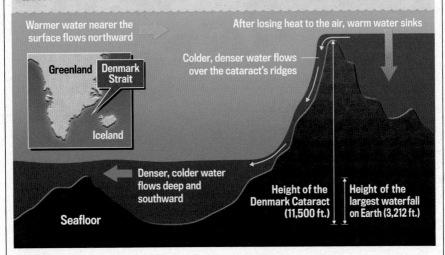

STRAIT DOWN

In the Denmark Strait between Greenland and Iceland, cold, dense ocean water (part of the down- and southward-flowing portion of the AMOC) sinks below warmer surface water onto a ridge that is 2,000 feet below the sea surface and then plunges to a depth of 11,500 feet. The Denmark Strait Cataract (waterfall) is more than three times the height of Angel Falls (aka Kerepakupai Merú) in Venezuela, which at 3,212 feet is the tallest waterfall on land.

Warmer water nearer the surface flows northward

After losing heat to the air, warm water sinks

Greenland

Denmark Strait

Iceland

Colder, denser water flows over the cataract's ridges

Denser, colder water flows deep and southward

Seafloor

Height of the Denmark Cataract (11,500 ft.)

Height of the largest waterfall on Earth (3,212 ft.)

of heat from the AMOC, northern Europe would be somewhat cooler. (This possibility would not completely offset global warming. Currently, projections suggest that any cooling in Europe from ocean heat transport would only reduce, not eliminate, atmospheric warming from greenhouse gas emissions.)

Similarly, the position of an ocean current can determine where there is moisture in the atmosphere, how much of it there is, and where it goes. This can affect the strength of storms and the whole climate system. For example, in the U.S. Midwest, a warmer North Atlantic is linked to droughts, including the Dust Bowl of the 1930s, while in the African Sahel, the same configuration is connected to increased rainfall.

The ocean is a slow yet massive part of our climate system. While the paths of future ocean currents are not clear, what is certain is that changes in ocean circulation today may have dramatic impacts on weather even far from the coasts, as well as possibly lead to climate changes that affect weather—and lives—for hundreds of years. ∎

Mara Freilich is an assistant professor of oceanography and applied mathematics at Brown University in Providence, Rhode Island. A hiker, backpacker, and bicyclist, she also enjoys ocean kayaking and snorkeling—despite her childhood fear of the sea.

Graphic adapted from NOAA

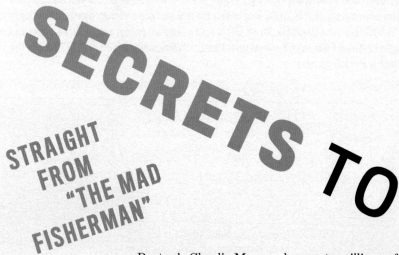

SECRETS TO

STRAIGHT FROM "THE MAD FISHERMAN"

Boston's Charlie Moore—known to millions of TV fans as "The Mad Fisherman"—is famous for his passionate pursuit of fish and boundless enthusiasm for the sport of angling. We asked him how he got started and how anyone can learn to love fishing as much as he does.

When I was a kid in the late '70s, I was lighting up Boston Harbor on my 14-foot Boston Whaler. My first rod and reel were a Penn deep-sea fishing setup. I loved bringing flounder back to the dock, filleting them up, and having them for dinner.

Even at age 8, I felt like I was ahead of my time when it came to fishing. A lot of commercial boats were docked at Crystal Cove Marina in Winthrop, Massachusetts, where

> "EVEN AT AGE 8, I FELT LIKE I WAS AHEAD OF MY TIME WHEN IT CAME TO FISHING."

my father had ours. Captain Norman's boat really caught a lot of fish. Almost every day during the summer, he would walk down and ask my father if I could go out with them—which I did every time I could! I learned a lot about striped bass, cod, bluefish, flounder, and haddock and really grew up with a lot of different ways to catch fish.

Fast-forward to my late teens, when I started learning the art of freshwater fishing from my future father-in-law,

FUN FISHING

BY CHARLIE MOORE

PHOTOS BY P. T. SULLIVAN

Dick Latini. Going out with him to small ponds around the North Shore area of Beverly, Massachusetts, was really how I came to enjoy freshwater bass fishing.

Am I crazy for fishing? Or just crazy? Probably a lot of both, but somehow people took notice of my great enthusiasm for the sport, and the rest is history, as I have now made more than 400 fishing shows.

IT'S ALL GOOD

But this isn't about *my* story. It's about people having more

"THERE ARE MANY, MANY DIFFERENT METHODS, TIMES, PLACES, AND LURES FOR CATCHING ANY FISH, AND THEY'RE ALL GOOD!"

fun when they fish, no matter who and where they are. There are many, many different methods, times, places, and lures for catching any fish—saltwater or freshwater—and they're all good! What's more, there's only one person who knows the "right" way for you to fish—*you!*

PRACTICE, PRACTICE, PRACTICE—OR NOT

Fishing is even more fun when you're *good* at it. The number one way to get better at anything is to make the most of your talents—and make no mistake about it, you already have what it takes.

Fishing is all about hand–eye coordination. Fish such as bass, bonefish, redfish, and snook require the cast to be precise, so anything that you can do to improve your overall strength and hand–eye coordination will help you over time. But we all do what we can with what we have, and any effort at all to hone your abilities is always great. Practice casting into a bucket in your backyard? Sounds good to me!

PUT IN THE TIME— ANY TIME, ANYTIME

The more time you put in at the water, the more adept you'll become. This doesn't have to mean going 10 miles out on a fancy boat—standing

by a pond or stream counts just as much. As the saying goes, "You can't catch a fish without a line in the water." Invest some time in gaining experience, and you'll definitely be rewarded. But *fish!*

TIMING ISN'T EVERYTHING

As far as time of year goes, sure: Fish move. They react differently in different seasons, but this doesn't happen as much as you'd think. When bass fishing, I always make my first casts into no more than 10 feet of water because I believe that I can always find catchable shallow-water fish. Plus, it's a lot easier to catch fish alongside visible underwater structure than it is to find them around an underwater hump in 60 feet of water. Don't worry about the timing. Think about where you can most easily reach the most fish.

IT'S A CONFIDENCE GAME

People are always asking me how to catch largemouth and smallmouth bass all year long. What are the secrets? The magical patterns? The special techniques?

Well, the answers always come down to an old adage: "Keep it simple, stupid." If you love a ½-ounce spinnerbait like I do, then throw it all day long, every day, for 12 months a year. *The best lure in your tack-*

> **"THE BEST LURE IN YOUR TACKLE BOX IS THE ONE THAT'S YOUR FAVORITE."**

le box is the one that's your favorite. This bait is called your "confidence bait."

Put together your own special tackle box with your top five favorite lures, in different sizes and colors. When you're toting this to the dock or boat ramp or shoreline, there's no question about it—you'll be feeling confident and success will lie just ahead!

DON'T BELIEVE THE HYPE!

With regard to lures, don't believe the hype! Don't believe

CELEBRATE YOUR LOVE OF GARDENING!

THE OLD FARMER'S ALMANAC
GARDENING CLUB

Your membership has privileges and benefits that are reserved exclusively for *you*—just look at what it includes!

IN PRINT . . .

THE 2024 OLD FARMER'S ALMANAC: The newest edition includes everything that you've come to expect from the world's premier Almanac—including gardening articles, Frosts and Growing Seasons, and more! You'll also have access to *The 2024 Old Farmer's Almanac* digital edition.

THE 2024 GARDENING CALENDAR: Enjoy beautiful botanical illustrations, useful gardening tips, inspirational quotes, and folklore.

THE 2023 *GARDEN GUIDE*: Grow herbs, vegetables, flowers, houseplants, and more.

GARDENING FOR EVERYONE: A curated collection of informative gardening articles.

ONLINE . . .

The following digital resources are available as soon as you activate your membership:

THE *GARDEN GUIDE* ONLINE LIBRARY: You'll find our complete collection of *Garden Guides* packed with no-nonsense tips, tricks, and inspiration!

DIGITAL BACK ISSUES: As part of your membership, you can read, download, or print past editions of *The Old Farmer's Almanac* going back to 2010!

EXTRA! Our monthly digital magazine features a lineup of valuable articles on topics such as gardening, food, weather, astronomy, and more!

Go to Almanac.com/Garden2024
or call 1-800-Almanac (800-256-2622) and select option 2.

U.S. Shipping Only

caught them on. After a while, you'll develop your own fishing patterns and styles, which will help you to catch more fish consistently during different times of year. As your success increases, so will your fun!

BE YOUR TRUE FISHING SELF

It's really funny. I tell people all the time that their personality will dictate their style of fishing. For example, I am high-energy and run at a million miles an hour. On the water, I am burning a ½-ounce Rat-L-Trap and a ½-ounce spinnerbait and then throwing them 400 times more than the average angler on any given day, which is upping my odds of catching more fish. But you can fish at any octane level you want—in whatever way is really *you*. If you're more slow-paced, no worries! Fish slow-paced. You'll still get good results if you make a lot of casts over time.

WHY WE'RE REALLY OUT THERE

Why is fishing so much fun for me? Well, it's the out-of-doors, the wildlife, the peacefulness, the excitement of rough water or bad weather, the ever-changing environment—you always need to be on your toes when fishing.

Unlike with almost any other sport, even when you have

in the latest and greatest lure or the latest and greatest color. *No, no, no.* Keep it *simple.* If your trusty Jitterbug lure worked in 1998, there's a good chance that the bass don't know what year it is now and will still bite it. Always stick with your "confidence" lures. You'll catch more fish.

WRITE YOU ARE

Keep a fishing journal, handwritten or on your phone or laptop, noting when and where you caught fish and what you

> "IF YOUR TRUSTY JITTERBUG LURE WORKED IN 1998, THERE'S A GOOD CHANCE THAT THE BASS DON'T KNOW WHAT YEAR IT IS NOW AND WILL STILL BITE IT."

Your Dream Garden Is Just a Click Away

Go from this . . .

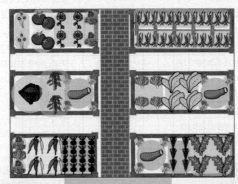

To this!

a bad day of fishing, it still offers up so much more. It's never a loss and always a big win, no matter what happens! For this reason, I always try to remember to be thankful for the opportunity to enjoy the natural world and the fun of fishing. We're out there to catch fish, sure, but we also should always appreciate that fishing is a total experience to be greeted with renewed gratitude every time we go out.

ONE MORE THING

Everybody has a different style. Everybody has a different technique. Everybody

> "WHEN IT COMES TO FISHING AND EVERYTHING ELSE THAT I DO IN MY LIFE, JUST LIKE FRANK SINATRA SANG, I DO IT MY WAY."

has an opinion: You should do this. You should do that. But in the end, I'm here to tell you that when it comes to fishing and everything else that I do in my life, just like Frank Sinatra sang, I do it my way— and to have the most fun fishing, *you* should, *too!*

And if you can take along an 8-year-old, please do! ∎

A TV host since 1996, irrepressible angler **Charlie Moore**—"The Mad Fisherman"—can be seen in *Charlie Moore: No Offense* (worldwide syndication, Roku TV, Apple TV) and *Charlie Moore Outdoors* on the New England Sports Network (NESN). For more information, go to CharlieMoore.com.

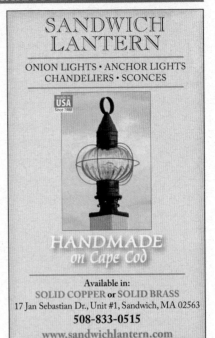

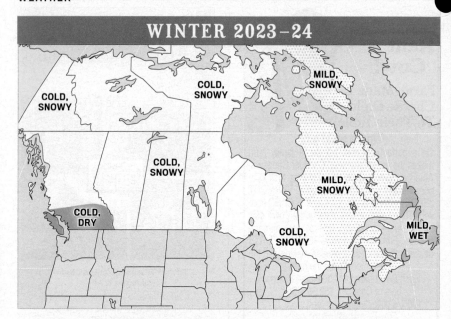

WINTER 2023–24

COLD, SNOWY

COLD, SNOWY

MILD, SNOWY

COLD, SNOWY

MILD, SNOWY

COLD, DRY

COLD, SNOWY

MILD, WET

These weather maps correspond to the winter and summer predictions in the General Weather Forecast (opposite) and on the regional forecast pages, 211–216. To learn more about how we make our forecasts, turn to page 209.

SUMMER 2024

WARM, RAINY

COOL, RAINY

WARM, RAINY

WARM, RAINY

WARM, DRY

WARM, DRY

COOL, RAINY

COOL, RAINY

HOT, DRY

HOT, RAINY

HOT, DRY

HOT, DRY

COOL, DRY

HOT, RAINY

WARM, RAINY

WARM, RAINY

Maps: AccuWeather, Inc.

THE GENERAL WEATHER REPORT AND FORECAST

FOR REGIONAL FORECASTS, SEE PAGES 211-216.

As we approach the middle of Solar Cycle 25, its increasing intensity is already as strong as that of Solar Cycle 24, which perhaps had the lowest solar activity in 200 years. This has usually meant cooler average temperatures across Earth, although this connection has become weaker. We expect a neutral to weak El Niño later in the year, a warm Atlantic Multidecadal Oscillation (AMO), and a cool Pacific Decadal Oscillation (PDO). Also important are the equatorial stratospheric winds in the Quasi-Biennial Oscillation, or QBO, which in certain combinations of conditions can contribute to the southward displacement of the polar vortex—and cold blasts for southern Canada this winter.

WINTER will be warmer than normal in Atlantic Canada and eastern Quebec and mostly colder elsewhere. Precipitation and snowfall will generally be above normal, except for in Southern British Columbia.

SPRING will be cooler than normal from Southern Ontario through Southern British Columbia and mostly warmer elsewhere. Precipitation will be above normal in southern Atlantic Canada, Southern Quebec, Southern Ontario, the Prairies, southeast British Columbia, southern Yukon, and the Northwest Territories and near to below normal elsewhere.

SUMMER will be hotter than normal, except for along the eastern side of Hudson Bay. Rainfall will be above normal from Atlantic Canada into eastern Southern Ontario and in southeast British Columbia, the Yukon, and the northern Northwest Territories and near to below normal elsewhere.

AUTUMN will be warmer than normal in Atlantic Canada and Southern Ontario, across the Prairies into Southern British Columbia, and in the Yukon and southern Northwest Territories; it will generally be cooler elsewhere. Precipitation will be below normal in northwest Ontario, the Prairies, and southwest British Columbia and near to above normal elsewhere.

The best chances for **TROPICAL STORMS** will occur from Atlantic Canada into Southern Ontario in early September and in Atlantic Canada in mid-October.

How Accurate Was Our Forecast Last Winter?

When looking at the direction of temperature departure for any one city in each region, our temperature forecasts for the December through February Canadian winter season were accurate in four of our seven zones, for a result of 57%. Our similar forecasts for precipitation were correct in six of the seven regions, which computes to an 86% accuracy rate. The Maritimes picked up less snow than we forecast, but, as we expected, there was greater snowfall in southern Ontario and Quebec, as well as in Vancouver. Our overall combined accuracy rate was 72%, which is a little below our traditional accuracy rate of 80%. As shown in the table below using one representative city from each region, the average difference between our winter season precipitation forecasts and the actual precipitation was 9mm.

REGION/CITY	Dec.–Feb. Precip. Departure From Normal (mm)		REGION/CITY	Dec.–Feb. Precip. Departure From Normal (mm)	
	PREDICTED	ACTUAL		PREDICTED	ACTUAL
1. Saint John, NB	53.3	38.1	5. Prince George, BC	−8.3	−12.1
2. Québec, QC	5.0	14.6	6. Whitehorse, YT	3.3	0.8
3. Toronto, ON	18.3	22.7	7. Resolute, NT	13.3	−3.8
4. Calgary, AB	26.7	12.6			

WEATHER

THE OLD
FARMER'S ALMANAC

Established in 1792 and published every year thereafter
ROBERT B. THOMAS, *founder* (1766–1846)

YANKEE PUBLISHING INC.
EDITORIAL AND PUBLISHING OFFICES
P.O. Box 520, 1121 Main Street, Dublin, NH 03444
Phone: 603-563-8111 • Fax: 603-563-8252

EDITOR *(13th since 1792):* Janice Stillman
CREATIVE DIRECTOR: Colleen Quinnell
MANAGING EDITOR: Jack Burnett
SENIOR EDITORS: Sarah Perreault, Heidi Stonehill
ASSOCIATE EDITOR: Tim Goodwin
WEATHER GRAPHICS AND CONSULTATION:
AccuWeather, Inc.

V.P., NEW MEDIA AND PRODUCTION:
Paul Belliveau
PRODUCTION DIRECTOR: David Ziarnowski
PRODUCTION MANAGER: Brian Johnson
SENIOR PRODUCTION ARTISTS:
Jennifer Freeman, Rachel Kipka, Janet Selle

WEB SITE: ALMANAC.CA
SENIOR DIGITAL EDITOR: Catherine Boeckmann
ASSOCIATE DIGITAL EDITOR: Jennifer Keating
SENIOR WEB DESIGNER: Amy O'Brien
DIGITAL MARKETING SPECIALISTS:
Jessica Garcia, Holly Sanderson
E-MAIL MARKETING SPECIALIST: Eric Bailey
E-COMMERCE MARKETING DIRECTOR: Alan Henning
PROGRAMMING: Peter Rukavina

CONTACT US
We welcome your questions and comments about articles and topics for this Almanac. Mail all editorial correspondence to Editor, The Old Farmer's Almanac, P.O. Box 520, Dublin, NH 03444-0520; fax us at 603-563-8252; or contact us through Almanac.ca/Contact. *The Old Farmer's Almanac* can not accept responsibility for unsolicited manuscripts and will not acknowledge any hard-copy queries or manuscripts that do not include a stamped and addressed return envelope.

All printing inks used in this edition of *The Old Farmer's Almanac* are soy-based. This product is recyclable. Consult local recycling regulations for the right way to do it.

Thank you for buying this Almanac! We hope that you find it "useful, with a pleasant degree of humour." Thanks, too, to everyone who had a hand in it, including advertisers, distributors, printers, and sales and delivery people.

OUR CONTRIBUTORS

BOB BERMAN, our astronomy editor, leads annual tours to Chilean observatories as well as to view solar eclipses and the northern lights. He is the author of 12 books, including *Zoom* (Little Brown, 2015) and *Earth-Shattering: Violent Supernovas, Galactic Explosions, Biological Mayhem, Nuclear Meltdowns, and Other Hazards to Life in Our Universe* (Little Brown, 2019).

DAN CLARK writes the weather doggerel verse that runs down the center of the Right-Hand Calendar Pages. His late father, Tim Clark, wrote the weather doggerel for more than 40 years.

BETHANY E. COBB, our astronomer, is an Associate Professor of Honors and Physics at George Washington University. In addition to conducting research on gamma-ray bursts and teaching astronomy and physics courses to non–science majors, she enjoys rock climbing, figure skating, and reading science fiction.

CELESTE LONGACRE, our astrologer, often refers to astrology as "a study of timing, and timing is everything." A New Hampshire native, she has been a practicing astrologer for more than 40 years. Her book, *Celeste's Garden Delights* (2015), is available on her Web site, CelesteLongacre.com.

BOB SMERBECK and **BRIAN THOMPSON,** our meteorologists, bring more than 50 years of forecasting expertise to the task, as well as some unique early accomplishments: a portable, wood-and-PVC-pipe tornado machine built by Bob and prescient 5-day forecasts made by Brian—in fourth grade.

TED WILLIAMS, a Massachusetts-based nature writer, pens the Farmer's Calendar essays. He serves on the Circle of Chiefs of the Outdoor Writers Association of America and writes about fish and wildlife for national publications. He is the author of *Earth Almanac* (Storey Publishing, 2020).

THE OLD
FARMER'S ALMANAC

Established in 1792 and published every year thereafter
ROBERT B. THOMAS, *founder* (1766–1846)

YANKEE PUBLISHING INC.
P.O. Box 520, 1121 Main Street, Dublin, NH 03444
Phone: 603-563-8111 • Fax: 603-563-8252

PUBLISHER *(23rd since 1792):* Sherin Pierce
EDITOR IN CHIEF: Judson D. Hale Sr.

FOR DISPLAY ADVERTISING RATES
Go to Almanac.ca/AdvertisingInfo or call 800-895-9265, ext. 109

Stephanie Bernbach-Crowe • 914-827-0015
Steve Hall • 800-736-1100, ext. 320

FOR CLASSIFIED ADVERTISING
Cindy Levine, RJ Media • 212-986-0016

SENIOR AD PRODUCTION COORDINATOR:
Janet Selle • 800-895-9265, ext. 168

PUBLIC RELATIONS
Vaughan Communications • 360-620-9107
Ginger Vaughan • ginger@vaughancomm.com

FOR ONLINE ORDERS,
go to Amazon.ca

RETAIL SALES
Stacey Korpi • 800-895-9265, ext. 160
Janice Edson, ext. 126

DISTRIBUTORS
NATIONAL: Comag Marketing Group
Smyrna, GA
BOOKSTORE: Firefly Books Ltd.
Richmond Hill, ON
NEWSSTAND CONSULTANT: PSCS Consulting
Linda Ruth • 603-924-4407

Old Farmer's Almanac publications are available for sales promotions or premiums. Contact Beacon Promotions, info@beaconpromotions.com.

YANKEE PUBLISHING INCORPORATED
A 100% EMPLOYEE-OWNED COMPANY

Jamie Trowbridge, *President;*
Paul Belliveau, Ernesto Burden, Judson D. Hale Jr.,
Brook Holmberg, Jennie Meister, Sherin Pierce,
Vice Presidents.

ECLIPSES

There will be four eclipses in 2024, two of the Sun and two of the Moon. Solar eclipses are visible only in certain areas and require eye protection to be viewed safely. Lunar eclipses are technically visible from the entire night side of Earth, but during a penumbral eclipse, the dimming of the Moon's illumination is slight. See the **Astronomical Glossary, page 110,** for explanations of the different types of eclipses.

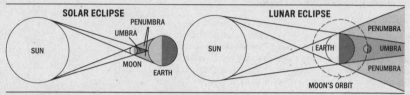

MARCH 24-25: PENUMBRAL ECLIPSE OF THE MOON. This eclipse is visible from North America. The Moon will enter the penumbra at 12:51 A.M. EDT on March 25 (9:51 P.M. PDT, March 24) and leave it at 5:35 A.M. EDT (2:35 A.M. PDT).

APRIL 8: TOTAL ECLIPSE OF THE SUN. This eclipse is visible from North America (except for Alaska). It will begin at 11:42 A.M. EDT and end at 4:52 P.M. EDT. The narrow path of totality in the U.S. extends northeast from Texas to Maine, crossing primarily through parts of Oklahoma, Arkansas, Missouri, Illinois, Kentucky, Indiana, Ohio, Pennsylvania, New York, Vermont, and New Hampshire. In Canada, it runs from southern Ontario to the island of Newfoundland, crossing through parts of southern Quebec, New Brunswick, and Prince Edward Island. For most other regions of North America, a partial eclipse will be visible. It is safe to look directly at the eclipse *only* during the brief period of totality. At all other times, you will need safety equipment such as "eclipse glasses" or a solar filter. (See "Behold Nature's Grandest Event!," page 158.)

SEPTEMBER 17-18: PARTIAL ECLIPSE OF THE MOON. Visible from most of North America, this is primarily a penumbral eclipse. On September 17, the Moon will enter the penumbra at 8:39 P.M. EDT (5:39 P.M. PDT) and umbra at 10:12 P.M. EDT (7:12 P.M. PDT). It will leave the umbra at 11:17 P.M. EDT (8:17 P.M. PDT) on September 17 and penumbra at 12:49 A.M. EDT on September 18 (9:49 P.M. PDT, September 17).

OCTOBER 2: ANNULAR ECLIPSE OF THE SUN. This eclipse is not visible from North America, although a partial eclipse will be visible from Hawaii. It will begin at 5:43 A.M. and end at 11:47 A.M. (HAT).

THE MOON'S PATH

The Moon's path across the sky changes with the seasons. Full Moons are very high in the sky (at midnight) between November and February and very low in the sky between May and July.

FULL-MOON DATES (ET)

	2024	2025	2026	2027	2028
JAN.	25	13	3	22	11
FEB.	24	12	1	20	10
MAR.	25	14	3	22	10
APR.	23	12	1	20	9
MAY	23	12	1 & 31	20	8
JUNE	21	11	29	18	7
JULY	21	10	29	18	6
AUG.	19	9	28	17	5
SEPT.	17	7	26	15	3
OCT.	17	6	26	15	3
NOV.	15	5	24	13	2
DEC.	15	4	23	13	1 & 31

New Blood Flow Breakthrough Helps Men Enjoy Strong, Long-Lasting Intimacy – At Any Age

Men across America are raving about a newly enhanced potency supplement that helps achieve healthy blood flow on demand

After age 40, it's common knowledge that performance begins to decline in many men. However, a new, performance empowering pill is showing that any relatively healthy man can now enjoy long-lasting, and frequent intimacy – at any age.

This doctor-designed formula, created by leading anti-aging expert Dr. Al Sears, has already helped men overcome low and sinking libido -- and has recently undergone a potency-enhancing update – with remarkable new results.

When the first pill -- **Primal Max Black** -- was first released, it quickly became a top-selling men's performance helper, promoting intimacy across America.

It worked by supporting healthy testosterone levels. However, Dr. Sears soon realized that this isn't the only challenge men face with performance. That's when he turned his attention to blood flow.

And this became **Primal Max Red**.

THIS PROVEN SOLUTION IS MORE MECHANICAL THAN HORMONAL

Truth is, once blood flow slows down for men, no matter how exciting it is, it won't be enough without the necessary amount...

So enjoying intimacy without healthy blood flow becomes difficult for most men.

Luckily, a Nobel prize-winning scientist discovered the simple answer to help support

performance strength and confidence -- by boosting vital blood flow -- and enhancing this essential performance function.

Using this landmark Nobel Prize as its basis, **Primal Max Red** enhanced healthy blood flow for untold millions of men around the world with the use of strong nitric oxide boosters.

While **Primal Max Black** helped maintain optimal testosterone, **Primal Max Red** tackles a lesser-known challenge.

Director, Al Sears MD, who has authored over 500 scientific papers and has appeared on more than 50 media outlets including ABC News, CNN, ESPN, Discovery, Lifetime, and many more say, *"Less than optimal blood flow can be part of a huge problem that affects a lot of men. And it needed to be addressed once and for all, so men would not dwell on it. Then, once we optimized it and had a great deal of success, we set out to see if we could do even better."*

The former formula had excellent results. However, new research showed that for even faster, anytime, anywhere results, increasing the dose of a key compound was needed.

So, one of the three nitric oxide boosters in the new **Primal Max Red**, L-Citrulline, was clinically boosted to 9000 mg, and the results were astounding. Which is no surprise considering that 5000 mg is considered a "normal amount" -- giving the new version nearly doubled the blood flow boosting power.

Men who had previously been unsure about their

A new discovery that increases nitric oxide availability was recently proven to boost blood flow 275% - resulting in improved performance.

power and stamina were overjoyed to be back to their old selves and to get and maintain a healthy bloodflow when they needed it.

BETTER BLOOD FLOW, STRONGER RESULTS

The best way to promote healthy blood flow throughout the body is with the use of **Primal Max Red**. By using it, when exciting signals leave the brain, blood flows much faster like it used to.

This critical action is how men across the country are enjoying full and satisfying performance at any age. No need to bother with testosterone-boosting shots, blue pills, or shady capsules that have no effect.

Primal Max Red can effectively promote healthy blood flow that most men can use for maximum intimacy. This is leading to more greater capacity and satisfaction, coupled with long-lasting performance.

"There was a time when men had little control when it came to boosting their blood flow," Dr. Sears said. "But science has come a long way in recent years. And now, with the creation of nitric oxide-boosting

Primal Max Red, men can perform better than ever, and enjoy intimacy at any age."

Now for men across America, it's much easier to stay at their performance peak as they get older.

HOW TO GET PRIMAL MAX RED (AND FREE PRIMAL MAX BLACK):

To secure free bottles of **Primal Max Black** and get the hot, new **Primal Max Red** formula, buyers should contact the Sears Health Hotline at **1-800-906-4782** TODAY. "It's not available in retail stores yet," says Dr. Sears. "The Hotline allows us to ship directly to the customer." Dr. Sears feels so strongly about **Primal Max**, all orders are backed by a 100% money-back guarantee. "Just send me back the bottle and any unused product within 90 days from purchase date, and I'll send you all your money back."

Call NOW at **1-800-906-4782** to secure your supply of **Primal Max Red** and free bottles of **Primal Max Black**. Use Promo Code **OFAPMX0823** when you call. Lines are frequently busy, but all calls will be answered!

BRIGHT STARS

TRANSIT TIMES

This table shows the time (ET) and altitude of a star as it transits the meridian (i.e., reaches its highest elevation while passing over the horizon's south point) at Ottawa on the dates shown. The transit time on any other date differs from that of the nearest date listed by approximately 4 minutes per day. To find the time of a star's transit for your location, convert its time at Ottawa using Key Letter C (see Time Corrections, page 240).

STAR	CONSTELLATION	MAGNITUDE	TIME OF TRANSIT (ET) BOLD = P.M. LIGHT = A.M.						ALTITUDE (DEGREES)
			JAN. 1	MAR. 1	MAY 1	JULY 1	SEPT. 1	NOV. 1	
Altair	Aquila	0.8	**1:11**	9:15	6:15	2:16	**10:08**	**6:08**	56.3
Deneb	Cygnus	1.3	**2:01**	10:05	7:06	3:06	**10:58**	**6:58**	92.8
Fomalhaut	Psc. Aus.	1.2	**4:18**	**12:22**	9:22	5:22	1:18	**9:15**	17.8
Algol	Perseus	2.2	**8:28**	**4:32**	**1:32**	9:32	5:28	1:29	88.5
Aldebaran	Taurus	0.9	**9:55**	**5:59**	**2:59**	10:59	6:56	2:56	64.1
Rigel	Orion	0.1	**10:33**	**6:37**	**3:38**	11:38	7:34	3:34	39.4
Capella	Auriga	0.1	**10:36**	**6:40**	**3:40**	11:41	7:37	3:37	93.6
Bellatrix	Orion	1.6	**10:44**	**6:48**	**3:48**	11:48	7:45	3:45	54.0
Betelgeuse	Orion	var. 0.4	**11:14**	**7:18**	**4:18**	**12:18**	8:15	4:15	55.0
Sirius	Can. Maj.	-1.4	12:08	**8:08**	**5:08**	**1:08**	9:04	5:05	31.0
Procyon	Can. Min.	0.4	1:02	**9:02**	**6:02**	**2:02**	9:59	5:59	52.9
Pollux	Gemini	1.2	1:08	**9:08**	**6:08**	**2:08**	10:05	6:05	75.7
Regulus	Leo	1.4	3:30	**11:31**	**8:31**	**4:31**	**12:27**	8:27	59.7
Spica	Virgo	var. 1.0	6:47	2:51	**11:47**	**7:47**	**3:43**	11:44	36.6
Arcturus	Boötes	-0.1	7:37	3:41	12:41	**8:37**	**4:34**	**12:34**	66.9
Antares	Scorpius	var. 0.9	9:51	5:55	2:55	**10:51**	6:47	**2:48**	21.3
Vega	Lyra	0	11:57	8:01	5:01	1:02	**8:54**	**4:54**	86.4

RISE AND SET TIMES

To find the time of a star's rising at Ottawa on any date, subtract the interval shown at right from the star's transit time on that date; add the interval to find the star's setting time. To find the rising and setting times for your city, convert the Ottawa transit times above using the Key Letter shown at right before applying the interval (see Time Corrections, page 240). Deneb, Algol, Capella, and Vega are circumpolar stars—they never set but appear to circle the celestial north pole.

STAR	INTERVAL (H.M.)	RISING KEY	DIR.*	SETTING KEY	DIR.*
Altair	6 36	B	EbN	E	WbN
Fomalhaut	3 59	E	SE	D	SW
Aldebaran	7 06	B	ENE	D	WNW
Rigel	5 33	D	EbS	B	WbS
Bellatrix	6 27	B	EbN	D	WbN
Betelgeuse	6 31	B	EbN	D	WbN
Sirius	5 00	D	ESE	B	WSW
Procyon	6 23	B	EbN	D	WbN
Pollux	8 01	A	NE	E	NW
Regulus	6 49	B	EbN	D	WbN
Spica	5 23	D	EbS	B	WbS
Arcturus	7 19	A	ENE	E	WNW
Antares	4 17	E	SEbE	A	SWbW

*b = "by"

THE TWILIGHT ZONE/METEOR SHOWERS

Twilight is the time when the sky is partially illuminated preceding sunrise and again following sunset. The ranges of twilight are defined according to the Sun's position below the horizon. **Civil twilight** occurs when the Sun's center is between the horizon and 6 degrees below the horizon (visually, the horizon is clearly defined). **Nautical twilight** occurs when the center is between 6 and 12 degrees below the horizon (the horizon is distinct). **Astronomical twilight** occurs when the center is between 12 and 18 degrees below the horizon (sky illumination is imperceptible). When the center is at 18 degrees (**dawn** or **dark**) or below, there is no illumination.

LENGTH OF ASTRONOMICAL TWILIGHT (HOURS AND MINUTES)

LATITUDE	JAN. 1–APR. 10	APR. 11–MAY 2	MAY 3–MAY 14	MAY 15–MAY 25	MAY 26–JULY 22	JULY 23–AUG. 3	AUG. 4–AUG. 14	AUG. 15–SEPT. 5	SEPT. 6–DEC. 31
37°N to 42°N	1 33	1 39	1 47	1 52	1 59	1 52	1 47	1 39	1 33
43°N to 47°N	1 42	1 51	2 02	2 13	2 27	2 13	2 02	1 51	1 42
48°N to 49°N	1 50	2 04	2 22	2 42	–	2 42	2 22	2 04	1 33
50°N to 55°N	1 54	2 15	2 52	3 25	–	3 11	2 37	2 10	1 53
56°N to 60°N	2 12	3 04	–	–	–	–	–	2 46	2 11

TO DETERMINE THE LENGTH OF TWILIGHT: The length of twilight changes with latitude and the time of year. See the **Time Corrections, page 240,** to find the latitude of your city or the city nearest you. Use that figure in the chart above with the appropriate date to calculate the length of twilight in your area.

TO DETERMINE ARRIVAL OF DAWN OR DARK: Calculate the sunrise/sunset times for your locality using the instructions in **How to Use This Almanac, page 116.**

Subtract the length of twilight from the time of sunrise to determine when dawn breaks. Add the length of twilight to the time of sunset to determine when dark descends.

EXAMPLE:
OTTAWA, ONT. (LATITUDE 45°25')

Sunrise, August 1	5:48 A.M. ET
Length of twilight	– 2 13
Dawn breaks	3:35 A.M.
Sunset, August 1	8:30 P.M. ET
Length of twilight	+2 13
Dark descends	10:43 P.M.

PRINCIPAL METEOR SHOWERS

SHOWER	BEST VIEWING	POINT OF ORIGIN	DATE OF MAXIMUM*	NO. PER HOUR**	ASSOCIATED COMET
Quadrantid	**Predawn**	**N**	**Jan. 4**	**25**	–
Lyrid	Predawn	S	Apr. 22	10	Thatcher
Eta Aquarid	Predawn	SE	May 4	10	Halley
Delta Aquarid	Predawn	S	July 30	10	–
Perseid	**Predawn**	**NE**	**Aug. 11–13**	**50**	**Swift-Tuttle**
Draconid	Late evening	NW	Oct. 9	6	Giacobini-Zinner
Orionid	Predawn	S	Oct. 21–22	15	Halley
Northern Taurid	Late evening	S	Nov. 9	3	Encke
Leonid	Predawn	S	Nov. 17–18	10	Tempel-Tuttle
Andromedid	Late evening	S	Nov. 25–27	5	Biela
Geminid	**All night**	**NE**	**Dec. 13–14**	**75**	–
Ursid	Predawn	N	Dec. 22	5	Tuttle

*May vary by 1 or 2 days   **In a moonless, rural sky   **Bold** = most prominent

Takes 10 Years Off Your Face in as Little as 10 Minutes

Women are raving about the life-changing effects of this powerful formula.

There's no denying that people — mostly women — are on a mission to discover the best way to eliminate fine lines and wrinkles permanently. The $14 billion dollars spent on aesthetic procedures in 2021 alone is a clear indication of that fact.

But now science appears to be offering a simpler solution. It's a special delivery technology adapted for skincare that gets superior results.

Known as advanced liposome technology, this powerful distribution system ensures that vital nutrients are delivered exactly where your skin needs them the most, providing your skin with maximum anti-aging benefits.

New Age-Defying 'Dermal Filler' Cream in High Demand

Al Sears, MD, of Palm Beach, Florida, recently released an anti-aging cream that adapts this breakthrough medical technology into the realm of skincare, and he's struggling to keep up with consumer demand.

Dr. Sears is South Florida's leading anti-aging pioneer. He has authored over 500 reports, scientific papers, and books on anti-aging. A frequent lecturer at global anti-aging conferences, Dr. Sears spoke at the WPBF 25 Health & Wellness Festival featuring Dr. Oz, along with special guest, Suzanne Somers. Thousands of people were in attendance as Dr. Sears discussed his latest anti-aging breakthroughs.

This powerful cream, known as **Restore**, keeps selling out faster than it's produced — and people are raving about the effect it's having on their skin.

"Within a few minutes of applying the cream, it visibly plumps out the under-eye area and my cheeks as well as those annoying lines that deepen as we age between the nose and lips. It also felt like it was tightening and smoothing my skin at the same time. I definitely feel I look younger whenever I use it," said Amy B., of Montville, New Jersey.

"The lines around my mouth and eyes are filled in and my skin is tightened. I love having younger-looking skin, so I will continue using **Restore**" raves Cathy C., of Florida.

The best part is that this cream has no adverse side effects, doesn't require a doctor's visit or prescription, and is 100% natural.

> "Advanced liposome technology ensures that vital nutrients are delivered exactly where your skin needs them the most."

Powerful Delivery System Ensures Nutrients Penetrate Deep into Your Skin

The dermis is the underlying layer of skin that supplies nourishment and oxygen, and removes waste. In other words, it's responsible for keeping your outer layer of skin healthy. Liposome technology is designed to support and nourish this deeper layer of skin by delivering nutrients directly to it.

"All of **Restore's** powerful ingredients are encapsulated in a liposome shell — an organic container that carries the beautifying agents deep into the skin cells," explained Dr. Sears.

"**Restore's** liposome shell is composed of phosphatidylcholine or PC for short. While cell membranes repel water, they absorb PC because they're actually made of it. As a result, **Restore** is delivered deep into the cell for maximum firming and volume."

When you apply liposome cream to your face, the liposomes in the skin cream work their way inside your skin, fuse with the skin cell membranes and then release their contents directly to the cells. Regular skin creams don't have this capability.

A Formula Designed to Take Years off Your Face in Minutes

Once it's penetrated the deeper layer of skin, **Restore** releases a unique blend of botanicals, vitamins and essential oils that reduces the appearance of fine lines and wrinkles, gives skin a more even tone, and moisturizes the interior layers of your dermal cells, firming and plumping your skin.

Restore's first skin-enhancing agent is Madonna lily leaf stem cell extract. It helps produce an even-toned complexion. In a clinical study reported in the Journal of Cosmetic Dermatology, participants treated with this extract for 28 days showed improvements in skin luminance and tone around the eyes.

Restore is also loaded with vitamin C, which British researchers have found reduces both wrinkles and dryness. "In **Restore** we use magnesium ascorbyl phosphate, a more stable form of vitamin C that doesn't break down in liquid as does ordinary C," explains Dr. Sears. "That means the antioxidant molecules stay intact within your skin cells where they can prevent damage from dangerous free radicals."

This powerful formula also features guarana seed extract, coenzyme Q10, and avocado oil. Japanese researchers have also found that coenzyme Q10 supports production of the thin membrane that separates layers of your skin, and French studies have shown that avocado oil improves skin cell metabolism and enhances skin thickness.

Where To Get Restore

To secure the hot, new **Restore** formula, buyers should contact the Sears Health Hotline at **1-800-690-1935** TODAY. "It's not available in retail stores yet," says Dr. Sears. "The Hotline allows us to ship directly to the customer." Dr. Sears feels so strongly about **Restore**, all orders are backed by a 100% money-back guarantee. "Just send me back the bottle and any unused product within 90 days from purchase date, and I'll send you all your money back."

Call NOW at **1-800-690-1935** to secure your supply of **Restore**. Use Promo Code **OFARS0823** when you call. Lines are frequently busy, but all calls will be answered!

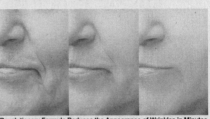

Revolutionary Formula Reduces the Appearance of Wrinkles in Minutes

107

THE VISIBLE PLANETS

Listed here for Ottawa are viewing suggestions for and the rise and set times (ET) of Venus, Mars, Jupiter, and Saturn on specific days each month, as well as when it is best to view Mercury. Approximate rise and set times for other days can be found by interpolation. Use the Key Letters at the right of each listing to convert the times for other localities **(see pages 116 and 240).**

GET ALL PLANET RISE AND SET TIMES BY POSTAL CODE VIA ALMANAC.CA/2024.

VENUS

Our nearest planetary neighbor starts 2024 as a morning star in the east just before dawn. On January 1, Venus shines at a dazzling magnitude –4.0, bright enough to cast shadows in rural areas when the Moon is absent. The splendor eventually fades as it falls closer to the sunrise while still a magnitude –3.9, which it maintains through mid-October. Its superior conjunction with the Sun happens on June 4, after which it can't be easily seen until late July, when the planet returns as an evening star moving upward in dusk's twilight. Look for a Venus–Moon conjunction on August 5. Autumn and then especially December bring a dramatic improvement, as Venus climbs to its maximum 47-degree separation from the Sun while brightening to a magnitude –4.4 at year's end.

Jan. 1	rise	4:44	E	Apr. 1	rise	6:17	C	July 1	set	9:27	E	Oct. 1	set	7:50	B
Jan. 11	rise	5:06	E	Apr. 11	rise	6:03	C	July 11	set	9:30	E	Oct. 11	set	7:40	A
Jan. 21	rise	5:26	E	Apr. 21	rise	5:49	B	July 21	set	9:26	E	Oct. 21	set	7:35	A
Feb. 1	rise	5:41	E	May 1	rise	5:36	B	Aug. 1	set	9:17	D	Nov. 1	set	7:37	A
Feb. 11	rise	5:50	E	May 11	rise	5:26	B	Aug. 11	set	9:05	D	Nov. 11	set	6:45	A
Feb. 21	rise	5:52	E	May 21	rise	5:19	A	Aug. 21	set	8:51	C	Nov. 21	set	7:00	A
Mar. 1	rise	5:49	D	June 1	rise	5:17	A	Sept. 1	set	8:33	C	Dec. 1	set	7:20	A
Mar. 11	rise	6:42	D	June 11	**set**	**9:00**	E	Sept. 11	set	8:18	C	Dec. 11	set	7:43	B
Mar. 21	rise	6:31	D	June 21	**set**	**9:17**	E	Sept. 21	set	8:03	B	Dec. 21	set	8:06	B
												Dec. 31	set	8:28	B

MARS

Earth and Mars meet every 26 months, so the Red Planet has alternating good and bad years for viewing—2024 being one of the latter. Mars starts off dim, distant, and tiny and remains that way during the entire first half of the year. It has neither a conjunction with the Sun nor an opposition to it in 2024, and it never brightens enough to outshine the stars. Attention will turn to Mars in the fall, though, as it reaches a very bright magnitude 0 in early November, in Cancer, and hovers just above the Moon on November 21. Mars's best moment will arrive on December 18, when it has an extremely close and beautiful conjunction with the Moon while shining at an eye-catching magnitude –0.89.

Jan. 1	rise	6:53	E	Apr. 1	rise	5:38	D	July 1	rise	2:09	B	Oct. 1	**rise**	**11:38**	A
Jan. 11	rise	6:47	E	Apr. 11	rise	5:15	D	July 11	rise	1:49	B	Oct. 11	**rise**	**11:23**	A
Jan. 21	rise	6:38	E	Apr. 21	rise	4:52	C	July 21	rise	1:30	A	Oct. 21	**rise**	**11:05**	A
Feb. 1	rise	6:26	E	May 1	rise	4:28	C	Aug. 1	rise	1:10	A	Nov. 1	**rise**	**10:43**	A
Feb. 11	rise	6:12	E	May 11	rise	4:05	C	Aug. 11	rise	12:54	A	Nov. 11	**rise**	**9:19**	A
Feb. 21	rise	5:57	E	May 21	rise	3:41	C	Aug. 21	rise	12:38	A	Nov. 21	**rise**	**8:51**	A
Mar. 1	rise	5:41	E	June 1	rise	3:16	B	Sept. 1	rise	12:22	A	Dec. 1	**rise**	**8:17**	A
Mar. 11	rise	6:22	D	June 11	rise	2:53	B	Sept. 11	rise	12:08	A	Dec. 11	**rise**	**7:35**	A
Mar. 21	rise	6:01	D	June 21	rise	2:31	B	Sept. 21	**rise**	**11:53**	A	Dec. 21	**rise**	**6:47**	A
												Dec. 31	**rise**	**5:51**	A

BOLD = P.M.   LIGHT = A.M.

JUPITER

The largest planet starts the year as a conspicuous evening star, high in the southeast at nightfall. It then steadily falls lower toward the sunset until it's too low to observe in April. Jupiter passes behind the Sun on May 18 and reappears as a morning star, in Taurus, in June. The fascinating gas giant steadily approaches Mars from August 1 to 13 until they hover together in a close conjunction from August 13 to 16. Rising 2 hours earlier each month, Jupiter is in opposition on December 7, its biggest and brightest night of the year.

Date				Date				Date				Date			
Jan. 1	set	2:30	D	Apr. 1	set	10:33	D	July 1	rise	3:15	A	Oct. 1	rise	9:57	A
Jan. 11	set	1:52	D	Apr. 11	set	10:05	E	July 11	rise	2:43	A	Oct. 11	rise	9:18	A
Jan. 21	set	1:16	D	Apr. 21	set	9:38	E	July 21	rise	2:10	A	Oct. 21	rise	8:37	A
Feb. 1	set	12:38	D	May 1	set	9:11	E	Aug. 1	rise	1:34	A	Nov. 1	rise	7:52	A
Feb. 11	set	12:05	D	May 11	set	8:44	E	Aug. 11	rise	1:01	A	Nov. 11	rise	6:09	A
Feb. 21	set	11:30	D	May 21	rise	5:26	A	Aug. 21	rise	12:28	A	Nov. 21	rise	5:25	A
Mar. 1	set	11:03	D	June 1	rise	4:50	A	Sept. 1	rise	11:47	A	Dec. 1	rise	4:41	A
Mar. 11	set	11:33	D	June 11	rise	4:18	A	Sept. 11	rise	11:11	A	Dec. 11	set	7:19	E
Mar. 21	set	11:04	D	June 21	rise	3:47	A	Sept. 21	rise	10:35	A	Dec. 21	set	6:34	E
												Dec. 31	set	5:49	E

SATURN

The universe's most beautiful planet begins 2024 as an evening star in Aquarius. After a decade-long occupation of the zodiac's most southerly constellations, Saturn finally moves up and away from that unfavorable position. Its rings—now almost edgewise to our view—can be seen through any telescope with more than 30× magnification. In mid-February, the Ringed Planet becomes too low to observe before gliding invisibly behind the Sun on February 28. It emerges as a morning star during the next few months, meeting Mars on April 10–11 low in the east 40 minutes before sunrise. Its opposition and closest approach occur on September 8, after which it remains high and glorious the rest of the year.

Date				Date				Date				Date			
Jan. 1	set	8:56	B	Apr. 1	rise	5:53	D	July 1	rise	12:09	C	Oct. 1	set	4:56	B
Jan. 11	set	8:22	B	Apr. 11	rise	5:17	D	July 11	rise	11:26	C	Oct. 11	set	4:13	B
Jan. 21	set	7:48	B	Apr. 21	rise	4:40	D	July 21	rise	10:47	D	Oct. 21	set	3:31	B
Feb. 1	set	7:11	B	May 1	rise	4:02	D	Aug. 1	rise	10:02	D	Nov. 1	set	2:46	B
Feb. 11	set	6:38	B	May 11	rise	3:25	D	Aug. 11	rise	9:22	D	Nov. 11	set	1:06	B
Feb. 21	set	6:05	B	May 21	rise	2:47	D	Aug. 21	rise	8:42	D	Nov. 21	set	12:27	B
Mar. 1	rise	6:47	D	June 1	rise	2:05	C	Sept. 1	rise	7:57	D	Dec. 1	set	11:45	B
Mar. 11	rise	7:11	D	June 11	rise	1:27	C	Sept. 11	set	6:22	B	Dec. 11	set	11:08	B
Mar. 21	rise	6:34	D	June 21	rise	12:48	C	Sept. 21	set	5:39	B	Dec. 21	set	10:31	B
												Dec. 31	set	9:56	B

MERCURY

The speedy innermost planet zips from morning to evening twilight and back again several times a year. Mercury appears as a predawn morning star from January 1–27, with a strikingly close but very low conjunction with Mars on January 27. As an evening star in the west, Mercury is both bright and easy to view from March 14–25. Its best moment is probably on July 7, when it hangs just below the crescent Moon while shining at a brilliant magnitude –0.2. From September 1 to 16, Mercury is again visible as a predawn morning star.

DO NOT CONFUSE: *Saturn with Mars on March 29 in the morning. Mars is higher and orange. • Mars with Taurus's brightest star, Aldebaran, on July 30, next to the crescent Moon. Both are orange, but Mars is slightly brighter. • Mars with Jupiter when they meet in mid-August. Jupiter is much brighter and yellow-white. • Uranus with the Pleiades star cluster during November. The planet is just to the right of the stars, looks distinctly green (through binoculars), and doesn't twinkle.*

ASTRONOMICAL GLOSSARY

APHELION (APH.): The point in a planet's orbit that is farthest from the Sun.

APOGEE (APO.): The point in the Moon's orbit that is farthest from Earth.

CELESTIAL EQUATOR (EQ.): The imaginary circle around the celestial sphere that can be thought of as the plane of Earth's equator projected out onto the sphere.

CELESTIAL SPHERE: An imaginary sphere projected into space that represents the entire sky, with an observer on Earth at its center. All celestial bodies other than Earth are imagined as being on its inside surface.

CIRCUMPOLAR: Always visible above the horizon, such as a circumpolar star.

CONJUNCTION: The time at which two or more celestial bodies appear closest in the sky. **Inferior (Inf.):** Mercury or Venus is between the Sun and Earth. **Superior (Sup.):** The Sun is between a planet and Earth. Actual dates for conjunctions are given on the **Right-Hand Calendar Pages, 121–147;** the best times for viewing the closely aligned bodies are given in **Sky Watch** on the **Left-Hand Calendar Pages, 120–146.**

DECLINATION: The celestial latitude of an object in the sky, measured in degrees north or south of the celestial equator; comparable to latitude on Earth. This Almanac gives the Sun's declination at noon.

ECLIPSE, LUNAR: The full Moon enters the shadow of Earth, which cuts off all or part of the sunlight reflected off the Moon. **Total:** The Moon passes completely through the umbra (central dark part) of Earth's shadow. **Partial:** Only part of the Moon passes through the umbra. **Penumbral:** The Moon passes through only the penumbra (area of partial darkness surrounding the umbra). See **page 102** for more information about eclipses.

ECLIPSE, SOLAR: Earth enters the shadow of the new Moon, which cuts off all or part of the Sun's light. **Total:** Earth passes through the umbra (central dark part) of the Moon's shadow, resulting in totality for observers within a narrow band on Earth. **Annular:** The Moon appears silhouetted against the Sun, with a ring of sunlight showing around it. **Partial:** The Moon blocks only part of the Sun.

ECLIPTIC: The apparent annual path of the Sun around the celestial sphere. The plane of the ecliptic is tipped 23½° from the celestial equator.

ELONGATION: The difference in degrees between the celestial longitudes of a planet and the Sun. **Greatest Elongation (Gr. Elong.):** The greatest apparent distance of a planet from the Sun, as seen from Earth.

EPACT: A number from 1 to 30 that indicates the Moon's age on January 1 at Greenwich, England; used in determining the date of Easter.

EQUINOX: When the Sun crosses the celestial equator. This event occurs two times each year: **Vernal** is around March 20 and **Autumnal** is around September 22.

EVENING STAR: A planet that is above the western horizon at sunset and less than 180° east of the Sun in right ascension.

GOLDEN NUMBER: A number in the 19-year Metonic cycle of the Moon, used in determining the date of Easter. See **page 149** for this year's Golden Number.

MAGNITUDE: A measure of a celestial object's brightness. **Apparent magnitude** measures the brightness of an object as seen from Earth. Objects with an apparent magnitude of 6 or less are observable to the naked eye. The lower the magnitude, the greater the brightness; an object with a magnitude of –1, e.g., is brighter than one with a magnitude of +1.

(continued)

ASTRONOMICAL GLOSSARY

MIDNIGHT: Astronomically, the time when the Sun is opposite its highest point in the sky. Both 12 hours before and after noon (so, technically, both A.M. and P.M.), midnight in civil time is usually treated as the beginning of the day. It is displayed as 12:00 A.M. on 12-hour digital clocks. On a 24-hour cycle, 00:00, not 24:00, usually indicates midnight.

MOON ON EQUATOR: The Moon is on the celestial equator.

MOON RIDES HIGH/RUNS LOW: The Moon is highest above or farthest below the celestial equator.

MOONRISE/MOONSET: When the Moon rises above or sets below the horizon.

MOON'S PHASES: The changing appearance of the Moon, caused by the different angles at which it is illuminated by the Sun. **First Quarter:** Right half of the Moon is illuminated. **Full:** The Sun and the Moon are in opposition; the entire disk of the Moon is illuminated. **Last Quarter:** Left half of the Moon is illuminated. **New:** The Sun and the Moon are in conjunction; the Moon is darkened because it lines up between Earth and the Sun.

MOON'S PLACE, Astronomical: The position of the Moon within the constellations on the celestial sphere at midnight. **Astrological:** The position of the Moon within the tropical zodiac, whose twelve 30° segments (signs) along the ecliptic were named more than 2,000 years ago after constellations within each area. Because of precession and other factors, the zodiac signs no longer match actual constellation positions.

MORNING STAR: A planet that is above the eastern horizon at sunrise and less than 180° west of the Sun in right ascension.

NODE: Either of the two points where a celestial body's orbit intersects the ecliptic. **Ascending:** When the body is moving from south to north of the ecliptic. **Descending:** When the body is moving from north to south of the ecliptic.

OCCULTATION (OCCN.): When the Moon or a planet eclipses a star or planet.

OPPOSITION: The Moon or a planet appears on the opposite side of the sky from the Sun (elongation 180°).

PERIGEE (PERIG.): The point in the Moon's orbit that is closest to Earth.

PERIHELION (PERIH.): The point in a planet's orbit that is closest to the Sun.

PRECESSION: The slowly changing position of the stars and equinoxes in the sky caused by a slight wobble as Earth rotates around its axis.

RIGHT ASCENSION (R.A.): The celestial longitude of an object in the sky, measured eastward along the celestial equator in hours of time from the vernal equinox; comparable to longitude on Earth.

SOLSTICE, Summer: When the Sun reaches its greatest declination (23½°) north of the celestial equator, around June 21. **Winter:** When the Sun reaches its greatest declination (23½°) south of the celestial equator, around December 21.

STATIONARY (STAT.): The brief period of apparent halted movement of a planet against the background of the stars shortly before it appears to move backward/westward (retrograde motion) or forward/eastward (direct motion).

SUN FAST/SLOW: When a sundial is ahead of (fast) or behind (slow) clock time.

SUNRISE/SUNSET: The visible rising/setting of the upper edge of the Sun's disk across the unobstructed horizon of an observer whose eyes are 15 feet above ground level.

TWILIGHT: See **page 106.** ∎

Note: These definitions apply to the Northern Hemisphere; some do not hold true for locations in the Southern Hemisphere.

2023

JANUARY
S	M	T	W	T	F	S
1	2	3	4	5	6	7
8	9	10	11	12	13	14
15	16	17	18	19	20	21
22	23	24	25	26	27	28
29	30	31				

FEBRUARY
S	M	T	W	T	F	S
			1	2	3	4
5	6	7	8	9	10	11
12	13	14	15	16	17	18
19	20	21	22	23	24	25
26	27	28				

MARCH
S	M	T	W	T	F	S
			1	2	3	4
5	6	7	8	9	10	11
12	13	14	15	16	17	18
19	20	21	22	23	24	25
26	27	28	29	30	31	

APRIL
S	M	T	W	T	F	S
						1
2	3	4	5	6	7	8
9	10	11	12	13	14	15
16	17	18	19	20	21	22
23	24	25	26	27	28	29
30						

MAY
S	M	T	W	T	F	S
	1	2	3	4	5	6
7	8	9	10	11	12	13
14	15	16	17	18	19	20
21	22	23	24	25	26	27
28	29	30	31			

JUNE
S	M	T	W	T	F	S
				1	2	3
4	5	6	7	8	9	10
11	12	13	14	15	16	17
18	19	20	21	22	23	24
25	26	27	28	29	30	

JULY
S	M	T	W	T	F	S
						1
2	3	4	5	6	7	8
9	10	11	12	13	14	15
16	17	18	19	20	21	22
23	24	25	26	27	28	29
30	31					

AUGUST
S	M	T	W	T	F	S
		1	2	3	4	5
6	7	8	9	10	11	12
13	14	15	16	17	18	19
20	21	22	23	24	25	26
27	28	29	30	31		

SEPTEMBER
S	M	T	W	T	F	S
					1	2
3	4	5	6	7	8	9
10	11	12	13	14	15	16
17	18	19	20	21	22	23
24	25	26	27	28	29	30

OCTOBER
S	M	T	W	T	F	S
1	2	3	4	5	6	7
8	9	10	11	12	13	14
15	16	17	18	19	20	21
22	23	24	25	26	27	28
29	30	31				

NOVEMBER
S	M	T	W	T	F	S
			1	2	3	4
5	6	7	8	9	10	11
12	13	14	15	16	17	18
19	20	21	22	23	24	25
26	27	28	29	30		

DECEMBER
S	M	T	W	T	F	S
					1	2
3	4	5	6	7	8	9
10	11	12	13	14	15	16
17	18	19	20	21	22	23
24	25	26	27	28	29	30
31						

2024

JANUARY
S	M	T	W	T	F	S
	1	2	3	4	5	6
7	8	9	10	11	12	13
14	15	16	17	18	19	20
21	22	23	24	25	26	27
28	29	30	31			

FEBRUARY
S	M	T	W	T	F	S
				1	2	3
4	5	6	7	8	9	10
11	12	13	14	15	16	17
18	19	20	21	22	23	24
25	26	27	28	29		

MARCH
S	M	T	W	T	F	S
					1	2
3	4	5	6	7	8	9
10	11	12	13	14	15	16
17	18	19	20	21	22	23
24	25	26	27	28	29	30
31						

APRIL
S	M	T	W	T	F	S
	1	2	3	4	5	6
7	8	9	10	11	12	13
14	15	16	17	18	19	20
21	22	23	24	25	26	27
28	29	30				

MAY
S	M	T	W	T	F	S
			1	2	3	4
5	6	7	8	9	10	11
12	13	14	15	16	17	18
19	20	21	22	23	24	25
26	27	28	29	30	31	

JUNE
S	M	T	W	T	F	S
						1
2	3	4	5	6	7	8
9	10	11	12	13	14	15
16	17	18	19	20	21	22
23	24	25	26	27	28	29
30						

JULY
S	M	T	W	T	F	S
	1	2	3	4	5	6
7	8	9	10	11	12	13
14	15	16	17	18	19	20
21	22	23	24	25	26	27
28	29	30	31			

AUGUST
S	M	T	W	T	F	S
				1	2	3
4	5	6	7	8	9	10
11	12	13	14	15	16	17
18	19	20	21	22	23	24
25	26	27	28	29	30	31

SEPTEMBER
S	M	T	W	T	F	S
1	2	3	4	5	6	7
8	9	10	11	12	13	14
15	16	17	18	19	20	21
22	23	24	25	26	27	28
29	30					

OCTOBER
S	M	T	W	T	F	S
		1	2	3	4	5
6	7	8	9	10	11	12
13	14	15	16	17	18	19
20	21	22	23	24	25	26
27	28	29	30	31		

NOVEMBER
S	M	T	W	T	F	S
					1	2
3	4	5	6	7	8	9
10	11	12	13	14	15	16
17	18	19	20	21	22	23
24	25	26	27	28	29	30

DECEMBER
S	M	T	W	T	F	S
1	2	3	4	5	6	7
8	9	10	11	12	13	14
15	16	17	18	19	20	21
22	23	24	25	26	27	28
29	30	31				

2025

JANUARY
S	M	T	W	T	F	S
			1	2	3	4
5	6	7	8	9	10	11
12	13	14	15	16	17	18
19	20	21	22	23	24	25
26	27	28	29	30	31	

FEBRUARY
S	M	T	W	T	F	S
						1
2	3	4	5	6	7	8
9	10	11	12	13	14	15
16	17	18	19	20	21	22
23	24	25	26	27	28	

MARCH
S	M	T	W	T	F	S
						1
2	3	4	5	6	7	8
9	10	11	12	13	14	15
16	17	18	19	20	21	22
23	24	25	26	27	28	29
30	31					

APRIL
S	M	T	W	T	F	S
		1	2	3	4	5
6	7	8	9	10	11	12
13	14	15	16	17	18	19
20	21	22	23	24	25	26
27	28	29	30			

MAY
S	M	T	W	T	F	S
				1	2	3
4	5	6	7	8	9	10
11	12	13	14	15	16	17
18	19	20	21	22	23	24
25	26	27	28	29	30	31

JUNE
S	M	T	W	T	F	S
1	2	3	4	5	6	7
8	9	10	11	12	13	14
15	16	17	18	19	20	21
22	23	24	25	26	27	28
29	30					

JULY
S	M	T	W	T	F	S
		1	2	3	4	5
6	7	8	9	10	11	12
13	14	15	16	17	18	19
20	21	22	23	24	25	26
27	28	29	30	31		

AUGUST
S	M	T	W	T	F	S
					1	2
3	4	5	6	7	8	9
10	11	12	13	14	15	16
17	18	19	20	21	22	23
24	25	26	27	28	29	30
31						

SEPTEMBER
S	M	T	W	T	F	S
	1	2	3	4	5	6
7	8	9	10	11	12	13
14	15	16	17	18	19	20
21	22	23	24	25	26	27
28	29	30				

OCTOBER
S	M	T	W	T	F	S
			1	2	3	4
5	6	7	8	9	10	11
12	13	14	15	16	17	18
19	20	21	22	23	24	25
26	27	28	29	30	31	

NOVEMBER
S	M	T	W	T	F	S
						1
2	3	4	5	6	7	8
9	10	11	12	13	14	15
16	17	18	19	20	21	22
23	24	25	26	27	28	29
30						

DECEMBER
S	M	T	W	T	F	S
	1	2	3	4	5	6
7	8	9	10	11	12	13
14	15	16	17	18	19	20
21	22	23	24	25	26	27
28	29	30	31			

A CALENDAR OF THE HEAVENS FOR 2024

–Beth Krommes

The Calendar Pages (120–147) are the heart of *The Old Farmer's Almanac*. They present sky sightings and astronomical data for the entire year and are what make this book a true almanac, a "calendar of the heavens." In essence, these pages are unchanged since 1792, when Robert B. Thomas published his first edition. The long columns of numbers and symbols reveal all of nature's precision, rhythm, and glory, providing an astronomical look at the year 2024.

HOW TO USE THE CALENDAR PAGES

The astronomical data on the **Calendar Pages (120–147)** are calculated for Ottawa, Ontario. Guidance for calculating the times of these events for your locale appears on **pages 116–117.** Note that the results will be *approximate*. Find the *exact* time of any astronomical event at your locale via **Almanac.ca/2024.** You can also go to **Almanac.ca/SkyMap** to print each month's "Sky Map," which can be useful for viewing with "Sky Watch" in the Calendar Pages.

For a list of 2024 holidays and observances, see **pages 148–149.** Also check out the **Glossary of Almanac Oddities** on **pages 150–151,** which describes some of the more obscure entries traditionally found on the **Right-Hand Calendar Pages (121–147).**

ABOUT THE TIMES: All times are given in ET (Eastern Time), except where otherwise noted as NT (Newfoundland Time, +1½ hours), AT (Atlantic Time, +1 hour), CT (Central Time, –1), MT (Mountain Time, –2), or PT (Pacific Time, –3). Between 2:00 A.M., March 10, and 2:00 A.M., November 3, Daylight Saving Time is assumed in those locales where it is observed.

ABOUT THE TIDES: For tidal information, see **pages 120–147, 237,** and **238–239.** Tide times and heights also are available via **Almanac.ca/2024.**

CALENDAR

The Left-Hand Calendar Pages, 120 to 146

On these pages are the year's astronomical predictions for Ottawa, Ontario (45°25' N, 75°42' W). Learn how to calculate the times of these events for your locale here or via **Almanac.ca/2024**.

A SAMPLE MONTH

SKY WATCH: The paragraph at the top of each Left-Hand Calendar Page describes the best times to view conjunctions, meteor showers, planets, and more. (Also see **How to Use the Right-Hand Calendar Pages, page 118.**)

	1		2		3	4		5		6		7	8
DAY OF YEAR	DAY OF MONTH	DAY OF WEEK	☀ RISES H. M.	RISE KEY	☀ SETS H. M.	SET KEY	LENGTH OF DAY H. M.	SUN FAST M.	SUN DECLINATION ° '	HIGH TIDE TIMES HALIFAX	☾ RISES H. M.	RISE KEY	☾ SETS H. M.	SET KEY	☾ ASTRON. PLACE	☾ AGE

DAY OF YEAR	DAY OF MONTH	DAY OF WEEK	RISES H. M.	RISE KEY	SETS H. M.	SET KEY	LENGTH OF DAY H. M.	SUN FAST M.	SUN DECLINATION	HIGH TIDE TIMES HALIFAX	RISES H. M.	RISE KEY	SETS H. M.	SET KEY	ASTRON. PLACE	AGE
60	1	Fr.	6:41	D	5:50	B	11 09	*15	7 s. 30	4 5	3:59	E	1:07	A	SAG	25
61	2	Sa.	6:40	D	5:51	B	11 11	*15	7 s. 07	5 6	4:45	E	2:01	A	SAG	26
62	3	**F**	6:38	D	5:52	C	11 14	*15	6 s. 44	6 6¾	5:24	E	2:58	A	CAP	27
63	4	M.	6:36	D	5:54	C	11 18	*14	6 s. 21	6¾ 7½	5:58	D	3:57	B	CAP	28

1. To calculate the sunrise time in your locale: Choose a day. Note its Sun Rise Key Letter. Find your (nearest) city on **page 240**. Add or subtract the minutes that correspond to the Sun Rise Key Letter to/from the sunrise time for Ottawa.[†]

EXAMPLE:

To calculate the sunrise time in Vancouver, British Columbia, on day 1:

Sunrise, Ottawa, with Key Letter D (above)	6:41 A.M. ET
Value of Key Letter D for Vancouver (p. 240)	+ 17 minutes
Sunrise, Vancouver	6:58 A.M. PT

To calculate your sunset time, repeat, using Ottawa's sunset time and its Sun Set Key Letter value.

2. To calculate the length of day: Choose a day. Note the Sun Rise and Sun Set Key Letters. Find your (nearest) city on **page 240**. Add or subtract the minutes that correspond to the Sun Set Key Letter to/from Ottawa's

[†] For locations where Daylight Saving Time is never observed, subtract 1 hour from results between the second Sunday of March and first Sunday of November.

length of day. *Reverse* the sign (e.g., minus to plus) of the Sun Rise Key Letter minutes. Add or subtract it to/from the first result.

EXAMPLE:

To calculate the length of day in Brandon, Manitoba, on day 1:

Length of day, Ottawa (above)	11h. 09m.
Sunset Key Letter B for Brandon (p. 240)	+ 28m.
	11h. 37m.
Reverse sunrise Key Letter D for Brandon (p. 240, +46 to –46)	– 46m.
Length of day, Brandon	10h. 51m.

3. Use Sun Fast to change sundial time to clock time. A sundial reads natural (Sun) time, which is neither Standard nor Daylight time. To calculate clock time on a sundial in Ottawa, subtract the minutes given in this column; add the minutes when preceded by an asterisk [*].

–Beth Krommes

To convert the time to your (nearest) city, use Key Letter C on **page 240.**

EXAMPLE:

To change sundial to clock time in Ottawa or Thunder Bay, Ont., on day 1:

Sundial reading (Ottawa or Thunder Bay)	12:00 noon
Add Sun Fast (p. 116)	+ 15 minutes
Clock time, Ottawa	12:15 P.M. ET**
Use Key Letter C for Thunder Bay (p. 241)	+ 53 minutes
Clock time, Thunder Bay	1:08 P.M. ET**

**Note: Add 1 hour to the results in locations where Daylight Saving Time is currently observed.

4. This column gives the degrees and minutes of the Sun from the celestial equator at noon ET.

5. This column gives the approximate times of high tides in Halifax. For example, the first high tide occurs at 4:00 A.M. and the second occurs at 5:00 P.M. the same day. (A dash indicates that high tide occurs on or after midnight and is recorded on the next day.) Because of the great variations in tide times and heights on both the east and west coasts, no one locality can be used as a mean. Twice-weekly times and heights of high tides at Churchill, Manitoba, and Vancouver, British Columbia, are provided on **page 238.**

6. To calculate the moonrise time in your locale: Choose a day. Note the Moon Rise Key Letter. Find your (nearest) city on **page 240.** Add or subtract the minutes that correspond to the Moon Rise

LONGITUDE OF CITY	CORRECTION MINUTES	LONGITUDE OF CITY	CORRECTION MINUTES
58°–76°	0	116°–127°	+4
77°–89°	+1	128°–141°	+5
90°–102°	+2	142°–155°	+6
103°–115°	+3		

Key Letter to/from the moonrise time given for Ottawa. (A dash indicates that the moonrise occurs on/after midnight and is recorded on the next day.) Find the longitude of your (nearest) city on **page 240.** Add a correction in minutes for your city's longitude (see table, bottom left). Use the same procedure with Ottawa's moonset time and the Moon Set Key Letter value to calculate the time of moonset in your locale.[†]

EXAMPLE:

To calculate the time of moonset in Toronto, Ontario, on day 1:

Moonset, Ottawa, with Key Letter A (p. 116)	1:07 P.M. ET
Value of Key Letter A for Toronto (p. 241)	+ 21 minutes
Correction for Toronto longitude, 79°23'	+ 1 minute
Moonset, Toronto	1:29 P.M. ET

7. This column gives the Moon's *astronomical* position among the constellations (not zodiac) at midnight. For *astrological* data, see **pages 224–227.**

Constellations have irregular borders; on successive nights, the midnight Moon may enter one, cross into another, and then move to a new area of the previous. It visits the 12 zodiacal constellations, as well as Auriga **(AUR),** a northern constellation between Perseus and Gemini; Cetus **(CET),** which lies south of the zodiac, just south of Pisces and Aries; Ophiuchus **(OPH),** primarily north of the zodiac but with a small corner between Scorpius and Sagittarius; Orion **(ORI),** whose northern limit first reaches the zodiac between Taurus and Gemini; and Sextans **(SEX),** which lies south of the zodiac except for a corner that just touches it near Leo.

8. This column gives the Moon's age: the number of days since the previous new Moon. (The average length of the lunar month is 29.53 days.) *(cont.)*

The Right-Hand Calendar Pages, 121 to 147

The Right-Hand Calendar Pages contain celestial events; religious observances; proverbs and poems; civil holidays; historical events; folklore; tide heights; weather prediction rhymes; Farmer's Calendar essays; and more.

A SAMPLE MONTH

1 2 3 4 5 6 7 8 9 10

1	Fr.	ALL FOOLS' • *If you want to make a fool of yourself, you'll find a lot of people ready to help you.*	*Flakes*	an inch long, who v
2	Sa.	Tap dancer Charles "Honi" Coles born, 1911 • Tides {5.1 5.0	*alive!*	in fresh water, pro pond across the r
3	**B**	2nd S. of Easter • Writer F. Scott Fitzgerald married Zelda Sayre, 1920	*Spring's*	emerged a month c
4	M.	Annunciation^{T} • ☌♆☾ • *Ben Hur* won 11 Academy Awards, 1960	*arrived!*	to spend the next 3 on land before ret
5	Tu.	☾ AT ☋ • Blizzard left 27.2" snow, St. John's, Nfld., 1999 • Tides {5.8 6.2	*Or is this*	their wet world.
6	W.	☾ ON EQ. • ☌♀☾ • Twin mongoose lemurs born, Busch Gardens, Tampa, Fla., 2012	*warmth*	You can't mis

1. The bold letter is the Dominical Letter (from A to G), a traditional ecclesiastical designation for Sunday determined by the date on which the year's first Sunday falls. For 2024, the Dominical Letter is **G** through February. It then reverts to **F** for the rest of the year.

2. Civil holidays and astronomical events.

3. Religious feasts: A^{T} indicates a major feast that the church has this year temporarily transferred to a date other than its usual one.

4. Sundays and special holy days.

5. Symbols for notable celestial events. For example, ☌♆☾ on the 4th day means that a conjunction (☌) of Neptune (♆) and the Moon (☾) occurs.

6. Proverbs, poems, and adages.

7. Noteworthy historical events, folklore, and legends.

8. High tide heights, in feet, at Halifax, Nova Scotia.

9. Weather prediction rhyme.

10. Farmer's Calendar essay.

Celestial Symbols

☉ Sun	⊕ Earth	⛢ Uranus	☌ Conjunction (on the same celestial longitude)	☋ Descending node
○●☾ Moon	♂ Mars	♆ Neptune	☊ Ascending node	☍ Opposition (180 degrees from Sun)
☿ Mercury	♃ Jupiter	♇ Pluto		
♀ Venus	♄ Saturn			

PREDICTING EARTHQUAKES

Note the dates in the Right-Hand Calendar Pages when the Moon rides high or runs low. The date of the high begins the most likely 5-day period of earthquakes in the Northern Hemisphere; the date of the low indicates a similar 5-day period in the Southern Hemisphere. Also noted are the 2 days each month when the Moon is on the celestial equator, indicating the most likely time for earthquakes in either hemisphere.

EARTH AT PERIHELION AND APHELION

Perihelion: January 2, 2024 (EST). Earth will be 91,404,095 miles from the Sun. **Aphelion:** July 5, 2024 (EDT). Earth will be 94,510,539 miles from the Sun.

Why We Have Seasons

–Beth Krommes

The seasons occur because as Earth revolves around the Sun, its axis remains tilted at 23.5 degrees from the perpendicular. This tilt causes different latitudes on Earth to receive varying amounts of sunlight throughout the year.

In the Northern Hemisphere, the summer solstice marks the beginning of summer and occurs when the North Pole is tilted toward the Sun. The winter solstice marks the beginning of winter and occurs when the North Pole is tilted away from the Sun.

The equinoxes occur when the hemispheres equally face the Sun. At this time, the Sun rises due east and sets due west. The vernal equinox marks the beginning of spring; the autumnal equinox marks the beginning of autumn.

In the Southern Hemisphere, the seasons are the reverse of those in the Northern Hemisphere.

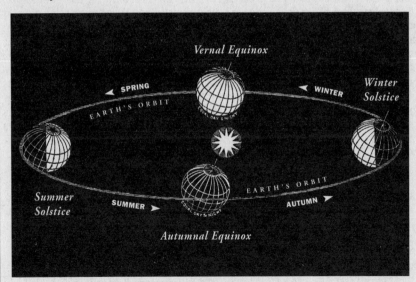

Vernal Equinox

SPRING

EARTH'S ORBIT

WINTER

Winter Solstice

Summer Solstice

SUMMER

EARTH'S ORBIT

AUTUMN

Autumnal Equinox

THE FIRST DAYS OF THE 2024 SEASONS

VERNAL (SPRING) EQUINOX:	March 19, 11:06 P.M. EDT
SUMMER SOLSTICE:	June 20, 4:51 P.M. EDT
AUTUMNAL (FALL) EQUINOX:	Sept. 22, 8:44 A.M. EDT
WINTER SOLSTICE:	Dec. 21, 4:21 A.M. EST

NOVEMBER 2023

SKY WATCH: Jupiter, in Aries, comes to opposition on the 3rd, rising at sunset; at its biggest and brightest of the year, the Giant World is visible all night. Saturn, in Aquarius, is also seen the entire night; any telescope using at least 30× magnification will capture its glorious rings. Uranus, in Aries, reaches opposition on the 13th, to the left of Jupiter, which is also in Aries. Binocular owners can easily find Uranus by looking for a green "star" halfway between Jupiter and the famous Pleiades star cluster. Since no star is green, identification should be easy. Not many meteors are expected when the Leonid shower peaks at night on the 18th and 19th. Look for the Moon to the right of Jupiter on the 24th.

◐ **LAST QUARTER** 5th day 3:37 A.M.
● **NEW MOON** 13th day 4:27 A.M.
◑ **FIRST QUARTER** 20th day 5:50 A.M.
○ **FULL MOON** 27th day 4:16 A.M.

After 2:00 A.M. on November 5, Eastern Standard Time is given.

GET THESE PAGES WITH TIMES SET TO YOUR POSTAL CODE VIA ALMANAC.CA/2024.

DAY OF YEAR	DAY OF MONTH	DAY OF WEEK	☼ RISES H.M.	RISE KEY	☼ SETS H.M.	SET KEY	LENGTH OF DAY H.M.	SUN FAST M.	SUN DECLINATION ° '	HIGH TIDE TIMES HALIFAX		☾ RISES H.M.	RISE KEY	☾ SETS H.M.	SET KEY	☾ ASTRON. PLACE	☾ AGE
305	1	W.	7:42	D	**5:50**	B	10 08	14	14 s. 29	11	11¾	**8:14**	A	**12:18**	E	TAU	18
306	2	Th.	7:43	D	**5:49**	B	10 06	14	14 s. 48	11¾	—	**9:12**	A	**1:14**	E	AUR	19
307	3	Fr.	7:45	D	**5:48**	B	10 03	14	15 s. 07	12½	12½	**10:16**	A	**1:58**	E	GEM	20
308	4	Sa.	7:46	D	**5:46**	B	10 00	14	15 s. 26	1½	1½	**11:23**	A	**2:31**	E	CAN	21
309	5	**A**	6:47	D	**4:45**	B	9 58	14	15 s. 44	1¼	1¼	**11:30**	A	**1:58**	E	CAN	22
310	6	M.	6:49	D	**4:43**	B	9 54	14	16 s. 02	2½	2½	—	-	**2:19**	D	LEO	23
311	7	Tu.	6:50	D	**4:42**	B	9 52	14	16 s. 20	3¾	3¾	12:35	B	**2:37**	D	LEO	24
312	8	W.	6:52	D	**4:41**	B	9 49	13	16 s. 37	4½	4¾	1:40	B	**2:53**	C	LEO	25
313	9	Th.	6:53	D	**4:40**	B	9 47	13	16 s. 55	5¼	5½	2:45	C	**3:09**	C	VIR	26
314	10	Fr.	6:54	D	**4:38**	B	9 44	13	17 s. 12	6	6¼	3:50	C	**3:25**	B	VIR	27
315	11	Sa.	6:56	D	**4:37**	B	9 41	13	17 s. 28	6½	6¾	4:57	D	**3:43**	B	VIR	28
316	12	**A**	6:57	D	**4:36**	B	9 39	13	17 s. 45	7	7½	6:08	E	**4:04**	A	VIR	29
317	13	M.	6:59	D	**4:35**	B	9 36	13	18 s. 01	7½	8¼	7:21	E	**4:30**	A	LIB	0
318	14	Tu.	7:00	E	**4:34**	B	9 34	13	18 s. 16	8¼	8¾	8:36	E	**5:04**	A	SCO	1
319	15	W.	7:01	E	**4:33**	B	9 32	13	18 s. 32	8¾	9½	9:50	E	**5:50**	A	OPH	2
320	16	Th.	7:03	E	**4:32**	B	9 29	12	18 s. 47	9½	10¼	10:55	E	**6:49**	A	SAG	3
321	17	Fr.	7:04	E	**4:31**	B	9 27	12	19 s. 02	10¼	11¼	11:50	E	**8:00**	A	SAG	4
322	18	Sa.	7:05	E	**4:30**	A	9 25	12	19 s. 16	11¼	—	**12:32**	E	**9:19**	A	SAG	5
323	19	**A**	7:07	E	**4:29**	A	9 22	12	19 s. 30	12	12	**1:04**	E	**10:40**	A	CAP	6
324	20	M.	7:08	E	**4:28**	A	9 20	12	19 s. 44	1	1	**1:30**	D	12:00	B	CAP	7
325	21	Tu.	7:09	E	**4:27**	A	9 18	11	19 s. 57	2¼	2¼	**1:51**	D	—	-	AQU	8
326	22	W.	7:11	E	**4:27**	A	9 16	11	20 s. 10	3½	3½	**2:11**	C	1:18	B	AQU	9
327	23	Th.	7:12	E	**4:26**	A	9 14	11	20 s. 23	4¼	4¾	**2:30**	C	2:35	C	CET	10
328	24	Fr.	7:13	E	**4:25**	A	9 12	11	20 s. 35	5¼	5¾	**2:50**	B	3:53	D	PSC	11
329	25	Sa.	7:15	E	**4:25**	A	9 10	10	20 s. 47	6	6½	**3:13**	A	5:11	D	ARI	12
330	26	**A**	7:16	E	**4:24**	A	9 08	10	20 s. 58	6¾	7¼	**3:42**	A	6:30	E	ARI	13
331	27	M.	7:17	E	**4:23**	A	9 06	10	21 s. 09	7½	8	**4:17**	A	7:47	E	TAU	14
332	28	Tu.	7:18	E	**4:23**	A	9 05	9	21 s. 20	8¼	8¾	**5:02**	A	8:59	E	TAU	15
333	29	W.	7:20	E	**4:22**	A	9 02	9	21 s. 30	9	9½	**5:57**	A	10:01	E	TAU	16
334	30	Th.	7:21	E	**4:22**	A	9 01	9	21 s. 40	9¾	10½	**7:00**	A	10:51	E	GEM	17

To use this page, see p. 116; for Key Letters, see p. 240. LIGHT = A.M. BOLD = P.M.

	Farmer's Calendar
	CALENDAR

The Frost Spirit comes! and the quiet lake shall feel
The torpid touch of his glazing breath.
–John Greenleaf Whittier

Farmer's Calendar

When nor'easters send Atlantic predator fish streaming south, winter flounder—aka mud dabs, blackbacks, lemon sole—begin their own migration, easing in from deep water to bays and estuaries from the Gulf of St. Lawrence to North Carolina. Protected from frigid water by "antifreeze" proteins in their blood, they'll spawn in winter, their eggs sinking unlike the buoyant offspring of most marine fish.

Winter flounder rest on the bottom, venturing higher in the water column less frequently than most members of the order. Early in their lives, their left eye migrates to the right side of their heads. Lying on their white blind sides, they're camouflaged against (or in) mud or sand. The first, and only, thing you're likely to see is their bulging eyes.

These fish lack the sharp teeth of their cousins, halibut and fluke, and their thick lips are permanently puckered, as if waiting for a kiss.

Few fish make better table fare, and now is the time to pursue them. Use small, long-shank hooks. Sea worms work best, but garden worms are nearly as effective and easier to come by. Flounders like bright colors, so paint your sinkers red.

DAY OF MONTH	DAY OF WEEK	DATES, FEASTS, FASTS, ASPECTS, TIDE HEIGHTS, AND WEATHER		
1	W.	All Saints' • Boston Female Medical Col., 1st U.S. medical school for women, opened, Boston, Mass., 1848		*Flurries*
2	Th.	All Souls' • ☾ RIDES HIGH • 1st titanium mill opened, Toronto, Ohio, 1957 • { 5.7 —		*again;*
3	Fr.	♃ AT � • Bob Kane, co-creator of *Batman* comic, died, 1998 • Tides { 5.3 5.4		*the bear*
4	Sa.	Sadie Hawkins Day • ♄ STAT. • Royal Montreal Golf Club founded, 1873		*makes*
5	**A**	23rd S. af. P. • DAYLIGHT SAVING TIME ENDS, 2:00 A.M. • { 5.0 5.0		*its den.*
6	M.	☾ AT APO. • 1st recorded sighting of supernova in Cassiopeia, 1572 • { 4.9 4.9		*St. Martin's*
7	Tu.	ELECTION DAY (U.S.) • Singer-songwriter Leonard Cohen died, 2016 • { 5.0 4.9		*summer,*
8	W.	Rodrigo Koxa surfed 80' wave, setting world record, Nazaré, Portugal, 2017 • Tides { 5.2 5.0		*but*
9	Th.	☾ ON EQ. • ♂♂☾ (• Alice Coachman, 1st Black woman to win Olympic gold medal, born, 1923		*showers*
10	Fr.	*If red the Sun begin his race,* *Be sure the rain will fall apace.* • Tides { 5.6 5.3		*a bummer.*
11	Sa.	St. Martin of Tours • REMEMBRANCE DAY • ☾ AT ☍ • { 5.8 5.5		*Veterans*
12	**A**	24th S. af. P. • Indian Summer • Tides { 6.0 5.6		*we thank*
13	M.	NEW ● • ♂♂☾ (• ☼ AT ☍ • Tides { 6.1 5.7		*as pull cords*
14	Tu.	♂♀☾ • UK's King Charles III born, 1948 • { 6.2 5.7		*we yank*
15	W.	America Recycles Day • Astronomer Sir William Herschel born, 1738 • { 6.3 5.7		*to start up*
16	Th.	☾ RUNS LOW • *Skylab 4* launched, 1973 • { 6.2 5.6		*ye olde*
17	Fr.	St. Hugh of Lincoln • Deadly tornado outbreak spawned 55 in Ill. and Ind., 2013		*snowblower*
18	Sa.	St. Hilda of Whitby • ♂♂☼☾ • ♂♄☾(• Astronaut Alan Shepard born, 1923		*in temps*
19	**A**	25th S. af. P. • U.S. pres. Abraham Lincoln delivered Gettysburg Address, 1863		*getting*
20	M.	♂♄☾(• *Gratitude is the heart's memory.* • { 5.4 5.5		*lower and*
21	Tu.	☾ AT PERIG. • *Nov. 19–21:* The "Long Storm" dropped 18" snow on N.Y.C., 1798 • { 5.4 5.4		*lower.*
22	W.	☾ ON EQ. • ♂♀☾ • Wiley Post, 1st pilot to fly solo around world, born, 1898		*Time for*
23	Th.	St. Clement • THANKSGIVING DAY (U.S.) • Tides { 5.9 5.5		*some turkey,*
24	Fr.	☾ AT ☍ (• Baseball player Steve Yeager born, 1948 • Pilot reported UFO, north Baffin Island, Nunavut, 2018		*but*
25	Sa.	♂♃☾ • Naturalist Kenneth Brugger, finder of Mex. winter home of monarch butterflies, died, 1998		*rain*
26	**A**	26th S. af. P. • ♂♂☼☾ • Thelma Chalifoux 1st Métis woman to become Canadian senator, Alta., 1997		*and snow*
27	M.	FULL BEAVER ○ • *A soft answer turneth away wrath.* • Tides { 6.4 5.9		*lurky.*
28	Tu.	1st U.S. automobile race held, Chicago, Ill., 1895 • { 6.3 5.8		*Mild,*
29	W.	☾ RIDES HIGH • Writer C. S. Lewis born, 1898 • { 6.2 5.7		*child!*
30	Th.	St. Andrew • 1st solar eclipse known to be recorded (Ireland), 3340 B.C. • { 6.0 5.6		

SKY WATCH: All this month, Jupiter is visible at night. Saturn, now solely an evening star, stands on the meridian due south at nightfall, in Aquarius. A bright star far to Saturn's lower left is the 1st magnitude star, Fomalhaut. During December's first few mornings, Venus—a morning star—guides observers to Virgo's blue main star, Spica, to its right. The 13th brings the year's best meteor shower, the Geminids, under perfect, moonless, dark conditions. Rural observers can see a meteor a minute at any time of night. On the 17th, the Moon dangles below Saturn before moving on to meet Jupiter on the 21st and 22nd. Winter in the Northern Hemisphere begins with the solstice on the night of the 21st at 10:27 P.M. EST.

◗ **LAST QUARTER** 5th day 12:49 A.M.　　◖ **FIRST QUARTER** 19th day 1:39 P.M.
● **NEW MOON** 12th day 6:32 P.M.　　○ **FULL MOON** 26th day 7:33 P.M.

All times are given in Eastern Standard Time.

GET THESE PAGES WITH TIMES SET TO YOUR POSTAL CODE VIA ALMANAC.CA/2024.

DAY OF YEAR	DAY OF MONTH	DAY OF WEEK	☼ RISES H. M.	RISE KEY	☼ SETS H. M.	SET KEY	LENGTH OF DAY H. M.	SUN FAST M.	SUN DECLINATION ° '	HIGH TIDE TIMES HALIFAX		☾ RISES H. M.	RISE KEY	☾ SETS H. M.	SET KEY	☾ ASTRON. PLACE	☾ AGE
335	1	Fr.	7:22	E	4:21	A	8 59	8	21 s. 49	10½	11¼	8:07	A	11:29	E	GEM	18
336	2	Sa.	7:23	E	4:21	A	8 58	8	21 s. 59	11¼	—	9:14	A	11:59	E	CAN	19
337	3	**A**	7:24	E	4:21	A	8 57	7	22 s. 07	12	12	10:21	B	12:22	D	LEO	20
338	4	M.	7:25	E	4:20	A	8 55	7	22 s. 15	12¾	12¾	11:26	B	12:41	D	LEO	21
339	5	Tu.	7:26	E	4:20	A	8 54	7	22 s. 23	1½	1½	—	-	12:58	D	LEO	22
340	6	W.	7:27	E	4:20	A	8 53	6	22 s. 30	2½	2¾	12:30	C	1:14	C	VIR	23
341	7	Th.	7:28	E	4:20	A	8 52	6	22 s. 37	3½	3¾	1:34	C	1:29	C	VIR	24
342	8	Fr.	7:29	E	4:20	A	8 51	5	22 s. 44	4¼	4¾	2:40	D	1:46	B	VIR	25
343	9	Sa.	7:30	E	4:20	A	8 50	5	22 s. 50	5	5½	3:48	D	2:05	B	VIR	26
344	10	**A**	7:31	E	4:20	A	8 49	4	22 s. 55	5¾	6¼	5:00	E	2:29	A	LIB	27
345	11	M.	7:32	E	4:20	A	8 48	4	23 s. 00	6½	7	6:15	E	3:00	A	LIB	28
346	12	Tu.	7:33	E	4:20	A	8 47	3	23 s. 05	7	7¾	7:31	E	3:42	A	SCO	0
347	13	W.	7:34	E	4:20	A	8 46	3	23 s. 09	7¾	8½	8:42	E	4:37	A	OPH	1
348	14	Th.	7:35	E	4:20	A	8 45	3	23 s. 13	8½	9¼	9:42	E	5:46	A	SAG	2
349	15	Fr.	7:35	E	4:20	A	8 45	2	23 s. 16	9¼	10¼	10:30	E	7:05	A	SAG	3
350	16	Sa.	7:36	E	4:20	A	8 44	2	23 s. 19	10¼	11	11:06	E	8:27	A	CAP	4
351	17	**A**	7:37	E	4:21	A	8 44	1	23 s. 21	11	11¾	11:34	D	9:49	B	CAP	5
352	18	M.	7:38	E	4:21	A	8 43	1	23 s. 23	12	—	11:57	D	11:08	B	AQU	6
353	19	Tu.	7:38	E	4:21	A	8 43	0	23 s. 24	12¾	1	12:17	C	—	-	AQU	7
354	20	W.	7:39	E	4:22	A	8 43	0	23 s. 25	1¾	2	12:35	C	12:25	C	PSC	8
355	21	Th.	7:39	E	4:22	A	8 43	*1	23 s. 26	2¾	3¼	12:55	B	1:41	C	PSC	9
356	22	Fr.	7:40	E	4:23	A	8 43	*1	23 s. 26	3¾	4½	1:16	B	2:57	D	ARI	10
357	23	Sa.	7:40	E	4:23	A	8 43	*2	23 s. 25	4¾	5½	1:42	A	4:13	E	ARI	11
358	24	**A**	7:41	E	4:24	A	8 43	*2	23 s. 24	5½	6¼	2:14	A	5:30	E	TAU	12
359	25	M.	7:41	E	4:25	A	8 44	*3	23 s. 23	6¼	7¼	2:54	A	6:42	E	TAU	13
360	26	Tu.	7:41	E	4:25	A	8 44	*3	23 s. 21	7¼	8	3:45	A	7:48	E	TAU	14
361	27	W.	7:42	E	4:26	A	8 44	*4	23 s. 19	8	8¾	4:45	A	8:42	E	AUR	15
362	28	Th.	7:42	E	4:27	A	8 45	*4	23 s. 16	8¾	9½	5:51	A	9:25	E	GEM	16
363	29	Fr.	7:42	E	4:27	A	8 45	*5	23 s. 12	9¼	10	6:59	A	9:58	E	CAN	17
364	30	Sa.	7:42	E	4:28	A	8 46	*5	23 s. 09	10	10¾	8:07	A	10:24	E	CAN	18
365	31	**A**	7:42	E	4:29	A	8 47	*6	23 s. 04	10¾	11½	9:12	B	10:44	D	LEO	19

DECEMBER

Hark! on the frozen ear of night, / The sleighs with silver bells—
On yonder hill top's snowy height, / The merry music swells.
–Richard George Holland

DAY OF MONTH	DAY OF WEEK	DATES, FEASTS, FASTS, ASPECTS, TIDE HEIGHTS, AND WEATHER	
1	Fr.	*Always put the saddle on the right horse.* • Tides {5.8 / 5.4	*C-c-c-cold*
2	Sa.	St. Viviana • Skier Bode Miller won his 33rd World Cup race, 2011 • {5.6 / 5.3	*and spitting,*
3	A	1st S. of Advent • *Pioneer 10* spacecraft's closest approach to Jupiter (EST), 1973	*snow*
4	M.	☾ AT APO. • ☿ GR. ELONG. (21° EAST) • National Cookie Day (U.S.) • Tides {5.2 / 5.1	*showers*
5	Tu.	Six U.S. Navy planes (Flight 19 and Training 49) disappeared over Bermuda Triangle, 1945 • {5.1 / 4.9	*hitting,*
6	W.	St. Nicholas • ☾ ON EQ. • ♆ STAT. • 1st U.S. presidential address via radio, 1923	*then*
7	Th.	St. Ambrose • Chanukah begins at sundown • NATIONAL PEARL HARBOR REMEMBRANCE DAY (U.S.)	*the*
8	Fr.	☾ AT ☋ • Bank of Canada announced human rights activist Viola Desmond to appear on $10 note, 2016	*real*
9	Sa.	☌♀☾ • "Weary Willie" clown Emmett Kelly born, 1898 • {5.6 / 5.1	*heavy stuff.*
10	A	2nd S. of Advent • Treaty of Paris officially ended Spanish-American war, 1898	*Chill*
11	M.	Astronomer Annie Jump Cannon born, 1863 • Tides {6.0 / 5.5	*abating, more*
12	Tu.	OUR LADY OF GUADALUPE • NEW ● • ☌♂☾ • ☿ STAT.	*snow waiting.*
13	W.	St. Lucia • ☾ RUNS LOW • *Apollo 17*'s lunar rover reached 11.18 mph, setting record, 1972	*Enough!*
14	Th.	Halcyon Days begin. • ☌☿☾ • Canadian Capt. Paul Triquet's WWII valor earned him later Victoria Cross, 1943	
15	Fr.	☌♇☾ • Leaning Tower of Pisa reopened after 11 years of repair, Italy, 2001 • {6.4 / 5.8	*Flakes with*
16	Sa.	☾ AT PERIG. • Boston Tea Party, 1773 • Tides {6.3 / 5.8	*mildness;*
17	A	3rd S. of Advent • ☌♄☾ • Tides {6.1 / 5.8	*snowstorm*
18	M.	*A fire hard to kindle indicates bad weather.* • Tides {5.8 / —	*with wildness—*
19	Tu.	☌♆☾ • Beware the Pogonip. • Writer Emily Brontë died, 1848 • {5.8 / 5.5	*Oh, well!*
20	W.	Ember Day • ☾ ON EQ. • At 81+, Queen Elizabeth II became oldest monarch in UK history, 2007	*Clear*
21	Th.	St. Thomas • WINTER SOLSTICE • ☾ AT ☊ • Tides {5.8 / 5.1	*sky*
22	Fr.	Ember Day • ☌♃☾ • ☿ IN INF. ☌ • Tides {5.9 / 5.2	*for*
23	Sa.	Ember Day • ☌♅☾ • *A Visit From St. Nicholas* 1st published, 1823 • {6.0 / 5.3	*Rudolph's*
24	A	4th S. of Advent • Entrepreneur Johns Hopkins died, 1873 • {6.0 / 5.4	*flight for*
25	M.	Christmas • 2.6" snow, Tucson, Ariz., 1987 • Tides {6.1 / 5.5	*Noël!*
26	Tu.	St. Stephen • BOXING DAY • FIRST DAY OF KWANZAA • FULL COLD ○ • ☾ RIDES HIGH	
27	W.	St. John • ☌☿♂ • Aeronautics pioneer Sir George Cayley born, 1773	*Freezing and*
28	Th.	Holy Innocents • Endangered Species Act (U.S.) became law, 1973	*snow showers*
29	Fr.	Isaac Roberts's photo of Great Nebula in Andromeda (M31) 1st to show its spiral structure, 1888	*galore—*
30	Sa.	*One touch of nature makes the whole world kin.* –Shakespeare • {5.9 / 5.5	*Now we leap*
31	A	1st S. af. Ch. • ♃ STAT. • Singer Donna Summer born, 1948	*to 2024!*

Farmer's Calendar

House mice, ship stowaways from Eurasia, infest human dwellings. Our cleaner, woodland-dwelling natives—white-footed mice—merely visit. If you live anywhere from Nova Scotia to Virginia and west to the Rockies, they are likely to enter your camp or house like poltergeists when the first frosts stiffen the grass.

Trying to block them is futile. By starlight, they always find openings unseen and unknown. You may see one of these creatures in the light of the dying fire, flowing over floor and hearth, pausing to preen its fur and tail, twitching its impossibly long whiskers, and fixing you with huge, obsidian eyes.

Your "polterguest" may even play music for you, especially if leaves have blown in through a door or window. For reasons not understood, they'll drum on them with their paws, creating a melodious buzz.

White-footed mice provide a service to forests by excreting spores of fungi that they eat. These fungi enhance the ability of trees to take up necessary nutrients.

Because these animals don't hibernate, they need a warm place. Beware: They'll poop, may chew soap, and can carry illnesses such as Lyme disease.

JANUARY

SKY WATCH: The year begins with Jupiter as the sky's brightest "star," high in the southeast at nightfall, while Saturn hovers in the lower half of the southwestern sky. Saturn's glorious rings—now almost edgewise to our view—can be seen through any telescope with more than 30× magnification; observe the Ringed Planet early, as it is too low to be seen after 7:00 P.M. Earth stands closest to the Sun (at perihelion) on the 2nd at 8:00 P.M. The Moon floats above Saturn on the 13th and below it on the 14th, before forming a close conjunction with Jupiter on the 18th. In the predawn sky, Venus, in Scorpius, is best seen in the east from 6:00 to 6:30 A.M., with Mercury to its lower left until the 27th. Both are extremely low, as is Mars when it joins Mercury on the morning of the 27th.

◐ **LAST QUARTER** 3rd day 10:30 P.M.   ◑ **FIRST QUARTER** 17th day 10:53 P.M.
● **NEW MOON** 11th day 6:57 A.M.   ○ **FULL MOON** 25th day 12:54 P.M.

All times are given in Eastern Standard Time.

GET THESE PAGES WITH TIMES SET TO YOUR POSTAL CODE VIA ALMANAC.CA/2024.

DAY OF YEAR	DAY OF MONTH	DAY OF WEEK	☼ RISES H.M.	RISE KEY	☼ SETS H.M.	SET KEY	LENGTH OF DAY H.M.	SUN FAST M.	SUN DECLINATION ° '	HIGH TIDE TIMES HALIFAX		☽ RISES H.M.	RISE KEY	☽ SETS H.M.	SET KEY	☽ ASTRON. PLACE	☽ AGE
1	1	M.	7:43	E	4:30	A	8 47	*6	23 s. 00	11½	—	10:16	B	11:02	D	LEO	20
2	2	Tu.	7:43	E	4:31	A	8 48	*7	22 s. 54	12	12	11:20	C	11:18	C	LEO	21
3	3	W.	7:43	E	4:32	A	8 49	*7	22 s. 49	12¾	12¾	—	-	11:33	C	VIR	22
4	4	Th.	7:42	E	4:33	A	8 51	*8	22 s. 43	1½	1¾	12:24	C	11:49	B	VIR	23
5	5	Fr.	7:42	E	4:34	A	8 52	*8	22 s. 36	2¼	2¾	1:30	D	12:07	B	VIR	24
6	6	Sa.	7:42	E	4:35	A	8 53	*8	22 s. 29	3¼	4	2:39	D	12:28	A	LIB	25
7	7	**G**	7:42	E	4:36	A	8 54	*9	22 s. 22	4	5	3:51	E	12:55	A	LIB	26
8	8	M.	7:42	E	4:37	A	8 55	*9	22 s. 14	5	5¾	5:06	E	1:31	A	SCO	27
9	9	Tu.	7:42	E	4:38	A	8 56	*10	22 s. 06	5¾	6¾	6:20	E	2:20	A	OPH	28
10	10	W.	7:41	E	4:39	A	8 58	*10	21 s. 57	6¾	7½	7:27	E	3:23	A	SAG	29
11	11	Th.	7:41	E	4:41	A	9 00	*11	21 s. 48	7½	8¼	8:21	E	4:40	A	SAG	0
12	12	Fr.	7:40	E	4:42	A	9 02	*11	21 s. 38	8¼	9	9:03	E	6:05	A	CAP	1
13	13	Sa.	7:40	E	4:43	A	9 03	*11	21 s. 28	9	10	9:35	E	7:30	B	CAP	2
14	14	**G**	7:39	E	4:44	A	9 05	*12	21 s. 18	10	10¾	10:00	D	8:53	B	AQU	3
15	15	M.	7:39	E	4:46	A	9 07	*12	21 s. 07	10¾	11½	10:21	C	10:13	C	AQU	4
16	16	Tu.	7:38	E	4:47	A	9 09	*12	20 s. 56	11½	—	10:41	C	11:31	C	PSC	5
17	17	W.	7:38	E	4:48	A	9 10	*13	20 s. 44	12¼	12½	11:00	B	—	-	PSC	6
18	18	Th.	7:37	E	4:49	A	9 12	*13	20 s. 32	1	1½	11:21	B	12:47	D	PSC	7
19	19	Fr.	7:36	E	4:51	A	9 15	*13	20 s. 20	2	2½	11:45	A	2:04	D	ARI	8
20	20	Sa.	7:36	E	4:52	A	9 16	*14	20 s. 07	3	4	12:14	A	3:20	E	TAU	9
21	21	**G**	7:35	E	4:54	A	9 19	*14	19 s. 54	4	5	12:52	A	4:33	E	TAU	10
22	22	M.	7:34	E	4:55	A	9 21	*14	19 s. 40	5¼	6¼	1:38	A	5:40	E	TAU	11
23	23	Tu.	7:32	E	4:56	A	9 23	*14	19 s. 26	6	7	2:34	A	6:37	E	AUR	12
24	24	W.	7:32	E	4:58	B	9 26	*15	19 s. 12	7	7¾	3:38	A	7:23	E	GEM	13
25	25	Th.	7:31	E	4:59	B	9 28	*15	18 s. 57	7¾	8½	4:46	A	7:59	E	CAN	14
26	26	Fr.	7:30	E	5:00	B	9 30	*15	18 s. 42	8½	9	5:54	A	8:26	E	CAN	15
27	27	Sa.	7:29	E	5:02	B	9 33	*15	18 s. 27	9	9¾	7:00	B	8:49	D	LEO	16
28	28	**G**	7:28	E	5:03	B	9 35	*16	18 s. 12	9¾	10¼	8:05	B	9:07	D	LEO	17
29	29	M.	7:27	E	5:05	B	9 38	*16	17 s. 56	10¼	10¾	9:09	C	9:23	C	LEO	18
30	30	Tu.	7:26	D	5:06	B	9 40	*16	17 s. 39	11	11¼	10:12	C	9:38	C	VIR	19
31	31	W.	7:25	D	5:08	B	9 43	*16	17 s. 23	11½	—	11:16	D	9:54	B	VIR	20

CALENDAR

JANUARY

We are standing on the threshold, we are in the opened door,
We are treading on a borderland we have never trod before.
–**Anonymous**

DAY OF MONTH	DAY OF WEEK	DATES, FEASTS, FASTS, ASPECTS, TIDE HEIGHTS, AND WEATHER	
1	M.	Holy Name • NEW YEAR'S DAY • ☾ AT APO. • ☿ STAT. • Tides {5.4 —	*New Year's*
2	Tu.	⊕ AT PERIHELION • *Luna-1,* 1st spacecraft to escape Earth's gravity, launched, 1959	*freeze,*
3	W.	☾ ON EQ. • Maya Angelou (American Women series) U.S. quarter released, 2022 • {5.4 4.9	*if you*
4	Th.	St. Elizabeth Ann Seton • ☾ AT ☋ • Teacher Louis Braille born, 1809 • {5.3 4.7	*please!*
5	Fr.	Twelfth Night • U.S. Brig. Gen. Zebulon Montgomery Pike born, 1779 • Tides {5.3 4.6	*Snow is*
6	Sa.	**Epiphany** • *At Twelfth Day, the days are lengthened a cock's stride.* • {5.3 4.7	*piling,*
7	**G**	**1st S. af. Ep.** • Orthodox Christmas (Julian) • Distaff Day • {5.4 4.8	*plow*
8	M.	Plough Monday • ☌♀☾ • Entertainer Elvis Presley born, 1935 • {5.6 5.1	*drivers*
9	Tu.	☌☿☾ • Runner Tom Longboat died, 1949 • Tides {5.9 5.3	*smiling.*
10	W.	☾ RUNS LOW • ☌♂☾ • *A good action is never thrown away.* • {6.2 5.6	*Let's all*
11	Th.	NEW ● • ☌♇☾ • Inventor Gail Borden died, 1874 • {6.4 5.8	*recall*
12	Fr.	☿ GR. ELONG. (24° WEST) • N.Y. Jets defeated Baltimore Colts, 16–7, in Super Bowl III, 1969	*a brave*
13	Sa.	St. Hilary • ☾ AT PERIG. • Discovery of 45,500-year-old painting in Sulawesi cave announced, 2021	
14	**G**	**2nd S. af. Ep.** • ☌♄☾ • Tides {6.5 6.2	*man's dream:*
15	M.	MARTIN LUTHER KING JR.'S BIRTHDAY (U.S.) • ☌♆☾ • 1st optical pulsar ID'd, 1969	*The King*
16	Tu.	☾ ON EQ. • Artist Andrew Wyeth died, 2009 • {5.9 —	*of*
17	W.	☾ AT ☊ • U.S. statesman Benjamin Franklin born, 1706 • Tides {6.1 5.6	*kindness*
18	Th.	☌♃☾ • Sale of pre-sliced bread banned in U.S. (law rescinded March 8), WWII, 1943	*reigns*
19	Fr.	National Popcorn Day • ☌♅☾ • Tides {5.8 4.9	*supreme.*
20	Sa.	☌♇⊙ • 1st bridge in U.S. to cross Columbia River opened, Wenatchee, Wash., 1908 • {5.6 4.8	*A*
21	**G**	**3rd S. af. Ep.** • Confederate general Thomas "Stonewall" Jackson born, 1824	*brief*
22	M.	St. Vincent • ☾ RIDES HIGH • Tides {5.5 5.0	*reprieve,*
23	Tu.	Elizabeth Blackwell 1st woman to receive medical degree, 1849 • Tides {5.6 5.2	*then*
24	W.	Warmest January on record across globe at time, 2020 • Tides {5.7 5.3	*frigid*
25	Th.	Conversion of Paul • FULL WOLF ○ • January thaw typically begins about now.	*eves!*
26	Fr.	Sts. Timothy & Titus • Canadian Red Ensign approved as official flag for govt. buildings, 1924	*Oh,*
27	Sa.	☌☿♂ • ♅ STAT. • 113-lb. 6-oz. black grouper caught, Dry Tortugas, Fla., 1990	*to see*
28	**G**	**Septuagesima** • *Every hill has its valley.* • Tides {5.8 5.6	*some*
29	M.	☾ AT APO. • Entrepreneur Oprah Winfrey born, 1954 • Tides {5.6 5.6	*palm*
30	Tu.	☾ ON EQ. • Raccoons mate now. • Tides {5.4 5.6	*tree*
31	W.	☾ AT ☋ • 0°F, San Antonio, Tex., 1949 • Film producer Samuel Goldwyn died, 1974	*leaves!*

Farmer's Calendar

They can be smaller than chocolate sprinkles, smaller even than some coffee grounds. Under a warm January Sun, they stretch over the snow's surface as if some mad grocer had slashed bags of pepper and danced over woods and meadow. Watch closely, and you'll see them launch. They are wingless, harmless snow fleas. Not real fleas, they belong to a group of arthropods called "springtails"—of an order so successful that it has not changed much in 410 million years.

The name "springtail" derives from an appendage under their abdomen, which, when released, can catapult the creature 4 inches into the air—the equivalent of a human jumping across a football field. Throughout North America, they live in leaf litter, bark, and decaying logs—sometimes 100,000 per cubic yard of soil.

There is no "dead of winter," and snow is not sterile. There's an ecosystem on and in it. When even muted sunlight strikes snow during a winter thaw, springtails scurry up from the forest floor to graze on the algae, fungi, bacteria, and decaying organic matter on its surface. Then, when night falls, they all scurry back.

FEBRUARY

SKY WATCH: From the 11th through the 13th, the crescent Moon appears as a smile in dusk's fading twilight—in contrast to the upward-aiming archer's bow orientation in which it can be seen for the rest of the year. Saturn is now too low to observe, but Jupiter remains the night's brightest "star" until 11:00 P.M. A Valentine's Day gift is Jupiter hovering just to the left of the Moon on the 14th, when early risers can also observe Venus above Mars low in the brightening dawn twilight to the southeast. Earth's two nearest planetary neighbors (Venus and Mars) form a close morning conjunction in the southeast from the 20th to the 24th.

◗ **LAST QUARTER** 2nd day 6:18 P.M. ◖ **FIRST QUARTER** 16th day 10:01 A.M.
● **NEW MOON** 9th day 5:59 P.M. ○ **FULL MOON** 24th day 7:30 A.M.

All times are given in Eastern Standard Time.

GET THESE PAGES WITH TIMES SET TO YOUR POSTAL CODE VIA ALMANAC.CA/2024.

DAY OF YEAR	DAY OF MONTH	DAY OF WEEK	☼ RISES H. M.	RISE KEY	☼ SETS H. M.	SET KEY	LENGTH OF DAY H. M.	SUN FAST M.	SUN DECLINATION ° ′	HIGH TIDE TIMES HALIFAX		☾ RISES H. M.	RISE KEY	☾ SETS H. M.	SET KEY	☾ ASTRON. PLACE	☾ AGE
32	1	Th.	7:24	D	5:09	B	9 45	*16	17 s. 06	12	12¼	—	-	10:10	B	VIR	21
33	2	Fr.	7:23	D	5:11	B	9 48	*16	16 s. 49	12½	1	12:23	D	10:29	B	VIR	22
34	3	Sa.	7:22	D	5:12	B	9 50	*16	16 s. 31	1¼	1¾	1:32	E	10:53	A	LIB	23
35	4	**G**	7:20	D	5:13	B	9 53	*17	16 s. 13	2	3	2:44	E	11:23	A	LIB	24
36	5	M.	7:19	D	5:15	B	9 56	*17	15 s. 55	3¼	4¼	3:57	E	**12:04**	A	SCO	25
37	6	Tu.	7:18	D	5:16	B	9 58	*17	15 s. 37	4¼	5½	5:06	E	**12:59**	A	OPH	26
38	7	W.	7:16	D	5:18	B	10 02	*17	15 s. 18	5¼	6¼	6:06	E	**2:09**	A	SAG	27
39	8	Th.	7:15	D	5:19	B	10 04	*17	14 s. 59	6¼	7¼	6:54	E	**3:31**	A	SAG	28
40	9	Fr.	7:14	D	5:21	B	10 07	*17	14 s. 40	7¼	8	7:31	E	**4:58**	A	CAP	0
41	10	Sa.	7:12	D	5:22	B	10 10	*17	14 s. 21	8	8¾	7:59	D	**6:25**	B	CAP	1
42	11	**G**	7:11	D	5:24	B	10 13	*17	14 s. 01	8¾	9½	8:23	D	**7:49**	B	AQU	2
43	12	M.	7:09	D	5:25	B	10 16	*17	13 s. 41	9¾	10¼	8:43	C	**9:11**	C	AQU	3
44	13	Tu.	7:08	D	5:27	B	10 19	*17	13 s. 21	10½	11	9:03	B	**10:31**	D	PSC	4
45	14	W.	7:06	D	5:28	B	10 22	*17	13 s. 01	11¼	11¾	9:24	B	**11:51**	D	PSC	5
46	15	Th.	7:05	D	5:29	B	10 24	*17	12 s. 40	12	—	9:48	A	—	-	ARI	6
47	16	Fr.	7:03	D	5:31	B	10 28	*17	12 s. 20	12½	1	10:16	A	**1:09**	E	ARI	7
48	17	Sa.	7:02	D	5:32	B	10 30	*17	11 s. 59	1½	2	10:50	A	**2:25**	E	TAU	8
49	18	**G**	7:00	D	5:34	B	10 34	*17	11 s. 38	2½	3½	11:34	A	**3:34**	E	TAU	9
50	19	M.	6:59	D	5:35	B	10 36	*17	11 s. 16	3½	5	**12:28**	A	**4:34**	E	AUR	10
51	20	Tu.	6:57	D	5:37	B	10 40	*16	10 s. 55	4¾	6	**1:29**	A	**5:23**	E	GEM	11
52	21	W.	6:55	D	5:38	B	10 43	*16	10 s. 33	5¾	6¾	**2:36**	A	**6:01**	E	GEM	12
53	22	Th.	6:54	D	5:39	B	10 45	*16	10 s. 12	6¾	7½	**3:43**	A	**6:31**	E	CAN	13
54	23	Fr.	6:52	D	5:41	B	10 49	*16	9 s. 50	7½	8	**4:50**	B	**6:54**	E	LEO	14
55	24	Sa.	6:50	D	5:42	B	10 52	*16	9 s. 28	8	8½	**5:56**	B	**7:13**	D	LEO	15
56	25	**G**	6:49	D	5:44	B	10 55	*16	9 s. 05	8¾	9¼	**7:00**	C	**7:30**	D	LEO	16
57	26	M.	6:47	D	5:45	B	10 58	*16	8 s. 43	9¼	9¾	**8:03**	C	**7:45**	C	VIR	17
58	27	Tu.	6:45	D	5:46	B	11 01	*15	8 s. 20	9¾	10¼	**9:07**	D	**8:00**	C	VIR	18
59	28	W.	6:44	D	5:48	B	11 04	*15	7 s. 58	10½	10¾	**10:12**	D	**8:16**	B	VIR	19
60	29	Th.	6:42	D	5:49	B	11 07	*15	7 s. 35	11	11¼	**11:20**	E	**8:34**	B	VIR	20

FEBRUARY

Outside the shivering ivy clings,
While on the hob the kettle sings.
–**William Wilfred Campbell**

DAY OF MONTH	DAY OF WEEK	DATES, FEASTS, FASTS, ASPECTS, TIDE HEIGHTS, AND WEATHER	
1	Th.	St. Brigid • Major snow and ice storm ended, Nashville, Tenn., 1951 • Tides {5.0 / —	*This*
2	Fr.	Candlemas • Groundhog Day • *At Candlemas, Cold come to us.* • {5.4 / 4.8	*shortest*
3	Sa.	Writer Gertrude Stein born, 1874 • –81.4°F, Snag, Y.T., 1947 • {5.3 / 4.6	*month*
4	**G**	**Sexagesima** • Distribution of Canadian penny stopped, 2013 • {5.3 / 4.6	*will*
5	M.	St. Agatha • ☌☿♇ • Botanist John Lindley born, 1799 • Tides {5.3 / 4.7	*grow by*
6	Tu.	☾ RUNS LOW • Woodrow Wilson 1st U.S. president buried in D.C., 1924 • {5.5 / 4.9	*a day;*
7	W.	☌♀☾ • Basketball player Steve Nash born, 1974 • Tides {5.7 / 5.3	*pray icy*
8	Th.	☌☿☾ • ☌♂☾ • ☌♇☾ • Tides {6.1 / 5.7	*winds*
9	Fr.	NEW ● • The Beatles made their U.S. live TV debut, 1964 • Tides {6.4 / 6.0	*don't*
10	Sa.	LUNAR NEW YEAR (CHINA) • ☾ AT PERIG. • ☌♄☾ • {6.6 / 6.3	*blow us*
11	**G**	**Quinquagesima** • Barbara Harris 1st female bishop in Anglican Communion, 1989	*away!*
12	M.	☾ ON EQ. • ☌♆☾ • U.S. president Abraham Lincoln born, 1809 • {6.5 / 6.6	*Sun*
13	Tu.	Shrove Tuesday • ☾ AT ☊ • –2°F, Tallahassee, Fla., 1899 • {6.3 / 6.5	*sends*
14	W.	Ash Wednesday • VALENTINE'S DAY • ☌♂♇ • Tides {5.9 / 6.2	*love,*
15	Th.	NATIONAL FLAG OF CANADA DAY • ☌♃☾ • ☌♅☾ • Social reformer Susan B. Anthony born, 1820	*but*
16	Fr.	73.2% of continental U.S. covered in snow, 2021 • Tides {5.9 / 5.1	*cold's*
17	Sa.	☌♀♇ • Winter's back breaks. • Artist Raphaelle Peale born, 1774 • {5.5 / 4.8	*the*
18	**G**	**1st. S. in Lent** • Auguste Bartholdi's statue design for "Liberty enlightening the world" patented, 1879	
19	M.	PRESIDENTS' DAY (U.S.) • ☾ RIDES HIGH • 1st N.Am. sighting of (beached) hoodwinker sunfish, Calif., 2019	*boss.*
20	Tu.	Film critic Gene Siskel died, 1999 • *If today will not, tomorrow may.* • Tides {5.1 / 4.8	*Heavens*
21	W.	Ember Day • 1st telephone directory published, New Haven, Conn., 1878 • {5.3 / 5.1	*above,*
22	Th.	☌♀♂ • U.S. president George Washington born, 1732 • Tides {5.5 / 5.3	*please*
23	Fr.	Ember Day • 1st mass Salk polio vaccine inoculation of children, Pittsburgh, Pa., 1954	*let us*
24	Sa.	St. Matthias • Ember Day • FULL SNOW ○ • Tides {5.7 / 5.6	*defrost!*
25	**G**	**2nd. S. in Lent** • ☾ AT APO. • Tides {5.7 / 5.7	*Sunshine*
26	M.	☾ ON EQ. • Skunks mate now. • 1st spacewalk outside ISS w/o crew member inside, 2004	*fizzles*
27	Tu.	Int'l Polar Bear Day • ☾ AT ☋ • 5-lb. 11-oz. Pacific bonefish caught, Honolulu, Hawaii, 2022	*in a*
28	W.	St. Romanus • ☌☿♄ • ☌♄☉ • ☿ IN SUP. ☌ • {5.4 / 5.6	*Leap Day*
29	Th.	LEAP DAY • *Leap year was ne'er a good sheep year.* • {5.2 / 5.6	*drizzle.*

Q: What is the difference between here and there? A: The letter "t"

Farmer's Calendar

Few mushrooms can be collected now. But almost anywhere in North America you are likely to encounter gelatinous fungi with the consistency of marmalade. Collectively, these particular jelly fungi are known as "witch's butter." If you find one in someone else's woods, you have nothing to worry about. But if it grows on your property—especially on your door frame—a witch has hexed you, and to rid yourself of the curse you must pierce and drain it with a sharp stick. Or so proclaim ancient texts.

Several species of witch's butter are edible: Yellow, or golden, jelly fungi (*Tremella mesenterica* and *Naematelia aurantia,* aka *T. aurantia*) prefer hardwood trees with attached bark and parasitize other fungi. Orange jelly fungus (*Dacrymyces chrysospermus,* aka *D. palmatus*) favors conifers, especially those without bark; instead of parasitizing fungi, it decomposes wood.

Witch's butter, known also by the endearing name of "yellow brain fungus," makes a superb base for soups. It has no taste of its own, however. So, after you have prudently dispelled the witch's hex by puncturing and draining it, do resist the temptation to eat it raw.

SKY WATCH: Venus remains glued in place as a brilliant morning star all month, low in the southeast at around 6:30 A.M. Look to Venus's right on the 7th, from 5:45 to 6:00 A.M., to see the hair-thin waning crescent Moon—in between them is Mercury. At dawn on the 21st, Venus closely meets Saturn very low in the east; use binoculars for viewing. Between midnight and dawn on the 25th, a penumbral eclipse of the Moon occurs, but this is the type of eclipse in which the appearance of the full Moon doesn't noticeably change. On the 29th at 6:30 A.M., look for Saturn halfway between low and brilliant Venus and higher and much dimmer Mars. Spring begins with the vernal equinox on the 19th at 11:06 P.M. EDT.

◐ LAST QUARTER	3rd day 10:23 A.M.	◑ FIRST QUARTER	17th day 12:11 A.M.
● NEW MOON	10th day 5:00 A.M.	○ FULL MOON	25th day 3:00 A.M.

After 2:00 A.M. on March 10, Eastern Daylight Time is given.

GET THESE PAGES WITH TIMES SET TO YOUR POSTAL CODE VIA ALMANAC.CA/2024.

DAY OF YEAR	DAY OF MONTH	DAY OF WEEK	☼ RISES H. M.	RISE KEY	☼ SETS H. M.	SET KEY	LENGTH OF DAY H. M.	SUN FAST M.	SUN DECLINATION ° ′	HIGH TIDE TIMES HALIFAX		☾ RISES H. M.	RISE KEY	☾ SETS H. M.	SET KEY	☾ ASTRON. PLACE	☾ AGE
61	1	Fr.	6:40	D	**5:51**	C	11 11	*15	7 s. 12	11¾	11¾	—	-	8:55	A	LIB	21
62	2	Sa.	6:38	D	**5:52**	C	11 14	*15	6 s. 49	12¼	—	12:30	E	9:21	A	LIB	22
63	3	**F**	6:36	C	**5:53**	C	11 17	*14	6 s. 26	12½	1¼	1:41	E	9:57	A	SCO	23
64	4	M.	6:35	C	**5:55**	C	11 20	*14	6 s. 03	1¼	2¼	2:50	E	10:44	A	OPH	24
65	5	Tu.	6:33	C	**5:56**	C	11 23	*14	5 s. 40	2½	3¾	3:53	E	11:45	A	SAG	25
66	6	W.	6:31	C	**5:57**	C	11 26	*14	5 s. 17	3¾	5	4:44	E	**1:00**	A	SAG	26
67	7	Th.	6:29	C	**5:59**	C	11 30	*14	4 s. 53	5	6	5:25	E	**2:23**	A	CAP	27
68	8	Fr.	6:27	C	**6:00**	C	11 33	*13	4 s. 30	6	6¾	5:56	E	**3:49**	A	CAP	28
69	9	Sa.	6:25	C	**6:02**	C	11 37	*13	4 s. 06	7	7½	6:22	D	**5:15**	B	AQU	29
70	10	**F**	7:24	C	**7:03**	C	11 39	*13	3 s. 43	8¾	9¼	7:44	C	**7:40**	C	AQU	0
71	11	M.	7:22	C	**7:04**	C	11 42	*12	3 s. 19	9½	10	8:04	C	**9:03**	C	PSC	1
72	12	Tu.	7:20	C	**7:06**	C	11 46	*12	2 s. 55	10¼	10¾	8:25	B	**10:26**	D	PSC	2
73	13	W.	7:18	C	**7:07**	C	11 49	*12	2 s. 32	11¼	11½	8:48	B	**11:49**	E	ARI	3
74	14	Th.	7:16	C	**7:08**	C	11 52	*12	2 s. 08	12	—	9:15	A	—	-	ARI	4
75	15	Fr.	7:14	C	**7:10**	C	11 56	*11	1 s. 44	12¼	12¾	9:48	A	**1:09**	E	TAU	5
76	16	Sa.	7:12	C	**7:11**	C	11 59	*11	1 s. 21	1	1¾	10:29	A	**2:23**	E	TAU	6
77	17	**F**	7:10	C	**7:12**	C	12 02	*11	0 s. 57	2	2¾	11:21	A	**3:29**	E	TAU	7
78	18	M.	7:09	C	**7:13**	C	12 04	*11	0 s. 33	3	4	**12:21**	A	**4:22**	E	GEM	8
79	19	Tu.	7:07	C	**7:15**	C	12 08	*10	0 s. 09	4¼	5½	**1:26**	A	**5:03**	E	GEM	9
80	20	W.	7:05	C	**7:16**	C	12 11	*10	0 N. 13	5½	6¾	**2:34**	A	**5:35**	E	CAN	10
81	21	Th.	7:03	C	**7:17**	C	12 14	*10	0 N. 37	6½	7½	**3:41**	A	**6:00**	E	LEO	11
82	22	Fr.	7:01	C	**7:19**	C	12 18	*9	1 N. 01	7¼	8	**4:47**	B	**6:20**	D	LEO	12
83	23	Sa.	6:59	C	**7:20**	C	12 21	*9	1 N. 24	8	8½	**5:51**	B	**6:37**	D	LEO	13
84	24	**F**	6:57	C	**7:21**	C	12 24	*9	1 N. 48	8¾	9	**6:55**	C	**6:53**	C	VIR	14
85	25	M.	6:55	C	**7:23**	C	12 28	*8	2 N. 11	9¼	9½	**7:59**	C	**7:08**	C	VIR	15
86	26	Tu.	6:53	C	**7:24**	C	12 31	*8	2 N. 35	9¾	10	**9:04**	D	**7:23**	B	VIR	16
87	27	W.	6:51	C	**7:25**	C	12 34	*8	2 N. 58	10½	10½	**10:11**	D	**7:40**	A	VIR	17
88	28	Th.	6:50	C	**7:26**	C	12 36	*8	3 N. 22	11	11	**11:20**	E	**8:00**	A	LIB	18
89	29	Fr.	6:48	C	**7:28**	C	12 40	*7	3 N. 45	11½	11¾	—	-	**8:24**	A	LIB	19
90	30	Sa.	6:46	C	**7:29**	C	12 43	*7	4 N. 08	12¼	—	**12:31**	E	**8:56**	A	SCO	20
91	31	**F**	6:44	C	**7:30**	C	12 46	*7	4 N. 32	12¼	1	**1:40**	E	**9:38**	A	OPH	21

MARCH

Not too hot nor yet too cold,
Graciously your charms unfold.
–Eugene Field, of spring

DAY OF MONTH	DAY OF WEEK	DATES, FEASTS, FASTS, ASPECTS, TIDE HEIGHTS, AND WEATHER	
1	Fr.	St. David • Director Ron Howard born, 1954 • Tides {5.1 / 5.5	*Still*
2	Sa.	St. Chad • Mount Rainier became national park, Wash., 1899 • Tides {4.9 / —	*cold,*
3	**F**	**3rd S. in Lent** • 1st U.S. international airmail delivery, Vancouver, B.C., to Seattle, Wash., 1919	*still*
4	M.	☾ RUNS LOW • Composer Antonio Vivaldi born, 1678 • Comedian John Candy died, 1994	*wet?*
5	Tu.	St. Piran • 13 tornadoes struck Iowa, 2022 • Tides {5.2 / 4.6	*You bet!*
6	W.	☌♇☾ • Toronto (Upper Canada) incorporated, 1834 • 4" snow in 24 hours, Milton Exp. Station, Fla., 1954	
7	Th.	St. Perpetua • Melvin Garlow 1st scheduled U.S. pilot to log 1,000,000 miles in jet planes, 1959	*Clocks*
8	Fr.	☌☿♆ • ☌♀☾ • ☌♂☾ • Baseball player Joe DiMaggio died, 1999	*ahead:*
9	Sa.	☌♄☾ • Hummingbirds migrate north now. • Tides {6.3 / 6.3	*Don't forget!*
10	**F**	DST BEGINS • RAMADAN BEGINS • NEW ● • ☾ AT PERIG. • ☌☿☾ • ☌♆☾	
11	M.	☾ ON EQ. • ☾ AT ☊ • *A Raisin in the Sun* opened on Broadway, N.Y.C., 1959 • {6.5 / 6.7	*Lawn*
12	Tu.	Inventor George Westinghouse died, 1914 • Tides {6.4 / 6.7	*busy*
13	W.	☌♃☾ • Major auroral display visible as far south as Cuba, 1989 • {6.2 / 6.4	*thawin';*
14	Th.	☌⛢☾ • *Knowledge without practice makes but half an artist.* • Tides {5.8 / —	*look*
15	Fr.	Beware the ides of March. • Tides {6.1 / 5.5	*for*
16	Sa.	Navigator Matthew Flinders born, 1774 • New Grand Ole Opry House opened, Nashville, Tenn., 1974	*shamrocks*
17	**F**	**5th S. in Lent** • ST. PATRICK'S DAY • ☾ RIDES HIGH • ☌♆☉	*upon!*
18	M.	**Orthodox Lent begins** • Daylilies returned to Earth via space shuttle *Discovery,* 1989	*Spring*
19	Tu.	St. Joseph • VERNAL EQUINOX • *A late spring is a great blessing.* • {4.8 / 4.6	*has begun,*
20	W.	Alfred Einstein submitted his theory of general relativity to physics journal, 1916 • Tides {4.9 / 4.9	*but*
21	Th.	☌♀♄ • Twitter co-founder Jack Dorsey sent out 1st tweet on platform, 2006 • {5.0 / 5.1	*snowy*
22	Fr.	Nurse Col. Elizabeth Lawrie Smellie born, 1884 • Tides {5.2 / 5.3	*showers*
23	Sa.	☾ AT APO. • Botanist John Bartram born, 1699 • Tides {5.4 / 5.5	*not*
24	**F**	**Palm Sunday** • ☾ ON EQ. • ☿ GR. ELONG. (19° EAST) • {5.5 / 5.6	*yet*
25	M.	FULL WORM ○ • ECLIPSE ☾ • *Words are the wings of action.* • {5.5 / 5.7	*done—*
26	Tu.	☾ AT ☋ • Poet Robert Frost born, 1874 • Tides {5.5 / 5.8	*big*
27	W.	9.2-magnitude earthquake, Prince William Sound, Alaska, 1964 • Tides {5.5 / 5.7	*earmuffs*
28	Th.	**Maundy Thursday** • Brewer August Anheuser Busch Jr. born, 1899	*for*
29	Fr.	**Good Friday** • *Mariner 10* completed 1st flyby of Mercury, 1974 • {5.3 / 5.6	*the*
30	Sa.	Chipmunks emerge from hibernation now. • {5.1 / —	*Easter*
31	**F**	**Easter** • Nfld. became Canada's 10th province, 1949 • Tides {5.5 / 5.0	*Bun!*

Farmer's Calendar

When the first chipmunk peeks over the rim of its winter burrow and scampers across your yard, spring can be only a few days away. In the eastern half of the country (except the extreme South), your harbinger will be the eastern chipmunk. In the West, it will be one of at least 20 species, all strikingly similar. The capacity of a chipmunk's cheeks is prodigious. One load was measured at 70 sunflower seeds, another at 12 acorns. So, it's easy for a chipmunk to empty and cache the entire contents of a bird feeder in 1 hour.

While chipmunks remain underground for most of the winter, they don't sleep through it. They have a bedroom in which they may sleep for several days before getting a snack from their pantry. Chipmunks are fastidious groomers; after eating they'll sit on their haunches, lick the inside of their paws, and rub their faces.

In the language of eastern chipmunks, loud "chips" may indicate alarm. "Chucking" warns of aerial predators. "Trills" indicate pursuit by a predator. But, when you hear an eastern chipmunk steadily chipping for several minutes, it's often simply saying, "I am a chipmunk, and I am here."

APRIL

SKY WATCH: On the 8th, a rare total solar eclipse can be seen from parts of Mexico, the U.S., and Canada. (See "Behold Nature's Grandest Event!," page 158.) Observers are strongly encouraged to travel to where it can be seen as a total eclipse rather than partial one. In early April, Jupiter sinks lower each nightfall until its close proximity to the horizon ends the gas giant's reign as an evening star. On the 6th, the waning crescent Moon forms a triangle with Saturn and Mars low in the east at 6:00 A.M. On the next morning, the thin crescent Moon stands to the right of dazzling Venus at 6:15 A.M. at a very low elevation, which will require an unobstructed view of the eastern horizon for observation.

◑ LAST QUARTER   1st day   11:15 P.M.   ● FIRST QUARTER   15th day   3:13 P.M.
● NEW MOON   8th day   2:21 P.M.   ○ FULL MOON   23rd day   7:49 P.M.

All times are given in Eastern Daylight Time.

GET THESE PAGES WITH TIMES SET TO YOUR POSTAL CODE VIA ALMANAC.CA/2024.

DAY OF YEAR	DAY OF MONTH	DAY OF WEEK	☼ RISES H.M.	RISE KEY	☼ SETS H.M.	SET KEY	LENGTH OF DAY H.M.	SUN FAST M.	SUN DECLINATION ° '	HIGH TIDE TIMES HALIFAX		☾ RISES H.M.	RISE KEY	☾ SETS H.M.	SET KEY	☾ ASTRON. PLACE	☾ AGE
92	1	M.	6:42	C	7:32	C	12 50	*6	4 N. 55	1	1¾	2:44	E	10:32	A	SAG	22
93	2	Tu.	6:40	C	7:33	D	12 53	*6	5 N. 18	1¾	2¾	3:38	E	11:40	A	SAG	23
94	3	W.	6:38	C	7:34	D	12 56	*6	5 N. 41	3	4½	4:21	E	12:57	A	SAG	24
95	4	Th.	6:36	C	7:36	D	13 00	*6	6 N. 04	4¼	5¾	4:55	E	2:20	A	CAP	25
96	5	Fr.	6:35	B	7:37	D	13 02	*5	6 N. 26	5½	6½	5:22	D	3:44	B	AQU	26
97	6	Sa.	6:33	B	7:38	D	13 05	*5	6 N. 49	6¾	7¼	5:45	D	5:07	B	AQU	27
98	7	**F**	6:31	B	7:39	D	13 08	*5	7 N. 11	7¾	8	6:05	C	6:30	C	AQU	28
99	8	M.	6:29	B	7:41	D	13 12	*4	7 N. 34	8½	8¾	6:26	C	7:54	D	PSC	0
100	9	Tu.	6:27	B	7:42	D	13 15	*4	7 N. 56	9¼	9½	6:47	B	9:18	D	PSC	1
101	10	W.	6:25	B	7:43	D	13 18	*4	8 N. 18	10	10¼	7:12	A	10:42	E	ARI	2
102	11	Th.	6:24	B	7:45	D	13 21	*4	8 N. 40	10¾	11	7:43	A	—	-	TAU	3
103	12	Fr.	6:22	B	7:46	D	13 24	*3	9 N. 02	11¾	11¾	8:21	A	12:02	E	TAU	4
104	13	Sa.	6:20	B	7:47	D	13 27	*3	9 N. 24	12½	—	9:10	A	1:15	E	TAU	5
105	14	**F**	6:18	B	7:48	D	13 30	*3	9 N. 45	12¾	1¼	10:09	A	2:15	E	AUR	6
106	15	M.	6:16	B	7:50	D	13 34	*3	10 N. 07	1½	2¼	11:14	A	3:02	E	GEM	7
107	16	Tu.	6:15	B	7:51	D	13 36	*2	10 N. 28	2½	3½	12:22	A	3:37	E	CAN	8
108	17	W.	6:13	B	7:52	D	13 39	*2	10 N. 49	3¾	5	1:30	A	4:05	E	CAN	9
109	18	Th.	6:11	B	7:54	D	13 43	*2	11 N. 10	5	6	2:37	B	4:26	D	LEO	10
110	19	Fr.	6:10	B	7:55	D	13 45	*2	11 N. 30	6	6¾	3:42	B	4:44	D	LEO	11
111	20	Sa.	6:08	B	7:56	D	13 48	*2	11 N. 51	6¾	7¼	4:45	C	5:00	C	LEO	12
112	21	**F**	6:06	B	7:57	D	13 51	*1	12 N. 11	7½	8	5:49	C	5:15	C	VIR	13
113	22	M.	6:04	B	7:59	D	13 55	*1	12 N. 31	8¼	8½	6:54	D	5:30	B	VIR	14
114	23	Tu.	6:03	B	8:00	D	13 57	*1	12 N. 51	8¾	9	8:01	D	5:46	B	VIR	15
115	24	W.	6:01	B	8:01	D	14 00	*1	13 N. 11	9½	9½	9:10	E	6:05	B	VIR	16
116	25	Th.	6:00	B	8:03	D	14 03	*1	13 N. 30	10	10	10:21	E	6:28	A	LIB	17
117	26	Fr.	5:58	B	8:04	D	14 06	*1	13 N. 49	10¾	10½	11:32	E	6:58	A	SCO	18
118	27	Sa.	5:56	B	8:05	D	14 09	0	14 N. 08	11¼	11¼	—	-	7:37	A	OPH	19
119	28	**F**	5:55	B	8:06	D	14 11	0	14 N. 27	12	—	12:38	E	8:27	A	SAG	20
120	29	M.	5:53	B	8:08	D	14 15	0	14 N. 46	12	12¾	1:35	E	9:30	A	SAG	21
121	30	Tu.	5:52	B	8:09	D	14 17	0	15 N. 04	12¾	1¾	2:20	E	10:44	A	SAG	22

Behold the Moon!—whose heavenly alchymy
Turns waves and clouds to silver.
–Park

Farmer's Calendar

In early spring, vernal pools—pockets of snowmelt and rain that vanish in the heat of summer—teem with life unseen by most woods wanderers. You can't be sure that you've found a vernal pool until you identify one of its obligate denizens such as fairy shrimp, of an order more ancient than dinosaurs. Under the dappled surface, you may see a translucent creature roughly an inch long materialize. Fairy shrimp glide along, swimming on their backs, breathing and rowing with 11 pairs of legs. They are there because fish are not. Ducks eat fairy shrimp but also serve to unknowingly transport their eggs to other vernal pools.

There are two kinds of eggs—one for times of plenty when males are scarce and one for occasions of low or no water. The first type, from unfertilized females of some species, quickly produce clones. The second, which are actually encysted embryos, are more common and result from male–female unions; these cysts remain viable for years. Development, drainage of wetlands, and other factors are causing the loss of vernal pools and consequent decline of fairy shrimp in much of North America.

DAY OF MONTH	DAY OF WEEK	DATES, FEASTS, FASTS, ASPECTS, TIDE HEIGHTS, AND WEATHER	
1	M.	Easter Monday • **All Fools'** • ☽RUNS LOW • ☿STAT. • Nunavut est., 1999	*Foolishly*
2	Tu.	*You can only take out of a bag what was already in it.* • Tides {5.2 {4.7	*assumin'*
3	W.	☿♀♅ • ☽♂☾ • Tsawwassen First Nation Final Agreement came into effect, 2009	*that soon*
4	Th.	North Atlantic Treaty signed, 1949 • Tides {5.2 {5.1	*we'll be*
5	Fr.	♂♂☾ • 26.9" snow, St. John's, Nfld., 1999 • Tides {5.4 {5.6	*bloomin'!*
6	Sa.	♂♄☾ • King Richard I, "the Lionheart," died, 1199 • Tides {5.7 {6.1	*As snow*
7	**F**	2nd S. of Easter • ☾ON EQ. • ☾AT PERIG. • ♂♀☾ • ♂♆☾	*reminds*
8	M.	Annunciation[T] • **NEW** ● • **ECLIPSE** ☉ • ☾AT ☋ • ♂♀☾	*us,*
9	Tu.	NASA introduced 1st seven astronauts to press, 1959 • Tides {6.2 {6.7	*winter's*
10	W.	♂♂♄ • ♂♃☾ • ♂♂☾ • Safety pin patented, 1849 • {6.1 {6.6	*not yet*
11	Th.	☿IN INF. ♂ • *Clouds that thunder do not always rain.* • Tides {6.0 {6.3	*behind us.*
12	Fr.	Dr. Peter Safar, "father of CPR," born, 1924 • Poet Gary Soto born, 1952 • Tides {5.7 {5.9	*With*
13	Sa.	☽RIDES HIGH • U.S. president Thomas Jefferson born, 1743 • Tides {5.4 {—	*Tax*
14	**F**	3rd S. of Easter • 1st MLB game in Canada, Montreal Expos vs. St. Louis Cardinals, 1969	*Day*
15	M.	George H. Shull, plant geneticist and "father of hybrid corn," born, 1874 • Tides {5.1 {4.8	*looming,*
16	Tu.	Two giant pandas, gift to U.S. from China, arrived at National Zoo, D.C., 1972 • {4.9 {4.7	*last*
17	W.	Geraldine "Jerrie" Mock 1st woman to complete solo flight around world, 1964 • {4.7 {4.8	*snowbanks*
18	Th.	♂♀♀ • Banshee, world's longest inverted roller coaster (4,124'), opened, Mason, Ohio, 2014	*melt,*
19	Fr.	☾AT APO. • *Little by little, one goes far.* • Tides {4.8 {5.2	*in the*
20	Sa.	♂♃☉ • 106°F, Del Rio, Tex., 1984 • Tides {5.0 {5.4	*chilliest*
21	**F**	4th S. of Easter • ☾ON EQ. • Naturalist John Muir born, 1838 • {5.1 {5.5	*spring*
22	M.	Passover begins at sundown • **Earth Day** • ☾AT ☋ • {5.3 {5.7	*we've*
23	Tu.	St. George • **Full Pink** ◯ • Olympic snowboarder Chloe Kim born, 2000 • {5.3 {5.7	*ever*
24	W.	☿STAT. • *The Old Farmer's Almanac founder* Robert B. Thomas born, 1766 • {5.4 {5.8	*felt.*
25	Th.	St. Mark • English statesman Oliver Cromwell born, 1599 • Tides {5.4 {5.8	*Dress*
26	Fr.	National Help a Horse Day (U.S.) • Geologist Eduard Suess died, 1914 • Tides {5.3 {5.8	*in*
27	Sa.	Poplars leaf out about now. • 27" snow in 24 hours, Minot, N.Dak., 1984	*layers*
28	**F**	5th S. of Easter • ☽RUNS LOW • Tides {5.2 {5.6	*for*
29	M.	Jazz pianist/bandleader Duke Ellington born, 1899 • Tides {5.1 {—	*Passover*
30	Tu.	♂♂♆ • Franklin D. Roosevelt 1st U.S. president to appear on TV, 1939 • {5.4 {5.0	*prayers!*

CALENDAR

MAY

SKY WATCH: This month's action is concentrated in the eastern sky during dawn's twilight. On the 1st at around 5:15 A.M., Saturn stands highest in the east, with Mercury below it and a dim, orange Mars halfway between them. On the 4th, Saturn and Mars stand on opposite sides of the thin, crescent Moon in the brightening twilight. Mars hovers to the upper right of the Moon on the 5th at 5:00 A.M. On the 6th at 5:15 A.M., an unobstructed view of the eastern horizon reveals Mercury to the lower right of the crescent Moon. On the evening of the 15th, the Moon is just above blue Spica, Virgo's brightest star. A gorgeous, super-close Saturn–Moon conjunction unfolds from 4:30 to 5:00 A.M. on the 31st.

◗ **LAST QUARTER**   1st day 7:27 A.M.   ○ **FULL MOON**   23rd day 9:53 A.M.
● **NEW MOON**   7th day 11:22 P.M.   ◑ **LAST QUARTER** 30th day 1:13 P.M.
◐ **FIRST QUARTER** 15th day 7:48 A.M.

All times are given in Eastern Daylight Time.

GET THESE PAGES WITH TIMES SET TO YOUR POSTAL CODE VIA ALMANAC.CA/2024.

DAY OF YEAR	DAY OF MONTH	DAY OF WEEK	☼ RISES H. M.	RISE KEY	☼ SETS H. M.	SET KEY	LENGTH OF DAY H. M.	SUN FAST M.	SUN DECLINATION ° '	HIGH TIDE TIMES HALIFAX		☾ RISES H. M.	RISE KEY	☾ SETS H. M.	SET KEY	☾ ASTRON. PLACE	☾ AGE
122	1	W.	5:50	B	8:10	D	14 20	0	15 N. 22	1¾	2¾	2:56	E	12:03	A	CAP	23
123	2	Th.	5:49	B	8:11	D	14 22	0	15 N. 40	2¾	4	3:24	E	1:23	B	CAP	24
124	3	Fr.	5:47	B	8:13	D	14 26	0	15 N. 57	4	5¼	3:48	D	2:44	B	AQU	25
125	4	Sa.	5:46	B	8:14	D	14 28	0	16 N. 15	5¼	6	4:08	C	4:04	C	AQU	26
126	5	F	5:44	B	8:15	E	14 31	0	16 N. 32	6½	6¾	4:28	C	5:25	C	PSC	27
127	6	M.	5:43	B	8:16	E	14 33	1	16 N. 48	7¼	7½	4:48	B	6:47	D	PSC	28
128	7	Tu.	5:42	B	8:18	E	14 36	1	17 N. 05	8¼	8¼	5:11	B	8:11	E	ARI	0
129	8	W.	5:40	B	8:19	E	14 39	1	17 N. 21	9	9	5:38	A	9:34	E	ARI	1
130	9	Th.	5:39	B	8:20	E	14 41	1	17 N. 37	9¾	10	6:13	A	10:52	E	TAU	2
131	10	Fr.	5:38	B	8:21	E	14 43	1	17 N. 52	10½	10¾	6:58	A	12:00	E	TAU	3
132	11	Sa.	5:37	B	8:23	E	14 46	1	18 N. 08	11½	11½	7:53	A	—	-	AUR	4
133	12	F	5:35	A	8:24	E	14 49	1	18 N. 22	12¼	—	8:58	A	12:54	E	GEM	5
134	13	M.	5:34	A	8:25	E	14 51	1	18 N. 37	12¼	1	10:07	A	1:35	E	CAN	6
135	14	Tu.	5:33	A	8:26	E	14 53	1	18 N. 51	1¼	2	11:16	A	2:06	E	CAN	7
136	15	W.	5:32	A	8:27	E	14 55	1	19 N. 05	2	3	12:24	B	2:30	E	LEO	8
137	16	Th.	5:31	A	8:28	E	14 57	1	19 N. 19	3	4¼	1:30	B	2:49	D	LEO	9
138	17	Fr.	5:30	A	8:30	E	15 00	1	19 N. 32	4¼	5	2:34	B	3:06	D	LEO	10
139	18	Sa.	5:29	A	8:31	E	15 02	1	19 N. 45	5¼	6	3:37	C	3:21	C	VIR	11
140	19	F	5:28	A	8:32	E	15 04	1	19 N. 58	6¼	6½	4:42	D	3:36	C	VIR	12
141	20	M.	5:27	A	8:33	E	15 06	0	20 N. 11	7	7¼	5:48	D	3:52	B	VIR	13
142	21	Tu.	5:26	A	8:34	E	15 08	0	20 N. 23	7¾	7¾	6:56	E	4:10	B	VIR	14
143	22	W.	5:25	A	8:35	E	15 10	0	20 N. 34	8¼	8¼	8:08	E	4:32	A	LIB	15
144	23	Th.	5:24	A	8:36	E	15 12	0	20 N. 45	9	9	9:20	E	4:59	A	LIB	16
145	24	Fr.	5:23	A	8:37	E	15 14	0	20 N. 56	9¾	9½	10:29	E	5:35	A	SCO	17
146	25	Sa.	5:22	A	8:38	E	15 16	0	21 N. 07	10¼	10¼	11:30	E	6:22	A	OPH	18
147	26	F	5:21	A	8:39	E	15 18	0	21 N. 17	11	11	—	-	7:23	A	SAG	19
148	27	M.	5:21	A	8:40	E	15 19	0	21 N. 27	11¾	11¾	12:19	E	8:34	A	SAG	20
149	28	Tu.	5:20	A	8:41	E	15 21	0	21 N. 36	12¾	—	12:58	E	9:52	A	CAP	21
150	29	W.	5:19	A	8:42	E	15 23	0	21 N. 46	12¾	1½	1:28	E	11:12	A	CAP	22
151	30	Th.	5:19	A	8:43	E	15 24	*1	21 N. 54	1½	2½	1:52	D	12:31	B	AQU	23
152	31	Fr.	5:18	A	8:44	E	15 26	*1	22 N. 03	2½	3½	2:13	D	1:49	C	AQU	24

How pleasant the life of a bird must be,
Flitting about in each leafy tree.
–Mary Howitt

DAY OF MONTH	DAY OF WEEK	DATES, FEASTS, FASTS, ASPECTS, TIDE HEIGHTS, AND WEATHER	
1	W.	Sts. Philip & James • May Day • Goddard Space Flight Center established, Greenbelt, Md., 1959	*Buy*
2	Th.	St. Athanasius • Artist/scientist Leonardo da Vinci died, 1519 • Tides {5.2/5.1	*fresh*
3	Fr.	☌♄☾ • ♇ stat. • Legally blind Dale Davis bowled perfect game, Alta, Iowa, 2008	*flowers,*
4	Sa.	☾ on eq. • ☌♂☾ • ☌♆☾ • Tides {5.3/5.9	*bake*
5	F	Rogation Sunday • Orthodox Easter • ☾ at perig. • ☾ at ☊ • {5.5/6.2	*a cake:*
6	M.	☌☿☾ • *Hindenburg* disaster, 1937 • Tides {5.7/6.4	*Celebrate,*
7	Tu.	new ● • ☌♀☾ • *A north wind with new Moon will hold until the full.*	*commemorate*
8	W.	St. Julian of Norwich • ☌♃☾ • ☌♅☾ • {5.9/6.5	*Mom*
9	Th.	Ascension • ☿ gr. elong. (26° west) • Musician Billy Joel born, 1949 • {5.8/6.3	*on*
10	Fr.	Anna Jarvis organized Mother's Day observance at Andrews Methodist Episcopal Church, Grafton, Va., 1908	*her*
11	Sa.	Three • ☾ rides high • 2-day Dust Bowl storm blew silt from Great Plains to East Coast, 1934	*special*
12	F	Chilly • 1st S. af. Asc. • Mother's Day • Tides {5.4/—	*date.*
13	M.	Saints • ☌♅☉ • Cranberries in bud now. • {5.4/5.2	*Wetness*
14	Tu.	Lewis and Clark expedition began, 1804 • Singer Frank Sinatra died, 1998 • {5.1/5.0	*chills us*
15	W.	Mickey Mouse 1st appeared in test screening for short film *Plane Crazy,* 1928 • {4.9/4.9	*to the*
16	Th.	Mill River dam break caused deadly flash flood, western Mass., 1874 • Tides {4.7/4.9	*core;*
17	Fr.	☾ at apo. • Fire destroyed large section of riverfront, St. Louis, Mo., 1849 • {4.6/5.0	*we want*
18	Sa.	☾ on eq. • ☌♀♅ • ☌♃☉ • Tides {4.6/5.2	*sun,*
19	F	Whit S. • Pentecost • ☾ at ☋ • Tides {4.7/5.3	*not rain*
20	M.	Victoria Day • *It is better to begin in the evening than not at all.* • {4.8/5.4	*galore!*
21	Tu.	New National Gallery of Canada opened, Ottawa, Ont., 1988 • Tides {5.0/5.6	*Windswept*
22	W.	Ember Day • Canadian Space Agency launched 3rd astronaut recruitment campaign, 2008	*lakes are*
23	Th.	Vesak • full flower ○ • ☌♀♃ • Tides {5.2/5.7	*flecked*
24	Fr.	Ember Day • Queen Victoria born, 1819 • Samuel Morse transmitted 1st telegraphic message, 1844	*with*
25	Sa.	St. Bede • Ember Day • ☾ runs low • Painter Rosa Bonheur died, 1899	*foam, as*
26	F	Trinity • 1st public elevator in Eiffel Tower opened, Paris, France, 1889 • {5.3/5.8	*thunder*
27	M.	Memorial Day, observed (U.S.) • ☌♇☾ • Reformer Julia Ward Howe born, 1819	*salutes*
28	Tu.	Hockey player Red Horner born, 1909 • Tides {5.3/—	*those*
29	W.	*Rebuke with soft words and hard arguments.* • {5.5/5.3	*who ne'er*
30	Th.	☌☿♅ • 2" hail, Deschutes, Grant, Umatilla counties, Oreg., 2020 • {5.3/5.3	*came*
31	Fr.	Visit. of Mary • ☌♄☾ • ☌♆☾ • Tides {5.1/5.5	*home.*

Farmer's Calendar

Robert Frost called them "sky flakes" and "flowers that fly and all but sing." Even when snow lingers on the greening earth, they start emerging from overwintering pupae to skip through woodlands, fields, marshes, prairies, and backyards from Atlantic to Pacific and tundra's edge to Gulf shores. They are azures—quarter-size butterflies dusted with cobalt scales.

Lepidopterists have recently discovered that what they'd been calling the "spring azure" may be at least a half-dozen species or subspecies. There is indeed a spring azure—one of our earliest emerging butterflies, whose flight period ends in May or early June and whose pupae go into diapause (a pause in development) until the following spring. Then there's the paler summer azure that, in most of its range, starts flying in May or June and produces up to three generations before its last flight period in autumn. Among other recently discovered varieties are the cherry gall azure, Appalachian azure, holly azure, and hops azure. If you see a diminutive blue butterfly during the flight periods of spring and summer azures, photograph it: You may have a new species.

JUNE

SKY WATCH: On the 1st at 4:30 A.M., look for the crescent Moon halfway between Saturn and Mars. Both planets share the same 1st-magnitude brightness. Due east on the mornings of the 2nd and 3rd, Mars is the bright orange "star" near the Moon at 4:30 A.M. After the 15th, Jupiter returns as a morning star due east at 4:30 A.M. On the 30th, Mars hovers halfway between the crescent Moon and brilliant Jupiter, a sight best seen at around 4:45 A.M. Summer in the Northern Hemisphere begins with the solstice on the 20th at 4:51 P.M. EDT. This is the day when the Sun is highest at midday, rises at its leftmost position, and sets at the year's rightmost spot on the horizon.

● **NEW MOON** 6th day 8:38 A.M.   ○ **FULL MOON** 21st day 9:08 P.M.
◐ **FIRST QUARTER** 14th day 1:18 A.M.   ◑ **LAST QUARTER** 28th day 5:53 P.M.

All times are given in Eastern Daylight Time.

GET THESE PAGES WITH TIMES SET TO YOUR POSTAL CODE VIA ALMANAC.CA/2024.

DAY OF YEAR	DAY OF MONTH	DAY OF WEEK	☼ RISES H. M.	RISE KEY	☼ SETS H. M.	SET KEY	LENGTH OF DAY H. M.	SUN FAST M.	SUN DECLINATION ° '	HIGH TIDE TIMES HALIFAX		☾ RISES H. M.	RISE KEY	☾ SETS H. M.	SET KEY	☾ ASTRON. PLACE	☾ AGE
153	1	Sa.	5:17	A	8:44	E	15 27	*1	22 N. 11	3¾	4½	2:32	C	3:07	C	PSC	25
154	2	**F**	5:17	A	8:45	E	15 28	*1	22 N. 18	5	5½	2:51	B	4:26	D	PSC	26
155	3	M.	5:16	A	8:46	E	15 30	*1	22 N. 25	6	6¼	3:12	B	5:47	D	ARI	27
156	4	Tu.	5:16	A	8:47	E	15 31	*1	22 N. 32	7	7¼	3:37	A	7:08	E	ARI	28
157	5	W.	5:16	A	8:48	E	15 32	*2	22 N. 39	8	8	4:08	A	8:28	E	TAU	29
158	6	Th.	5:15	A	8:48	E	15 33	*2	22 N. 45	8¾	8¾	4:48	A	9:41	E	TAU	0
159	7	Fr.	5:15	A	8:49	E	15 34	*2	22 N. 50	9½	9½	5:38	A	10:42	E	TAU	1
160	8	Sa.	5:15	A	8:50	E	15 35	*2	22 N. 55	10¼	10½	6:40	A	11:29	E	GEM	2
161	9	**F**	5:14	A	8:50	E	15 36	*2	23 N. 00	11¼	11¼	7:48	A	—	-	GEM	3
162	10	M.	5:14	A	8:51	E	15 37	*3	23 N. 05	12	—	8:59	A	12:04	E	CAN	4
163	11	Tu.	5:14	A	8:51	E	15 37	*3	23 N. 08	12	12¾	10:09	A	12:31	E	LEO	5
164	12	W.	5:14	A	8:52	E	15 38	*3	23 N. 12	12¾	1½	11:16	B	12:53	D	LEO	6
165	13	Th.	5:14	A	8:52	E	15 38	*3	23 N. 15	1½	2¼	12:21	B	1:10	D	LEO	7
166	14	Fr.	5:14	A	8:53	E	15 39	*3	23 N. 18	2¼	3¼	1:25	C	1:26	C	VIR	8
167	15	Sa.	5:14	A	8:53	E	15 39	*4	23 N. 20	3¼	4	2:28	C	1:41	C	VIR	9
168	16	**F**	5:14	A	8:54	E	15 40	*4	23 N. 22	4½	5	3:33	D	1:57	B	VIR	10
169	17	M.	5:14	A	8:54	E	15 40	*4	23 N. 24	5½	5¾	4:40	D	2:14	B	VIR	11
170	18	Tu.	5:14	A	8:54	E	15 40	*4	23 N. 25	6¼	6½	5:51	E	2:34	A	LIB	12
171	19	W.	5:14	A	8:55	E	15 41	*4	23 N. 26	7¼	7	7:03	E	2:59	A	LIB	13
172	20	Th.	5:14	A	8:55	E	15 41	*5	23 N. 26	8	7¾	8:14	E	3:31	A	SCO	14
173	21	Fr.	5:14	A	8:55	E	15 41	*5	23 N. 26	8¾	8½	9:19	E	4:14	A	OPH	15
174	22	Sa.	5:15	A	8:55	E	15 40	*5	23 N. 25	9¼	9¼	10:14	E	5:11	A	SAG	16
175	23	**F**	5:15	A	8:55	E	15 40	*5	23 N. 24	10¼	10	10:57	E	6:20	A	SAG	17
176	24	M.	5:15	A	8:55	E	15 40	*6	23 N. 23	11	10¾	11:30	E	7:39	A	CAP	18
177	25	Tu.	5:16	A	8:55	E	15 39	*6	23 N. 21	11¾	11¾	11:57	D	9:00	A	CAP	19
178	26	W.	5:16	A	8:55	E	15 39	*6	23 N. 19	12½	—	—	-	10:20	B	AQU	20
179	27	Th.	5:17	A	8:55	E	15 38	*6	23 N. 16	12½	1¼	12:18	D	11:39	B	AQU	21
180	28	Fr.	5:17	A	8:55	E	15 38	*6	23 N. 13	1½	2	12:38	C	12:57	C	PSC	22
181	29	Sa.	5:17	A	8:55	E	15 38	*7	23 N. 10	2¼	3	12:57	C	2:14	D	PSC	23
182	30	**F**	5:18	A	8:55	E	15 37	*7	23 N. 06	3½	4	1:17	B	3:33	D	PSC	24

JUNE

Th' indented bean beneath its clay / Moves cautiously and slow, Curves its white stem to meet the ray, / And hides its head below.
–Peter Sherston

DAY OF MONTH	DAY OF WEEK	DATES, FEASTS, FASTS, ASPECTS, TIDE HEIGHTS, AND WEATHER	
1	Sa.	☾ on Eq. • ☾ at ☊ • EF3 tornado struck western Mass., 2011 • {5.0 5.7	*Storming,*
2	F	**Corpus Christi** • ☾ at perig. • ☌♂☾ • Tides {5.0 5.9	*then*
3	M.	*There is no general rule without some exception.* • {5.2 6.0	*warming!*
4	Tu.	☌☿♃ • ☌♅☾ • ♀ in sup. ☌ • Tides {5.3 6.1	*Plants*
5	W.	St. Boniface • ☌☿☾ • ☌♃☾ • Tides {5.4 6.1	*now,*
6	Th.	New ● • ☌♀☾ • Canadian Nat'l Railway Co. incorporated, 1919 • D-Day, 1944	*forming,*
7	Fr.	☾ rides high • *A good name keeps its luster in the dark.* • Tides {5.5 6.0	*school*
8	Sa.	Kathy Sullivan 1st woman to reach Challenger Deep, Mariana Trench, 2020 • {5.5 5.8	*bells*
9	F	**3rd S. af. P.** • Church of England fully adopted *Book of Common Prayer,* 1549	*ring:*
10	M.	Agriculturist David Lubin born, 1849 • Tides {5.4 5.4	*Caps*
11	Tu.	St. Barnabas • Shavuot begins at sundown • Actor DeForest Kelley died, 1999 • {5.3 —	*and*
12	W.	Little League 1st allowed girls, 1974 • Tides {5.2 5.2	*gowns*
13	Th.	Orthodox Ascension • Yellowstone Nat'l Park closed due to flooding and other hazards, Idaho/Mont./Wyo., 2022	*mean*
14	Fr.	St. Basil • Flag Day (U.S.) • ☾ on Eq. • ☾ at apo. • ☿ in sup. ☌	*everything!*
15	Sa.	☾ at ☋ • Hinkle Tree planted, 79th U.S. Golf Open, Inverness Club, Toledo, Ohio, 1979	*Happy*
16	F	**4th S. af. P.** • Father's Day • Sea turtle biologist Archie Carr born, 1909	*dads*
17	M.	☌☿♀ • 1st successful kidney transplant, Evergreen Park, Ill., 1950 • Tides {4.5 5.2	*wear*
18	Tu.	Edward Fincke 1st U.S. astronaut in space during birth of his child, 2004 • Tides {4.6 5.3	*brand-*
19	W.	Juneteenth National Independence Day (U.S.)	*new*
20	Th.	Summer Solstice • Singer Lionel Richie born, 1949 • {4.9 5.6	*ties;*
21	Fr.	Full Strawberry ○ • ☾ runs low • Astronomer William Morgan died, 1994	*summer*
22	Sa.	St. Alban • Actress Meryl Streep born, 1949 • 1st operational use of Canadarm, 1983	*arrives and*
23	F	**5th S. af. P.** • Orthodox Pentecost • Tides {5.4 5.9	*finally dries!*
24	M.	Nativ. John the Baptist • Midsummer Day • ☌♇☾	*Clouds*
25	Tu.	*Before the storm the crab his briny home / Sidelong forsakes, and strives on land to roam.* • {5.6 5.8	*loom in*
26	W.	Physicist William Thomson, Baron Kelvin, born, 1824 • Tides {5.6 —	*flashing skies,*
27	Th.	National Sunglasses Day (U.S.) • ☾ at perig. • ☌♄☾ • {5.6 5.7	*and flowers*
28	Fr.	St. Irenaeus • ☾ on Eq. • ☌♆☾ • Stonewall Riots began, N.Y.C., 1969	*bloom*
29	Sa.	Sts. Peter & Paul • ☾ at ☊ • Chef Jordi Cruz Mas born, 1978 • {5.1 5.7	*before*
30	F	**6th S. af. P.** • Orthodox All Saints' • ♄ stat. • Tides {4.9 5.7	*our eyes.*

Farmer's Calendar

The pileated, our largest woodpecker, which can knock 14-inch chips out of even live trees, has spent late winter and early spring mating and nest-building. Now both male and female are incubating eggs and taking care of the nestlings.

Throughout wooded North America, from Nova Scotia down through the eastern United States and west to the Pacific Coast from British Columbia to California, you may hear the maniacal laughter of this crow-size, scarlet-crested bird, which, along with the acorn woodpecker, served as the model for Walter Lantz's Woody Woodpecker.

If you pound a hollow tree with a stick, a male may fly in to defend his territory. When courting, the two birds do much bobbing, head-swinging, wing-flailing, and crest-raising. They'll meet on a limb or trunk; dance; bow; stretch their necks; appear to kiss; and inscribe lazy circles with fluttering, silver-lined wings. The pair mates for life, usually cutting a new nest hole each year. "Pileated," which means "capped," can be pronounced "pile" or "pill." Either way, reports ornithologist John Eastman, "will be wrong in whatever field group one happens to join."

JULY

SKY WATCH: On the morning of the 1st, the thin crescent Moon can be seen above Mars at 4:45 A.M. On the 2nd, the Moon stands between Jupiter and Mars due east at 4:45 A.M. On the 3rd, Jupiter is very close to the Moon, a lovely conjunction best seen due east between 4:45 and 5:00 A.M. On the 14th and 15th, Mars meets Uranus at 4:45 A.M., due east at a comfortable 30 degrees high. Use binoculars to enjoy the orange color of Mars and the green of Uranus, both seen to the right of the Pleiades and upper right of Jupiter. Mars and Jupiter steadily approach each other all month, culminating in the formation of a tight triangle with the crescent Moon on the 30th.

● **NEW MOON** 5th day 6:57 P.M.   ○ **FULL MOON** 21st day 6:17 A.M.
◐ **FIRST QUARTER** 13th day 6:49 P.M.   ◑ **LAST QUARTER** 27th day 10:52 P.M.

All times are given in Eastern Daylight Time.

GET THESE PAGES WITH TIMES SET TO YOUR POSTAL CODE VIA ALMANAC.CA/2024.

DAY OF YEAR	DAY OF MONTH	DAY OF WEEK	☼ RISES H. M.	RISE KEY	☼ SETS H. M.	SET KEY	LENGTH OF DAY H. M.	SUN FAST M.	SUN DECLINATION ° '	HIGH TIDE TIMES HALIFAX		☾ RISES H. M.	RISE KEY	☾ SETS H. M.	SET KEY	☾ ASTRON. PLACE	☾ AGE
183	1	M.	5:19	A	8:55	E	15 36	*7	23 N. 02	4½	5	1:40	B	4:52	E	ARI	25
184	2	Tu.	5:19	A	8:55	E	15 36	*7	22 N. 57	5¾	6	2:07	A	6:11	E	ARI	26
185	3	W.	5:20	A	8:54	E	15 34	*7	22 N. 52	6¾	6¾	2:43	A	7:25	E	TAU	27
186	4	Th.	5:20	A	8:54	E	15 34	*7	22 N. 47	7¾	7¾	3:28	A	8:30	E	TAU	28
187	5	Fr.	5:21	A	8:54	E	15 33	*8	22 N. 41	8½	8½	4:25	A	9:22	E	AUR	0
188	6	Sa.	5:22	A	8:53	E	15 31	*8	22 N. 34	9½	9¼	5:31	A	10:02	E	GEM	1
189	7	F	5:23	A	8:53	E	15 30	*8	22 N. 28	10¼	10¼	6:42	A	10:32	E	CAN	2
190	8	M.	5:23	A	8:52	E	15 29	*8	22 N. 21	11	10¾	7:53	A	10:55	D	CAN	3
191	9	Tu.	5:24	A	8:52	E	15 28	*8	22 N. 13	11½	11½	9:01	B	11:14	D	LEO	4
192	10	W.	5:25	A	8:51	E	15 26	*8	22 N. 06	12¼	—	10:08	B	11:31	C	LEO	5
193	11	Th.	5:26	A	8:51	E	15 25	*8	21 N. 58	12¼	1	11:12	C	11:46	C	LEO	6
194	12	Fr.	5:27	A	8:50	E	15 23	*9	21 N. 49	1	1½	12:15	C	—	-	VIR	7
195	13	Sa.	5:28	A	8:49	E	15 21	*9	21 N. 40	1¾	2¼	1:19	D	12:01	C	VIR	8
196	14	F	5:29	A	8:49	E	15 20	*9	21 N. 31	2½	3	2:25	D	12:17	B	VIR	9
197	15	M.	5:29	A	8:48	E	15 19	*9	21 N. 21	3½	3¾	3:33	E	12:36	B	VIR	10
198	16	Tu.	5:30	A	8:47	E	15 17	*9	21 N. 11	4½	4¾	4:43	E	12:58	A	LIB	11
199	17	W.	5:31	A	8:46	E	15 15	*9	21 N. 01	5½	5½	5:55	E	1:26	A	SCO	12
200	18	Th.	5:32	A	8:45	E	15 13	*9	20 N. 50	6½	6½	7:03	E	2:04	A	OPH	13
201	19	Fr.	5:33	A	8:44	E	15 11	*9	20 N. 39	7½	7¼	8:03	E	2:55	A	SAG	14
202	20	Sa.	5:34	A	8:43	E	15 09	*9	20 N. 28	8¼	8¼	8:52	E	4:00	A	SAG	15
203	21	F	5:35	A	8:43	E	15 08	*9	20 N. 16	9	9	9:29	E	5:17	A	SAG	16
204	22	M.	5:36	A	8:42	E	15 06	*9	20 N. 04	9¾	9¾	9:59	D	6:39	A	CAP	17
205	23	Tu.	5:37	A	8:40	E	15 03	*9	19 N. 51	10½	10½	10:22	B	8:03	B	CAP	18
206	24	W.	5:39	A	8:39	E	15 00	*9	19 N. 39	11¼	11½	10:43	C	9:25	B	AQU	19
207	25	Th.	5:40	A	8:38	E	14 58	*9	19 N. 26	12	—	11:02	C	10:45	C	AQU	20
208	26	Fr.	5:41	A	8:37	E	14 56	*9	19 N. 12	12¼	12¾	11:22	B	12:04	C	PSC	21
209	27	Sa.	5:42	A	8:36	E	14 54	*9	18 N. 58	1	1½	11:44	B	1:22	D	PSC	22
210	28	F	5:43	A	8:35	E	14 52	*9	18 N. 44	2	2½	—	-	2:42	E	ARI	23
211	29	M.	5:44	A	8:34	E	14 50	*9	18 N. 30	3	3½	12:10	A	4:01	E	ARI	24
212	30	Tu.	5:45	A	8:32	E	14 47	*9	18 N. 15	4¼	4½	12:42	A	5:16	E	TAU	25
213	31	W.	5:46	B	8:31	E	14 45	*9	18 N. 00	5½	5½	1:24	A	6:23	E	TAU	26

JULY

JULY HATH 31 DAYS

All things on earth, in ocean, or in air
Do in the clouds some rude resemblance find.
–John Askham

DAY OF MONTH	DAY OF WEEK	DATES, FEASTS, FASTS, ASPECTS, TIDE HEIGHTS, AND WEATHER	
1	M.	CANADA DAY • ☌♂☾ • 18-month International Geophysical Year began, 1957	*Nighttime*
2	Tu.	☌♅☾ • ♆ STAT. • Civil Rights Act (U.S.) signed into law, 1964 • {4.9 5.7	*brightening*
3	W.	Dog Days begin. • ☌♃☾ • *Dog days bright and clear Indicate a happy year.* • {5.0 5.7	*as*
4	Th.	INDEPENDENCE DAY (U.S.) • ☾ RIDES HIGH • Writer Nathaniel Hawthorne born, 1804	*fireworks*
5	Fr.	NEW ● • ⊕ AT APHELION • 113°F (45°C), Midale and Yellow Grass, Sask., 1937	*boom,*
6	Sa.	☌♀☾ • Pirate "Capt. Kidd" arrested, Boston, Mass., 1699 • Tides {5.3 5.8	*joined*
7	**F**	7th S. af. P. • First of Muharram begins at sundown • ☌☿☾ • {5.4 5.7	*by*
8	M.	Armadillos mate now. • Chef Wolfgang Puck born, 1949 • {5.5 5.6	*lightning!*
9	Tu.	Traveling at 0.92 ft./sec., Bertie set record for fastest tortoise, Brasside, UK, 2014 • {5.5 5.4	*(Where's*
10	W.	*When a friend asks, there is no tomorrow.* • Tides {5.4 —	*the*
11	Th.	National Blueberry Muffin Day (U.S.) • Writer E. B. White born, 1899 • {5.2 5.3	*Moon?)*
12	Fr.	☾ ON EQ. • ☾ AT ☋ • ☾ AT APO. • Webb telescope's 1st images released, 2022	*Storms*
13	Sa.	Cornscateous air is everywhere. • Tides {4.7 5.2	*will*
14	**F**	8th S. af. P. • Bastille Day • Folk singer Woody Guthrie born, 1912 • {4.5 5.1	*briefly*
15	M.	St. Swithin • ☌♂♅ • 3"-diameter hail fell, SE Conn., 1799 • {4.4 5.0	*brew,*
16	Tu.	Millennium Park opened, Chicago, Ill., 2004 • {4.3 5.1	*then*
17	W.	Montreal, Que., 1st Canadian city to host Summer Olympics, 1976 • Tides {4.4 5.2	*skies are*
18	Th.	Writer Jane Austen died, 1817 • Hockey player Jamie Benn born, 1989 • {4.6 5.4	*chiefly*
19	Fr.	☾ RUNS LOW • *By Love Possessed* 1st scheduled in-flight movie (TWA), 1961 • Tides {4.8 5.6	*blue,*
20	Sa.	"One giant leap for mankind," Apollo 11, 1969 • {5.1 5.8	*prompting*
21	**F**	9th S. af. P. • FULL BUCK ○ • ☌♇☾ • Actor Don Knotts born, 1924 • {5.4 6.1	
22	M.	St. Mary Magdalene • ☿ GR. ELONG. (27° EAST) • Tides {5.6 6.2	*pies*
23	Tu.	♇ AT ☍ • Astronaut Eileen Collins 1st woman to command space shuttle mission, 1999 • {5.9 6.1	*and*
24	W.	☾ AT PERIG. • ☌♄☾ • Black-eyed Susans in bloom now. • {6.0 6.0	*barbecue.*
25	Th.	Sts. James & Christopher • ☾ ON EQ. • ☌♆☾ • {6.1 —	*Campers*
26	Fr.	St. Anne • ☾ AT ☊ • Van McCoy's "The Hustle" topped U.S. charts amid hustle dance craze, 1975	*be*
27	Sa.	*Be silent and pass for a philosopher.* • Tides {5.4 5.9	*warned:*
28	**F**	10th S. af. P. • 1st public auction of Gorgosaurus dinosaur skeleton, 2022	*Watch*
29	M.	St. Martha • ☌♅☾ • Singer "Mama Cass" Elliot died, 1974 • {4.8 5.5	*out*
30	Tu.	☌♂☾ • ☌♃☾ • 33-lb. 8-oz. tripletail caught off Hilton Head, S.C., 2005 • {4.7 5.4	*for*
31	W.	St. Ignatius of Loyola • French became sole official language of Quebec, 1974 • Tides {4.7 5.3	*storms!*

Farmer's Calendar

The profusion of zucchini, eggplants, green peppers, basil leaves, tomatoes, onions, and other vegetables that ripen now render waste a common affliction. You can't eat all of these, so stew them into ratatouille, then freeze in several portions. Size matters with zucchini: It's inverse to quality. But don't compost the giant zucchini; hollow them out and stuff them with cooked ground beef, tomatoes, and onions; top with mozzarella cheese; and bake. Surplus beans can be blanched in boiling water for 3 minutes, plunged into ice water to arrest ripening enzymes, then frozen. Thawed and steamed, they'll taste almost fresh. Sauté surplus tomatoes with basil, garlic, and onions; freeze the stew. In the garden, onions started in January now have droopy brown stalks, which means that the bulbs are ready to harvest. Leave them in the sun for 2 days before storing them somewhere dark and cool for 2 weeks.

And always remember to put away tools—a painful lesson that Robert Frost learned only too well: "At the end of the row / I stepped on the toe / Of an unemployed hoe. / It rose in offense / And struck me a blow / In the seat of my sense."

AUGUST

SKY WATCH: On the 1st between 4:30 and 5:00 A.M., look for a lovely triangle in the east composed of Jupiter to the lower left; the orange Taurus star, Aldebaran, to the lower right; and Mars at the upper apex—all to the right of the crescent Moon. From the 1st through the 13th, Mars and Jupiter draw closer together in the predawn sky. From the 13th to the 16th, the two planets are wonderfully close, creating a glorious conjunction. On the 11th and 12th, the Perseid meteor shower is not affected by the Moon, which sets before midnight—just as the most intense meteors appear. On the 27th, look for the crescent Moon to the upper left of dazzling Jupiter in the east, especially between 4:30 and 5:30 A.M.

● **NEW MOON** 4th day 7:13 A.M.   ○ **FULL MOON** 19th day 2:26 P.M.
◐ **FIRST QUARTER** 12th day 11:19 A.M.   ◑ **LAST QUARTER** 26th day 5:26 A.M.

All times are given in Eastern Daylight Time.

GET THESE PAGES WITH TIMES SET TO YOUR POSTAL CODE VIA ALMANAC.CA/2024.

DAY OF YEAR	DAY OF MONTH	DAY OF WEEK	☀ RISES H. M.	RISE KEY	☀ SETS H. M.	SET KEY	LENGTH OF DAY H. M.	SUN FAST M.	SUN DECLINATION ° ′	HIGH TIDE TIMES HALIFAX		☾ RISES H. M.	RISE KEY	☾ SETS H. M.	SET KEY	☾ ASTRON. PLACE	☾ AGE
214	1	Th.	5:48	B	8:30	E	14 42	*9	17 N. 45	6¾	6½	2:16	A	7:18	E	AUR	27
215	2	Fr.	5:49	B	8:29	E	14 40	*9	17 N. 30	7¾	7½	3:18	A	8:01	E	GEM	28
216	3	Sa.	5:50	B	8:27	E	14 37	*9	17 N. 14	8½	8¼	4:27	A	8:34	E	CAN	29
217	4	**F**	5:51	B	8:26	E	14 35	*9	16 N. 58	9¼	9	5:38	A	8:59	E	CAN	0
218	5	M.	5:52	B	8:24	D	14 32	*9	16 N. 41	9¾	9¾	6:48	B	9:19	D	LEO	1
219	6	Tu.	5:53	B	8:23	D	14 30	*9	16 N. 25	10½	10½	7:55	B	9:36	D	LEO	2
220	7	W.	5:55	B	8:22	D	14 27	*8	16 N. 08	11	11¼	9:00	B	9:52	C	LEO	3
221	8	Th.	5:56	B	8:20	D	14 24	*8	15 N. 51	11¾	11¾	10:04	C	10:07	C	VIR	4
222	9	Fr.	5:57	B	8:19	D	14 22	*8	15 N. 33	12¼	—	11:07	C	10:22	B	VIR	5
223	10	Sa.	5:58	B	8:17	D	14 19	*8	15 N. 15	12½	12¾	12:11	D	10:39	B	VIR	6
224	11	**F**	5:59	B	8:16	D	14 17	*8	14 N. 58	1	1¼	1:18	D	10:59	A	VIR	7
225	12	M.	6:01	B	8:14	D	14 13	*8	14 N. 39	1¾	2	2:26	E	11:24	A	LIB	8
226	13	Tu.	6:02	B	8:12	D	14 10	*8	14 N. 21	2½	2¾	3:37	E	11:57	A	LIB	9
227	14	W.	6:03	B	8:11	D	14 08	*7	14 N. 02	3¾	3¾	4:46	E	—	-	SCO	10
228	15	Th.	6:04	B	8:09	D	14 05	*7	13 N. 44	5	5	5:49	E	12:41	A	OPH	11
229	16	Fr.	6:05	B	8:08	D	14 03	*7	13 N. 25	6	6	6:42	E	1:38	A	SAG	12
230	17	Sa.	6:07	B	8:06	D	13 59	*7	13 N. 05	7	7	7:24	E	2:49	A	SAG	13
231	18	**F**	6:08	B	8:04	D	13 56	*6	12 N. 46	8	7¾	7:57	E	4:10	A	CAP	14
232	19	M.	6:09	B	8:03	D	13 54	*6	12 N. 26	8¾	8¾	8:23	D	5:35	A	CAP	15
233	20	Tu.	6:10	B	8:01	D	13 51	*6	12 N. 06	9½	9½	8:46	D	7:00	B	AQU	16
234	21	W.	6:12	B	7:59	D	13 47	*6	11 N. 46	10	10¼	9:06	C	8:23	C	AQU	17
235	22	Th.	6:13	B	7:57	D	13 44	*5	11 N. 26	10¾	11	9:26	B	9:45	C	PSC	18
236	23	Fr.	6:14	B	7:56	D	13 42	*5	11 N. 06	11½	—	9:47	B	11:07	D	PSC	19
237	24	Sa.	6:15	B	7:54	D	13 39	*5	10 N. 45	12	12¼	10:12	A	12:28	D	ARI	20
238	25	**F**	6:16	B	7:52	D	13 36	*5	10 N. 24	12¾	1	10:43	A	1:50	E	ARI	21
239	26	M.	6:18	B	7:50	D	13 32	*4	10 N. 03	1¾	2	11:21	A	3:07	E	TAU	22
240	27	Tu.	6:19	B	7:49	D	13 30	*4	9 N. 42	2½	3	—	-	4:17	E	TAU	23
241	28	W.	6:20	B	7:47	D	13 27	*4	9 N. 21	3¾	4	12:11	A	5:16	E	AUR	24
242	29	Th.	6:21	B	7:45	D	13 24	*3	9 N. 00	5¼	5¼	1:10	A	6:02	E	GEM	25
243	30	Fr.	6:22	B	7:43	D	13 21	*3	8 N. 38	6½	6½	2:17	A	6:37	E	GEM	26
244	31	Sa.	6:24	B	7:41	D	13 17	*3	8 N. 16	7½	7¼	3:27	A	7:04	E	CAN	27

THE EIGHTH MONTH • 2024

AUGUST

AUGUST HATH 31 DAYS

'Twas summer, and parched by the merciless drouth,
The earth gaped with hope long deferred.
–**Abel Beach**

DAY OF MONTH	DAY OF WEEK	DATES, FEASTS, FASTS, ASPECTS, TIDE HEIGHTS, AND WEATHER	
1	Th.	Lammas Day • ☾ RIDES HIGH • U.S. Olympic gold medalist and diver Sammy Lee born, 1920	*Bees*
2	Fr.	*When it rains in August, it rains honey and wine.* • {5.0 5.5	*are*
3	Sa.	National Basketball Association formed from merger, 1949 • Tides {5.1 5.6	*humming,*
4	**F**	**11th S. af. P.** • NEW ● • ☿ STAT. • Tides {5.3 5.7	*thunder*
5	M.	**Civic Holiday** • ☌☿☾ • ☌♀☾ • Tides {5.4 5.7	*rumbles—*
6	Tu.	Transfiguration • ☌☿♀ • Poet Alfred, Lord Tennyson, born, 1809	*school's*
7	W.	Explorer La Salle's *Griffon* launched on Great Lakes, to vanish later that year, 1679 • {5.5 5.4	*a-coming,*
8	Th.	St. Dominic • ☾ ON EQ. • ☾ AT ☋ • ☾ AT APO. • {5.5 5.2	*children*
9	Fr.	Ragweed in bloom. • Richard Nixon resigned as U.S. president, 1974 • Tides {5.4 —	*grumble.*
10	Sa.	St. Lawrence • Ground-breaking ceremony for St. Lawrence Seaway, 1954 • {5.0 5.4	*Humid*
11	**F**	**12th S. af. P.** • Dog Days end. • Tides {4.8 5.2	*days,*
12	M.	232-day MLB baseball strike began, 1994 • Gray squirrels have second litters now. • {4.6 5.1	*lightning*
13	Tu.	Filmmaker Sir Alfred Hitchcock born, 1899 • {4.4 5.0	*flashes,*
14	W.	☌♂♃ • 1st game of Canadian Football League, 1958 • Tides {4.3 5.0	*stay*
15	Th.	**Assumption** • ☾ RUNS LOW • Emperor Napoleon Bonaparte born, 1769	*away*
16	Fr.	Chemist Robert Bunsen died, 1899 • Tides {4.6 5.3	*from*
17	Sa.	Cat Nights commence. • ☌♇☾ • Hurricane Camille made landfall, Miss., 1969 • {4.9 5.7	*curbside*
18	**F**	**13th S. af. P.** • ☿ IN INF. ☌ • Explorer Meriwether Lewis born, 1774	*splashes!*
19	M.	FULL STURGEON ○ • *A mariner must have his eye upon rock and sands as well as upon the North Star.*	*Rain*
20	Tu.	☌♄☾ • Greatest global temperature differential in 1 day (250.2 degrees F, Calif. and Antarctica), 1992	*is*
21	W.	☾ ON EQ. • ☾ AT PERIG. • ☌♆☾ • Hawaii statehood, 1959 • {6.3 6.3	*soaking*
22	Th.	☾ AT ☊ • 1.7 earthquake near Rochester, N.H., 2021 • Tides {6.4 6.1	*but*
23	Fr.	Physician Antonia Novello, 1st woman and Hispanic to serve as U.S. Surgeon General, born, 1944	*puddles*
24	Sa.	St. Bartholomew • Pianist Louis Teicher born, 1924 • {6.2 —	*are*
25	**F**	**14th S. af. P.** • ☌⛢☾ • *Voyager 2* closest approach to Neptune, 1989	*fun,*
26	M.	Aviator Charles Lindbergh died, 1974 • Hummingbirds migrate south. • {5.1 5.6	*bullfrog's*
27	Tu.	☌♂☾ • ☌♃☾ • ☿ STAT. • Tides {4.8 5.3	*croaking*
28	W.	St. Augustine of Hippo • ☾ RIDES HIGH • Polymath Johann Wolfgang von Goethe born, 1749	*will*
29	Th.	St. John the Baptist • 13-lb. 3-oz. barred sand bass caught, Huntington Flats, Calif., 1988 • {4.6 5.1	*bring*
30	Fr.	*Good nature is the proper soil upon which virtue grows.* • Tides {4.8 5.2	*back*
31	Sa.	National Trail Mix Day • Actor Richard Gere born, 1949 • Tides {5.0 5.4	*the Sun.*

Farmer's Calendar

Chestnut-flanked and flecked with scarlet spots centered in azure halos, eastern brook trout are gaudy in any season. But as spawning approaches in August, the bellies of males turn sunrise-orange, and the ivory trim on the edges of their bottom fins gets even whiter. These fish are native to the eastern United States and Canada, but they've been stocked all across the continent. The brook trout's scientific name, *Salvelinus fontinalis,* means "dweller of springs." Look for it where cold water tumbles over mossy ledges and curls off through alder runs and boggy meadows. These are not true trout but descendants of oceangoing arctic char landlocked by glaciers.

Populations can adjust to fit the habitat. In big lakes like Superior and Nipigon, such trout can reach 10 pounds in weight. But no perennial rill is too small for these glacial relics: Adults can be no longer than your thumb. Walk along almost any high-country or north-country stream, and you'll see them. Or maybe when swamp maples blush and woodcock twitter, you'll find them paired up, hovering over gravel in water so clear that you can't tell where it stops and the air begins.

SEPTEMBER

SKY WATCH: On the 8th, Saturn comes to opposition. Surrounded by the dim stars of Aquarius, the planet's rings can be seen as almost edgewise this year. Any telescope using more than 30× magnification will capture its rings. Saturn leaves the far southern regions of the zodiac that it has inhabited for nearly a decade, causing it to be low in the sky and telescopically blurry for U.S. and Canadian observers. On the 17th, a strange partial lunar eclipse is visible from most of the U.S. and Canada. Even at the time of the Moon's maximum obscuration at 10:44 P.M., only 9 percent of it is dark. Fall begins with the autumnal equinox on the 22nd at 8:44 A.M. EDT.

● **NEW MOON** 2nd day 9:56 P.M. ○ **FULL MOON** 17th day 10:34 P.M.
◐ **FIRST QUARTER** 11th day 2:06 A.M. ◑ **LAST QUARTER** 24th day 2:50 P.M.

All times are given in Eastern Daylight Time.

GET THESE PAGES WITH TIMES SET TO YOUR POSTAL CODE VIA ALMANAC.CA/2024.

DAY OF YEAR	DAY OF MONTH	DAY OF WEEK	☼ RISES H. M.	RISE KEY	☼ SETS H. M.	SET KEY	LENGTH OF DAY H. M.	SUN FAST M.	SUN DECLINATION ° '	HIGH TIDE TIMES HALIFAX	☾ RISES H. M.	RISE KEY	☾ SETS H. M.	SET KEY	☾ ASTRON. PLACE	☾ AGE
245	1	**F**	6:25	B	**7:39**	D	13 14	*3	7 N. 55	8¼ — 8	4:37	A	**7:25**	D	LEO	28
246	2	M.	6:26	B	**7:38**	D	13 12	*2	7 N. 33	8¾ — 8¾	5:44	B	**7:43**	D	LEO	0
247	3	Tu.	6:27	B	**7:36**	D	13 09	*2	7 N. 10	9¼ — 9½	6:50	B	**7:59**	C	LEO	1
248	4	W.	6:29	B	**7:34**	D	13 05	*2	6 N. 48	10 — 10	7:54	C	**8:13**	C	VIR	2
249	5	Th.	6:30	B	**7:32**	D	13 02	*1	6 N. 26	10½ — 10¾	8:57	C	**8:28**	B	VIR	3
250	6	Fr.	6:31	B	**7:30**	D	12 59	*1	6 N. 04	11 — 11¼	10:01	D	**8:44**	B	VIR	4
251	7	Sa.	6:32	B	**7:28**	D	12 56	*1	5 N. 41	11½ — 11¾	11:07	D	**9:03**	B	VIR	5
252	8	**F**	6:33	C	**7:26**	C	12 53	0	5 N. 18	12 — —	12:14	E	**9:26**	A	LIB	6
253	9	M.	6:35	C	**7:24**	C	12 49	0	4 N. 56	12½ — 12½	1:23	E	**9:54**	A	LIB	7
254	10	Tu.	6:36	C	**7:22**	C	12 46	0	4 N. 33	1¼ — 1¼	2:31	E	**10:32**	A	SCO	8
255	11	W.	6:37	C	**7:20**	C	12 43	1	4 N. 10	2 — 2	3:35	E	**11:22**	A	OPH	9
256	12	Th.	6:38	C	**7:19**	C	12 41	1	3 N. 47	3 — 3	4:32	E	—	-	SAG	10
257	13	Fr.	6:39	C	**7:17**	C	12 38	2	3 N. 24	4¼ — 4¼	5:18	E	**12:26**	A	SAG	11
258	14	Sa.	6:41	C	**7:15**	C	12 34	2	3 N. 01	5¾ — 5½	5:54	E	**1:41**	A	CAP	12
259	15	**F**	6:42	C	**7:13**	C	12 31	2	2 N. 38	6¾ — 6½	6:22	D	**3:03**	A	CAP	13
260	16	M.	6:43	C	**7:11**	C	12 28	3	2 N. 15	7½ — 7½	6:46	D	**4:27**	B	AQU	14
261	17	Tu.	6:44	C	**7:09**	C	12 25	3	1 N. 52	8¼ — 8¼	7:07	C	**5:51**	B	AQU	15
262	18	W.	6:46	C	**7:07**	C	12 21	3	1 N. 29	9 — 9¼	7:27	C	**7:16**	C	PSC	16
263	19	Th.	6:47	C	**7:05**	C	12 18	4	1 N. 05	9½ — 10	7:49	B	**8:40**	D	PSC	17
264	20	Fr.	6:48	C	**7:03**	C	12 15	4	0 N. 42	10¼ — 10¾	8:13	B	**10:04**	D	PSC	18
265	21	Sa.	6:49	C	**7:01**	C	12 12	4	0 N. 19	11 — 11½	8:41	A	**11:29**	E	ARI	19
266	22	**F**	6:50	C	**6:59**	C	12 09	5	0 s. 04	11¾ — —	9:18	A	**12:52**	E	TAU	20
267	23	M.	6:52	C	**6:57**	C	12 05	5	0 s. 27	12½ — 12¾	10:05	A	**2:07**	E	TAU	21
268	24	Tu.	6:53	C	**6:55**	C	12 02	5	0 s. 50	1¼ — 1½	11:02	A	**3:11**	E	TAU	22
269	25	W.	6:54	C	**6:53**	C	11 59	6	1 s. 14	2¼ — 2½	—	-	**4:02**	E	AUR	23
270	26	Th.	6:55	C	**6:52**	C	11 57	6	1 s. 37	3½ — 3¾	12:08	A	**4:40**	E	GEM	24
271	27	Fr.	6:57	C	**6:50**	C	11 53	6	2 s. 00	5¼ — 5	1:18	A	**5:09**	E	CAN	25
272	28	Sa.	6:58	C	**6:48**	C	11 50	7	2 s. 24	6¼ — 6¼	2:27	A	**5:32**	D	CAN	26
273	29	**F**	6:59	C	**6:46**	C	11 47	7	2 s. 47	7 — 7	3:36	B	**5:50**	D	LEO	27
274	30	M.	7:00	C	**6:44**	C	11 44	7	3 s. 10	7¾ — 7¾	4:41	B	**6:06**	C	LEO	28

To use this page, see p. 116; for Key Letters, see p. 240. LIGHT = A.M. **BOLD = P.M.**

THE NINTH MONTH • 2024

SEPTEMBER

SEPTEMBER HATH 30 DAYS

Now the last load, now merry tune the pipe,
To celebrate the harvest—rich and ripe.
–**John Evans**

DAY OF MONTH	DAY OF WEEK	DATES, FEASTS, FASTS, ASPECTS, TIDE HEIGHTS, AND WEATHER	
1	F	15th S.af.P. • ☌☿☾ • ⛢ STAT. • Tides {5.2 5.6	*Labour*
2	M.	LABOUR DAY • NEW ● • 103.3°F (39.6°C), Lytton, B.C., 2022 • Tides {5.4 5.6	*Day*
3	Tu.	Writer Sarah Orne Jewett born, 1849 • Astronaut Peggy Whitson spent 665 days in space over career, setting record, 2017	*is*
4	W.	☾ ON EQ. • ☿ GR. ELONG. (18° WEST) • Bob Barker began hosting *The Price is Right*, 1972 • {5.6 5.6	*mild*
5	Th.	☾ AT ☋ • ☾ AT APO. • ☌♀☾ • Tides {5.6 5.4	*and*
6	Fr.	"Yellow Day" in Northeast, due to yellow haze from Thumb Fire in Mich., 1881 • {5.6 5.3	*gray,*
7	Sa.	Nolan Ryan 1st to pitch baseball at more than 100 mph (100.8), 1974 • {5.5 5.1	*neighborhood*
8	F	16th S.af.P. • ♄ AT ☍ • Composer Richard Strauss died, 1949	*kids*
9	M.	Cranberry bog harvest begins, Cape Cod, Mass. • Tides {4.9 5.3	*have a*
10	Tu.	*When the rain is from the east, / It is for four-and-twenty hours at least.* • Tides {4.8 5.2	*last chance*
11	W.	PATRIOT DAY (U.S.) • Explorer Henry Hudson anchored at Lenape island of Mannahatta (now Manhattan, N.Y.C.), 1609	
12	Th.	☾ RUNS LOW • Agricultural scientist Norman Ernest Borlaug died, 2009 • Tides {4.5 5.0	*to play.*
13	Fr.	International Chocolate Day • Tides {4.5 5.1	*Back to*
14	Sa.	Holy Cross • ☌♇☾ • Jasper Forest Park (later, Jasper Nat'l Park) established, Alta., 1907	*school,*
15	F	17th S.af.P. • Entomologist Frank Eugene Lutz born, 1879 • Tides {5.2 5.7	*it's rainy*
16	M.	Actress Lauren Bacall born, 1924 • Tides {5.7 6.1	*and cool.*
17	Tu.	FULL HARVEST ○ • ECLIPSE ☾ • ☌♄☾ • {6.1 6.3	*Here's*
18	W.	Ember Day • ☾ ON EQ. • ☾ AT ☊ • ☾ AT PERIG. • ☌♆☾ • {6.5 6.4	*sun*
19	Th.	Astronomer Jean-Baptiste-Joseph Delambre born, 1749 • Tides {6.7 6.4	*instead,*
20	Fr.	Ember Day • ♆ AT ☍ • *He who will eat the kernel must crack the nut.* • {6.7 6.2	*as*
21	Sa.	St. Matthew • Ember Day • *MAVEN* spacecraft entered orbit around Mars, 2014 • {6.6 5.9	*leaves*
22	F	18th S.af.P. • AUTUMNAL EQUINOX • Harvest Home • ☌⛢☾ • {6.2 —	*turn*
23	M.	☌♃☾ • Judy Reed thought to be 1st Black woman to receive U.S. patent, 1884 • {5.6 5.9	*red,*
24	Tu.	☾ RIDES HIGH • Large meteoric fireball caught on video, N.C., 2021 • Tides {5.2 5.5	*then*
25	W.	☌♂☾ • Architect Francesco Borromini born, 1599 • Tides {4.9 5.1	*rain*
26	Th.	Woodchucks hibernate now. • Nurseryman John Chapman (aka "Johnny Appleseed") born, 1774	*will*
27	Fr.	St. Vincent de Paul • 33-lb. 4-oz. coho salmon caught, Salmon River, Pulaski, N.Y., 1989 • {4.8 5.0	*chase*
28	Sa.	Canada won Summit Series hockey game vs. Soviet Union, 6 to 5, 1972 • Tides {5.0 5.2	*you*
29	F	19th S.af.P. • *Fruit ripens not well in the shade.* • {5.2 5.4	*back*
30	M.	St. Michael[T] • ☿ IN SUP. ☌ • USS *Nautilus*, world's 1st nuclear submarine, commissioned, 1954	*to bed.*

Farmer's Calendar

Any morning now, your lawn may be draped with silver fabric so fine that it seems to have no mass. Chaucer called the phenomenon one of the unsolved mysteries of the universe. Subsequent investigators attributed it to evaporated dew. It took a pig to pin it down: "The baby spiders felt the warm updraft. One spider climbed to the top of the fence. Then it did something that came as a great surprise to Wilbur. The spider stood on its head, pointed its spinnerets in the air, and let loose a cloud of fine silk. The silk formed a balloon. As Wilbur watched, the spider let go of the fence and rose into the air." This passage from E. B. White's *Charlotte's Web* remains one of the best descriptions of how many juvenile spiders disperse.

Darwin observed silkriding spiderlings when his ship was 60 miles off Argentina. In May 1884, 9 months after one of the planet's most powerful volcanic explosions sterilized the island of Krakatoa, scientists found only one life form—a spider. Census traps mounted on airplanes have caught spiderlings at 15,000 feet. Occasionally, they'll ascend to the jet stream and cross oceans.

OCTOBER

SKY WATCH: On the 2nd, an annular solar eclipse resembling a ring of fire can be seen in Patagonia, the southernmost regions of Chile and Argentina. Venus returns as an evening star early in the month and hovers next to the waxing crescent Moon on the 5th. On the 14th, the Moon meets Saturn at nightfall and is visible throughout the night. Jupiter rises by 9:30 P.M. at midmonth and meets the Moon on the 20th. The Moon hovers above Mars starting at midnight on the 22nd and is to the left of Mars on the 23rd. From the 24th to the 28th, look for Venus, now brightening to magnitude –4.0, standing above Scorpius's famous orange-color "heart," Antares. With an unobstructed horizon, the pair can be seen low in the southwest at around 6:00 P.M.

● NEW MOON	2nd day 2:49 P.M.	○ FULL MOON	17th day 7:26 A.M.
◐ FIRST QUARTER	10th day 2:55 P.M.	◑ LAST QUARTER	24th day 4:03 A.M.

All times are given in Eastern Daylight Time.

GET THESE PAGES WITH TIMES SET TO YOUR POSTAL CODE VIA ALMANAC.CA/2024.

DAY OF YEAR	DAY OF MONTH	DAY OF WEEK	☼ RISES	RISE KEY	☼ SETS	SET KEY	LENGTH OF DAY	SUN FAST	SUN DECLINATION		HIGH TIDE TIMES HALIFAX		☾ RISES	RISE KEY	☾ SETS	SET KEY	☾ ASTRON. PLACE	☾ AGE
			H. M.		H. M.		H. M.	M.	°	'			H. M.		H. M.			
275	1	Tu.	7:02	C	**6:42**	C	11 40	8	3 s.	34	8¼	**8½**	5:46	C	**6:21**	C	LEO	29
276	2	W.	7:03	C	**6:40**	C	11 37	8	3 s.	57	8¾	**9**	6:49	C	**6:36**	C	VIR	0
277	3	Th.	7:04	C	**6:38**	C	11 34	8	4 s.	20	9¼	**9½**	7:53	D	**6:51**	B	VIR	1
278	4	Fr.	7:05	C	**6:36**	C	11 31	9	4 s.	43	9¾	**10¼**	8:58	D	**7:09**	B	VIR	2
279	5	Sa.	7:07	C	**6:35**	C	11 28	9	5 s.	06	10¼	**10¾**	10:04	E	**7:30**	A	LIB	3
280	6	**F**	7:08	C	**6:33**	C	11 25	9	5 s.	29	10¾	**11½**	11:13	E	**7:56**	A	LIB	4
281	7	M.	7:09	C	**6:31**	C	11 22	10	5 s.	52	11½	—	**12:21**	E	**8:31**	A	SCO	5
282	8	Tu.	7:11	D	**6:29**	C	11 18	10	6 s.	15	12	**12**	**1:26**	E	**9:15**	A	OPH	6
283	9	W.	7:12	D	**6:27**	C	11 15	10	6 s.	38	12¾	**12¾**	**2:24**	E	**10:12**	A	SAG	7
284	10	Th.	7:13	D	**6:25**	B	11 12	10	7 s.	00	1½	**1½**	**3:12**	E	**11:21**	A	SAG	8
285	11	Fr.	7:14	D	**6:24**	B	11 10	11	7 s.	23	2½	**2½**	**3:51**	E	—	-	SAG	9
286	12	Sa.	7:16	D	**6:22**	B	11 06	11	7 s.	45	4	**4**	**4:22**	E	12:37	A	CAP	10
287	13	**F**	7:17	D	**6:20**	B	11 03	11	8 s.	08	5¼	**5¼**	**4:46**	D	1:58	A	CAP	11
288	14	M.	7:18	D	**6:18**	B	11 00	11	8 s.	30	6¼	**6¼**	**5:08**	D	3:20	B	AQU	12
289	15	Tu.	7:20	D	**6:16**	B	10 56	12	8 s.	52	7	**7¼**	**5:28**	C	4:42	B	AQU	13
290	16	W.	7:21	D	**6:15**	B	10 54	12	9 s.	14	7¾	**8**	**5:49**	B	6:06	C	PSC	14
291	17	Th.	7:22	D	**6:13**	B	10 51	12	9 s.	36	8½	**8¾**	**6:11**	B	7:31	D	PSC	15
292	18	Fr.	7:24	D	**6:11**	B	10 47	12	9 s.	58	9¼	**9½**	**6:38**	A	8:57	D	ARI	16
293	19	Sa.	7:25	D	**6:10**	B	10 45	12	10 s.	19	9¾	**10½**	**7:12**	A	10:24	E	ARI	17
294	20	**F**	7:26	D	**6:08**	B	10 42	13	10 s.	41	10¾	**11¼**	**7:55**	A	11:46	E	TAU	18
295	21	M.	7:28	D	**6:06**	B	10 38	13	11 s.	02	11½	—	**8:50**	A	**12:58**	E	TAU	19
296	22	Tu.	7:29	D	**6:05**	B	10 36	13	11 s.	23	12	**12¼**	**9:55**	A	**1:56**	E	AUR	20
297	23	W.	7:30	D	**6:03**	B	10 33	13	11 s.	44	1	**1¼**	**11:06**	A	**2:40**	E	GEM	21
298	24	Th.	7:32	D	**6:01**	B	10 29	13	12 s.	05	2	**2¼**	—	-	**3:12**	E	CAN	22
299	25	Fr.	7:33	D	**6:00**	B	10 27	13	12 s.	25	3¼	**3¼**	12:17	A	**3:37**	E	CAN	23
300	26	Sa.	7:35	D	**5:58**	B	10 23	13	12 s.	46	4½	**4¾**	1:26	B	**3:57**	D	LEO	24
301	27	**F**	7:36	D	**5:57**	B	10 21	13	13 s.	06	5¾	**5¾**	2:33	B	**4:13**	D	LEO	25
302	28	M.	7:37	D	**5:55**	B	10 18	13	13 s.	26	6½	**6½**	3:37	B	**4:29**	C	LEO	26
303	29	Tu.	7:39	D	**5:54**	B	10 15	14	13 s.	46	7	**7¼**	4:41	C	**4:43**	C	VIR	27
304	30	W.	7:40	D	**5:52**	B	10 12	14	14 s.	05	7½	**8**	5:44	C	**4:59**	B	VIR	28
305	31	Th.	7:41	D	**5:51**	B	10 10	14	14 s.	25	8¼	**8½**	6:48	D	**5:16**	B	VIR	29

To use this page, see p. 116; for Key Letters, see p. 240. LIGHT = A.M. **BOLD** = P.M.

THE TENTH MONTH • 2024

OCTOBER

OCTOBER HATH 31 DAYS

Thou, from whose unseen presence the leaves dead
Are driven, like ghosts from an enchanter fleeing.
–**Percy Bysshe Shelley, of the west wind**

DAY OF MONTH	DAY OF WEEK	DATES, FEASTS, FASTS, ASPECTS, TIDE HEIGHTS, AND WEATHER
1	Tu.	☾ ON EQ. • Yosemite Nat'l Park established, 1890 • {5.6 / 5.6 *Witness autumn's*
2	W.	Rosh Hashanah begins at sundown • NEW ● • ECLIPSE ⊙ • ☾ AT ☋ • ☾ AT APO. • ☌☿☾
3	Th.	Watch for banded woolly bear caterpillars now. *convocation:*
4	Fr.	St. Francis of Assisi • World Animal Day • {5.8 / 5.5 *blue*
5	Sa.	☌♀☾ • Shawnee chief Tecumseh died (War of 1812), 1813 • Tides {5.7 / 5.3 *skies*
6	**F**	**20th S. af. P.** • Groundbreaking for Red River Floodway, Winnipeg, Man., 1962 *and*
7	M.	1st images rec'd of Moon's far side, 1959 • Tornado struck near Jenner, Alta., 2017 • {5.6 / — *leafy*
8	Tu.	Actress Sigourney Weaver born, 1949 • *The mill does not grind with water that is past.* *conflagration.*
9	W.	☾ RUNS LOW • ♃ STAT. • Meteorite hit car in Peekskill, N.Y., 1992 • Tides {5.0 / 5.4 *A*
10	Th.	Little brown bats hibernate now. • Tides {4.8 / 5.2 *football win,*
11	Fr.	Yom Kippur begins at sundown • ☌♇☾ • ♇ STAT. • {4.7 / 5.2 *congratulations!*
12	Sa.	National Farmer's Day (U.S.) • Basketball player Wilt Chamberlain died, 1999 *Cool,*
13	**F**	**21st S. af. P.** • TV personality Ed Sullivan died, 1974 • Tides {5.1 / 5.4 *with*
14	M.	Thanksgiving Day • Columbus Day, observed (U.S.) • ☌♄☾ • Tides {5.6 / 5.8
15	Tu.	☾ ON EQ. • ☌♆☾ • Green Bay Packers/Denver Broncos played football in blizzard, Denver, Colo., 1984 *rain*
16	W.	Sukkoth begins at sundown • ☾ AT ☊ • ☾ AT PERIG. • Tides {6.5 / 6.3 *in*
17	Th.	St. Ignatius of Antioch • FULL HUNTER'S ○ • Composer Frederic Chopin died, 1849 *isolation,*
18	Fr.	St. Luke • St. Luke's little summer. • Tides {6.9 / 6.3 *then*
19	Sa.	☌♅☾ • Outdoorsman Eddie Bauer born, 1899 • Tides {6.8 / 6.2 *sun*
20	**F**	**22nd S. af. P.** • "Black Friday Storm" sank 4 ships on Lake Erie, 1916 • {6.6 / 5.9 *spreads*
21	M.	☾ RIDES HIGH • ☌♃☾ • Joseph Aspdin granted UK patent for Portland cement, 1824 *a warm*
22	Tu.	*The dews of the evening industriously shun, / They're the tears of the sky for the loss of the sun.* • {5.7 / 5.8 *sensation.*
23	W.	St. James of Jerusalem • ☌♂☾ • Musician Weird Al Yankovic born, 1959 • {5.4 / 5.5 *Stockpile*
24	Th.	Bar-tailed godwit flew 8,425 miles nonstop (Alaska to Tasmania), setting record, 2022 • {5.1 / 5.2 *candy*
25	Fr.	Frederic Edwin Church's "The Icebergs" auctioned for $2.5 million, setting record for U.S. paintings, 1979 *for*
26	Sa.	Timber rattlesnakes move to winter dens. • {5.0 / 5.0 *Halloween*
27	**F**	**23rd S. af. P.** • Nat'l Council of Women of Canada formed, Toronto, Ont., 1893 *Nation:*
28	M.	Sts. Simon & Jude • Discovery of 3.4-billion-yr.-old 1-cell fossils announced in *Science* journal, 1977 *Cool*
29	Tu.	☾ ON EQ. • ☾ AT ☋ • ☾ AT APO. • Tides {5.6 / 5.4 *night*
30	W.	*Fear has no understanding.* • Tides {5.7 / 5.5 *tricks bring*
31	Th.	All Hallows' Eve • Reformation Day • Nev. statehood, 1864 *consternation!*

CALENDAR

Farmer's Calendar

From Newfoundland south to Delaware and northwest to Alaska the leaves of the quaking aspen, our most widely distributed tree, dance in the wind, glowing neon yellow as they catch the rays of the low-arcing Sun. Unlike other trees, aspens also photosynthesize through their bark, so they continue to produce energy and sugar in winter.

Seventy years is ancient for a quaking aspen tree. Aspens, however, should be thought of not as trees but as root systems. The "trees" are clones sent up by the main part of the organism. Inject dye or a radioactive isotope into one tree, and it will show up in another. From this perspective, the quaking aspen is the largest and heaviest organism on Earth. In Minnesota, one clone root system has been estimated to be 8,000 years old. In Utah, a 100-acre root system weighs an estimated 6,600 tons and is thought to be 80,000 years old.

Preferring moist sites, aspen doesn't do well in dry habitats such as Yellowstone National Park. So why is there so much of it there? Botanist Roy Renkin thinks that aspen got started in the park when the climate there was cold and wet—that is, during the last Ice Age.

SKY WATCH: On the 1st, Mars, now a brilliant magnitude 0, rises at midnight just below the Gemini twins, Castor and Pollux, with dazzling Jupiter high above them. On the 10th, don't miss the very close conjunction of the Moon and Saturn, with the best viewing between 9:30 and 10:00 P.M. Jupiter, now rising at around 6:30 P.M., hangs just below the Moon on the 16th. On this same night, Uranus comes to opposition, at its closest and brightest appearance of the year. Just to the right of the famous Pleiades star cluster, Uranus's magnitude of 5.6 means that it can be seen as a faint star from dark rural sites, although binoculars make for easier viewing of its green color. On the 20th, Mars rises by 9:30 P.M. and hovers next to the Moon.

● NEW MOON	1st day 8:47 A.M.	○ FULL MOON	15th day 4:29 P.M.
◑ FIRST QUARTER	9th day 12:55 A.M.	◐ LAST QUARTER	22nd day 8:28 P.M.

After 2:00 A.M. on November 3, Eastern Standard Time is given.

GET THESE PAGES WITH TIMES SET TO YOUR POSTAL CODE VIA ALMANAC.CA/2024.

DAY OF YEAR	DAY OF MONTH	DAY OF WEEK	☼ RISES H.M.	RISE KEY	☼ SETS H.M.	SET KEY	LENGTH OF DAY H.M.	SUN FAST M.	SUN DECLINATION ° '	HIGH TIDE TIMES HALIFAX		☽ RISES H.M.	RISE KEY	☽ SETS H.M.	SET KEY	☽ ASTRON. PLACE	☽ AGE
306	1	Fr.	7:43	D	5:49	B	10 06	14	14 s. 44	8¾	9¼	7:55	D	5:36	A	VIR	0
307	2	Sa.	7:44	D	5:48	B	10 04	14	15 s. 03	9¼	9¾	9:03	E	6:00	A	LIB	1
308	3	**F**	6:46	D	4:46	B	10 00	14	15 s. 21	8¾	9¼	9:12	E	5:32	A	SCO	2
309	4	M.	6:47	D	4:45	B	9 58	14	15 s. 40	9¼	10	10:18	E	6:14	A	SCO	3
310	5	Tu.	6:48	D	4:44	B	9 56	14	15 s. 58	10	10¾	11:19	E	7:06	A	OPH	4
311	6	W.	6:50	D	4:42	B	9 52	14	16 s. 16	10½	11½	12:10	E	8:11	A	SAG	5
312	7	Th.	6:51	D	4:41	B	9 50	13	16 s. 33	11½	—	12:51	E	9:23	A	SAG	6
313	8	Fr.	6:53	D	4:40	B	9 47	13	16 s. 51	12¼	12¼	1:23	E	10:40	A	CAP	7
314	9	Sa.	6:54	D	4:39	B	9 45	13	17 s. 08	1¼	1¼	1:49	E	11:59	B	CAP	8
315	10	**F**	6:55	D	4:38	B	9 43	13	17 s. 24	2½	2½	2:10	D	—	-	AQU	9
316	11	M.	6:57	E	4:36	B	9 39	13	17 s. 41	3½	3¾	2:30	C	1:17	B	AQU	10
317	12	Tu.	6:58	E	4:35	B	9 37	13	17 s. 57	4½	5	2:50	C	2:37	C	PSC	11
318	13	W.	7:00	E	4:34	B	9 34	13	18 s. 13	5¼	5¾	3:11	B	3:58	C	PSC	12
319	14	Th.	7:01	E	4:33	B	9 32	13	18 s. 28	6	6¾	3:35	B	5:22	D	PSC	13
320	15	Fr.	7:02	E	4:32	B	9 30	12	18 s. 43	7	7½	4:05	A	6:49	E	ARI	14
321	16	Sa.	7:04	E	4:31	B	9 27	12	18 s. 58	7¾	8¼	4:43	A	8:15	E	TAU	15
322	17	**F**	7:05	E	4:30	A	9 25	12	19 s. 12	8½	9¼	5:34	A	9:34	E	TAU	16
323	18	M.	7:06	E	4:29	A	9 23	12	19 s. 27	9¼	10	6:36	A	10:41	E	TAU	17
324	19	Tu.	7:08	E	4:28	A	9 20	12	19 s. 40	10	10¾	7:47	A	11:32	E	GEM	18
325	20	W.	7:09	E	4:28	A	9 19	11	19 s. 54	11	11¾	9:01	A	12:10	E	GEM	19
326	21	Th.	7:10	E	4:27	A	9 17	11	20 s. 07	11¾	—	10:12	A	12:39	E	CAN	20
327	22	Fr.	7:12	E	4:26	A	9 14	11	20 s. 20	12¾	12¾	11:21	B	1:01	D	LEO	21
328	23	Sa.	7:13	E	4:25	A	9 12	11	20 s. 32	1¾	1¾	—	-	1:19	D	LEO	22
329	24	**F**	7:14	E	4:25	A	9 11	10	20 s. 44	2¾	3	12:27	B	1:35	C	LEO	23
330	25	M.	7:16	E	4:24	A	9 08	10	20 s. 55	3¾	4	1:31	C	1:50	C	VIR	24
331	26	Tu.	7:17	E	4:23	A	9 06	10	21 s. 07	4½	5	2:34	C	2:05	C	VIR	25
332	27	W.	7:18	E	4:23	A	9 05	9	21 s. 17	5¼	5¾	3:38	D	2:21	B	VIR	26
333	28	Th.	7:19	E	4:22	A	9 03	9	21 s. 28	6	6½	4:43	D	2:40	A	VIR	27
334	29	Fr.	7:20	E	4:22	A	9 02	9	21 s. 38	6½	7	5:51	E	3:03	A	LIB	28
335	30	Sa.	7:22	E	4:21	A	8 59	8	21 s. 47	7¼	7¾	7:00	E	3:33	A	LIB	29

NOVEMBER

In slack wind of November
The fog forms and shifts.
–**Christina Georgina Rossetti**

DAY OF MONTH	DAY OF WEEK	DATES, FEASTS, FASTS, ASPECTS, TIDE HEIGHTS, AND WEATHER	
1	Fr.	All Saints' • NEW ● • Baseball player Fernando Valenzuela born, 1960	*Snowflakes*
2	Sa.	All Souls' • Sadie Hawkins Day • N.Dak. and S.Dak. statehood, 1889 • Tides {5.9 5.5	*fall*
3	**F**	24th S. af. P. • DAYLIGHT SAVING TIME ENDS, 2:00 A.M. • ☌☿☾ • {5.9 5.4	*on*
4	M.	☌♀☾ • Humorist Will Rogers born, 1879 • Tides {5.9 5.4	*people*
5	Tu.	ELECTION DAY (U.S.) • ☾ RUNS LOW • "Cotton candy" lobster caught, Casco Bay, Maine, 2021	*voting*
6	W.	*Sleep is the equalizer of all.* • Tides {5.7 5.2	*(for those*
7	Th.	☌♇☾ • 1st robot-assisted human hip replacement, 1992 • Tides {5.6 —	*up*
8	Fr.	Poet John Milton likely died, 1674 • Mont. statehood, 1889 • Tides {5.1 5.4	*north,*
9	Sa.	Canada joined the United Nations, 1945 • Tides {5.1 5.3	*a*
10	**F**	25th S. af. P. • ☌♄☾ • "Charmed quark" discovered, 1974 • {5.2 5.3	*decent*
11	M.	St. Martin of Tours • REMEMBRANCE DAY • ☌♆☾ • {5.5 5.4	*coating).*
12	Tu.	Indian Summer • ☾ ON EQ. • ☾ AT ☊ • Tides {5.9 5.6	*Chills*
13	W.	1st modern-day cloud-seeding experiment, Mt. Greylock, Mass., 1946 • Tides {6.3 5.9	*retreat*
14	Th.	☾ AT PERIG. • Home improvement expert Chip Gaines born, 1974 • USS *Nimitz* "Tic Tac" UFO incident, off Calif., 2004	
15	Fr.	FULL BEAVER ○ • ☌⛢☾ • 1st U.S. poultry show began, Boston, Mass., 1849	*from sun*
16	Sa.	♄ STAT. • ⛢ AT ☍ • ☿ GR. ELONG. (23° EAST) • Tides {6.8 6.2	*serene,*
17	**F**	26th S. af. P. • ☌♃☾ • Sculptor Auguste Rodin died, 1917 • {6.7 6.1	*then*
18	M.	St. Hilda of Whitby • ☾ RIDES HIGH • Ballerina Evelyn Cisneros-Legate born, 1958	*rain*
19	Tu.	World's first surviving septuplets born, Des Moines, Iowa, 1997 • Tides {6.2 5.7	*and heat*
20	W.	☌♂☾ • *What has been, may be.* • Tides {5.9 5.5	*go to*
21	Th.	World Hello Day • N.C. statehood, 1789 • {5.6 —	*extremes!*
22	Fr.	Humane Society of the United States founded, 1954 • 15 tornadoes hit Ind., 1992 • {5.3 5.3	*Prepare*
23	Sa.	St. Clement • 1st smartphone (IBM Simon) introduced, COMDEX show, Las Vegas, Nev., 1992	*a feast,*
24	**F**	27th S. af. P. • Artist Henri de Toulouse-Lautrec born, 1864	*and as*
25	M.	☾ ON EQ. • ☾ AT ☋ • ☿ STAT. • Tides {5.3 4.9	*ice*
26	Tu.	☾ AT APO. • *Evening red and morning gray Help the traveler on his way.* • {5.4 5.0	*melts,*
27	W.	Mauna Loa eruption began, Hawaii, 2022 • {5.5 5.1	*do give*
28	Th.	THANKSGIVING DAY (U.S.) • Basketball game inventor James Naismith died, 1939 • {5.6 5.2	*thanks for*
29	Fr.	Entertainer Garry Shandling born, 1949 • Tides {5.7 5.3	*loosened*
30	Sa.	St. Andrew • Writer Lucy Maud Montgomery born, 1874 • {5.8 5.4	*belts!*

Farmer's Calendar

Most "traditional food" that we enjoy on Thanksgiving wasn't consumed by the Pilgrims. Turkey is a notable exception. The wild turkeys around Plimoth were the likely quarry of the "fowling" party dispatched in 1621 by Governor William Bradford in preparation for the 3-day (first Thanksgiving) event. The Pilgrims couldn't have eaten mashed potatoes because potatoes weren't cultivated in North America until the 1700s, and cranberry sauce and pumpkin pie wouldn't have been on the menu because sugar, flour, and butter were in short supply. Seafood was probably part of the feast. As colonist Edward Winslow reported, "In September, we can take a hogshead of eels in a night. . . . We have mussels . . . at our doors." Recently harvested corn, onions, beans, lettuce, spinach, cabbage, and carrots were probably served. Wampanoag guests contributed five deer.

In 1939, Franklin Roosevelt attempted to boost retail sales by moving Thanksgiving up a week. Such was the opposition to "Franksgiving," that in 1941 he reluctantly signed a bill codifying Thanksgiving on November's fourth Thursday instead.

DECEMBER

SKY WATCH: Venus, now a bright magnitude –4.2, is an evening star in the west from 5:00 to 6:30 P.M. On the 6th, look for Mercury low in the southeast at dawn, after which it remains visible until the 15th. Jupiter floats below the Moon on the 6th and is in opposition on the morning of the 7th, creating a conjunction with the Moon. Now at its brightest of the year, Jupiter rises at around 9:30 P.M. before hovering close to the Moon on the 14th. The Geminid meteor shower arrives on the 13th and is best seen before the Moon rises at around 1:00 A.M. On the 28th, Mercury hovers to the left of the crescent Moon in dawn's twilight. Winter in the Northern Hemisphere begins with the solstice on the 21st at 4:21 A.M. EST.

● **NEW MOON** 1st day 1:21 A.M. ◑ **LAST QUARTER** 22nd day 5:18 P.M.
◐ **FIRST QUARTER** 8th day 10:27 A.M. ● **NEW MOON** 30th day 5:27 P.M.
○ **FULL MOON** 15th day 4:02 A.M.

All times are given in Eastern Standard Time.

GET THESE PAGES WITH TIMES SET TO YOUR POSTAL CODE VIA ALMANAC.CA/2024.

DAY OF YEAR	DAY OF MONTH	DAY OF WEEK	☼ RISES H. M.	RISE KEY	☼ SETS H. M.	SET KEY	LENGTH OF DAY H. M.	SUN FAST M.	SUN DECLINATION ° '	HIGH TIDE TIMES HALIFAX	☾ RISES H. M.	RISE KEY	☾ SETS H. M.	SET KEY	☾ ASTRON. PLACE	☾ AGE
336	1	F	7:23	E	4:21	A	8 58	8	21 s. 56	7¾ 8½	8:09	E	4:12	A	SCO	0
337	2	M.	7:24	E	4:21	A	8 57	7	22 s. 05	8¼ 9	9:12	E	5:02	A	OPH	1
338	3	Tu.	7:25	E	4:20	A	8 55	7	22 s. 13	9 9¾	10:07	E	6:03	A	SAG	2
339	4	W.	7:26	E	4:20	A	8 54	7	22 s. 21	9¾ 10½	10:51	E	7:14	A	SAG	3
340	5	Th.	7:27	E	4:20	A	8 53	6	22 s. 29	10½ 11¼	11:25	E	8:30	A	CAP	4
341	6	Fr.	7:28	E	4:20	A	8 52	6	22 s. 36	11¼ —	11:52	E	9:47	B	CAP	5
342	7	Sa.	7:29	E	4:20	A	8 51	5	22 s. 42	12 12	12:15	D	11:04	B	AQU	6
343	8	F	7:30	E	4:20	A	8 50	5	22 s. 48	1 1	12:35	C	—	-	AQU	7
344	9	M.	7:31	E	4:20	A	8 49	5	22 s. 54	2 2	12:53	C	12:21	C	PSC	8
345	10	Tu.	7:32	E	4:20	A	8 48	4	22 s. 59	3 3¼	1:13	B	1:38	C	PSC	9
346	11	W.	7:33	E	4:20	A	8 47	4	23 s. 04	4 4½	1:34	B	2:58	D	PSC	10
347	12	Th.	7:34	E	4:20	A	8 46	3	23 s. 08	4¾ 5½	2:01	A	4:21	D	ARI	11
348	13	Fr.	7:35	E	4:20	A	8 45	3	23 s. 12	5¾ 6½	2:34	A	5:45	E	ARI	12
349	14	Sa.	7:35	E	4:20	A	8 45	2	23 s. 15	6½ 7¼	3:19	A	7:06	E	TAU	13
350	15	F	7:36	E	4:20	A	8 44	2	23 s. 18	7¼ 8	4:16	A	8:20	E	TAU	14
351	16	M.	7:37	E	4:21	A	8 44	1	23 s. 21	8¼ 9	5:24	A	9:19	E	AUR	15
352	17	Tu.	7:37	E	4:21	A	8 44	1	23 s. 23	9 9¾	6:38	A	10:04	E	GEM	16
353	18	W.	7:38	E	4:21	A	8 43	0	23 s. 24	9¾ 10½	7:52	A	10:37	E	CAN	17
354	19	Th.	7:39	E	4:22	A	8 43	0	23 s. 25	10½ 11¼	9:04	B	11:02	D	CAN	18
355	20	Fr.	7:39	E	4:22	A	8 43	*1	23 s. 26	11½ —	10:12	B	11:22	D	LEO	19
356	21	Sa.	7:40	E	4:23	A	8 43	*1	23 s. 26	12¼ 12¼	11:18	C	11:39	C	LEO	20
357	22	F	7:40	E	4:23	A	8 43	*2	23 s. 25	1 1	—	-	11:55	C	VIR	21
358	23	M.	7:41	E	4:24	A	8 43	*2	23 s. 25	1¾ 2	12:21	C	12:10	C	VIR	22
359	24	Tu.	7:41	E	4:24	A	8 43	*3	23 s. 23	2¾ 3	1:25	D	12:26	B	VIR	23
360	25	W.	7:41	E	4:25	A	8 44	*3	23 s. 21	3½ 4¼	2:30	D	12:43	B	VIR	24
361	26	Th.	7:42	E	4:26	A	8 44	*4	23 s. 19	4½ 5¼	3:37	A	1:05	A	LIB	25
362	27	Fr.	7:42	E	4:27	A	8 45	*4	23 s. 16	5¼ 6	4:45	A	1:32	A	LIB	26
363	28	Sa.	7:42	E	4:27	A	8 45	*5	23 s. 13	6 6¾	5:54	A	2:07	A	SCO	27
364	29	F	7:42	E	4:28	A	8 46	*5	23 s. 10	6½ 7½	7:00	A	2:53	A	OPH	28
365	30	M.	7:42	E	4:29	A	8 47	*6	23 s. 05	7¼ 8	7:59	A	3:52	A	SAG	0
366	31	Tu.	7:42	E	4:30	A	8 48	*6	23 s. 01	8 8¾	8:48	E	5:01	A	SAG	1

THE TWELFTH MONTH • 2024

DECEMBER

DECEMBER HATH 31 DAYS

Welcome all and make good cheer,
Welcome all another year.
–Anonymous

DAY OF MONTH	DAY OF WEEK	DATES, FEASTS, FASTS, ASPECTS, TIDE HEIGHTS, AND WEATHER	
1	F	1st S. of Advent • NEW ● • ☌☿☾ • {5.9/5.4	*Mulled*
2	M.	St. Viviana • ☾ runs low • Major League Baseball agreed to accept cowhide baseballs, 1974	*wine or*
3	Tu.	John Backus, who led team that designed FORTRAN programming language, born, 1924 • {6.0/5.5	*ciders*
4	W.	☌♀☾ • ☌♇☾ • Montreal Canadiens founded, 1909 • Tides {6.0/5.5	*warm*
5	Th.	☿ in inf. ☌ • Chemist Hazel Bishop died, 1998 • Tides {5.9/5.5	*snowboard*
6	Fr.	St. Nicholas • *Joy that we can not share with others is only half enjoyed.* • {5.8/—	*riders,*
7	Sa.	St. Ambrose • Pearl Harbor Day (U.S.) • ☌♀♇ • ♂ stat. • ♃ at ☍	
8	F	2nd S. of Advent • ☌♄☾ • ♆ stat.	*alpine sliders,*
9	M.	☾ on Eq. • ☾ at ☊ • ☌♆☾ • {5.6/5.3	*and cross-country*
10	Tu.	St. Eulalia • Colonel John P. Stapp attained 632 mph on rocket sled, 1954 • {5.8/5.2	*gliders.*
11	W.	Actress Rita Moreno born, 1931 • Statute of Westminster passed, 1931 • {6.0/5.3	*They're*
12	Th.	Our Lady of Guadalupe • ☾ at perig. • F3 waterspout-turned-tornado, Des Moines to Kent, Wash., 1969	*all*
13	Fr.	St. Lucia • ☌♅☾ • Royal charter for Dartmouth College (Hanover, N.H.) granted, 1769	*out in*
14	Sa.	Halcyon Days begin. • ☌♃☾ • U.S. president George Washington died, 1799 • {6.5/5.8	*frigid*
15	F	3rd S. of Advent • Full Cold ○ • ☾ rides high • ☿ stat.	*air,*
16	M.	Discovery of 1st millipede species having more than 1,000 legs (1,306), announced, 2021 • {6.5/5.9	*while*
17	Tu.	105.6°F national average set record for hottest day, Australia, 2019 • Tides {6.4/5.9	*others*
18	W.	Ember Day • ☌♂☾ • *How the Grinch Stole Christmas!* TV special 1st aired, 1966	*hibernate*
19	Th.	Beware the Pogonip. • Gustl, a terrier mix, undid 10 knots in 1 minute, setting record, 2012	*like*
20	Fr.	Ember Day • *When the night's darkest, the dawn is nearest.* • {5.6/—	*bears.*
21	Sa.	St. Thomas • Ember Day • Winter Solstice • Tides {5.5/5.3	*Raise*
22	F	4th S. of Advent • ☾ on Eq. • ☾ at ☋ • Tides {5.4/5.0	*a toast,*
23	M.	20-lb. 9-oz. southern flounder caught, Nassau Sound, Fla., 1983 • Tides {5.3/4.8	*give*
24	Tu.	☾ at apo. • ☿ gr. elong. (22° west) • –57°F (–82°F old formula) wind chill, Chicago, Ill., 1983	*a cheer,*
25	W.	Christmas • Chanukah begins at sundown • Actor Humphrey Bogart born, 1899	*here's*
26	Th.	St. Stephen • Boxing Day • First Day of Kwanzaa • {5.3/4.8	*wishing*
27	Fr.	St. John • Radio City Music Hall opened, N.Y.C., 1932 • Tides {5.4/4.9	*all*
28	Sa.	Holy Innocents • National Call a Friend Day (U.S.) • ☌☿☾ • Tides {5.6/5.1	*a*
29	F	1st S. af. Ch. • *Be it dry or be it wet, The weather'll always pay its debt.*	*grand*
30	M.	NEW ● • ☾ runs low • Musician Artie Shaw died, 2004 • Tides {5.9/5.4	*New*
31	Tu.	St. Sylvester • Educator Jaime Escalante born, 1930 • Tides {6.1/5.6	*Year!*

Farmer's Calendar

If you stand under wild American mistletoe, which grows from New Jersey to Florida and west through Texas, you may get something less welcome than a kiss. This is because the juicy white berries, now ripe, are relished by birds. The plant's seeds pass through avian digestive tracts, germinate on the bark of trees, and then send roots into sap-conducting tissues. But most mistletoe species are only partially parasitic; their evergreen leaves contain chlorophyll, which enables them to manufacture their own food once they have purloined water and nutrients from their host trees. In some of the range, foresters consider American mistletoe a pest because it can retard tree growth and break branches. However, ecologists recognize it as a keystone species because not only do many forest creatures forage on its leaves and shoots but also its berries help to sustain birds.

Ancient Europeans reasoned that because mistletoe stayed green in the dead of winter, it must provide shelter for woodland spirits—hence its use in rituals for fertility, health, peace, safety, and good luck.

HOLIDAYS AND OBSERVANCES

2024 HOLIDAYS

JAN. 1: New Year's Day*

JAN. 7: Orthodox Christmas (Julian)

FEB. 1: First day of Black History Month

FEB. 2: Groundhog Day

FEB. 14: Valentine's Day

FEB. 15: National Flag of Canada Day

FEB. 19: Family Day *(Alta., B.C., N.B., Ont., Sask.)*
Louis Riel Day *(Man.)*
Nova Scotia Heritage Day *(N.S.)*
Islander Day *(P.E.I.)*

FEB. 23: Heritage Day *(Y.T.)*

FEB. 29: Leap Day

MAR. 8: International Women's Day

MAR. 11: Commonwealth Day

MAR. 17: St. Patrick's Day

MAR. 29: Good Friday

APR. 1: Easter Monday

APR. 22: Earth Day
St. George's Day, observed *(N.L.)*

MAY 1: First day of Asian Heritage Month

MAY 5: Holocaust Remembrance Day begins at sundown

MAY 12: Mother's Day

MAY 20: Victoria Day

JUNE 1: First day of Pride Month

JUNE 2: Canadian Armed Forces Day

JUNE 5: World Environment Day

JUNE 6: D-Day

JUNE 16: Father's Day

JUNE 21: National Indigenous Peoples Day

JUNE 24: Fête Nationale *(Qué.)*
June Holiday *(N.L.)*

JULY 1: Canada Day*

JULY 9: Nunavut Day

JULY 15: Orangemen's Day, observed *(N.L.)*

AUG. 1: Emancipation Day

AUG. 5: Civic Holiday *(Alta., B.C., Man., N.B., N.W.T., N.S., Nunavut, Ont., P.E.I., Sask.)*

AUG. 19: Discovery Day *(Y.T.)*

SEPT. 2: Labour Day

SEPT. 30: National Day for Truth and Reconciliation*

OCT. 1: First day of Hispanic/Latin American Heritage Month

OCT. 14: Thanksgiving Day

OCT. 31: Halloween

NOV. 11: Remembrance Day*

NOV. 20: National Child Day

DEC. 25: Christmas Day*

DEC. 26: Boxing Day
First day of Kwanzaa

When this day falls on a Saturday or Sunday, the following Monday is observed as a holiday.

–PGC photo/Jacob Dingel

GROUNDHOG DAY

Traditionally, on February 2, farmers looked for signs of what the weather would be for the next 6 weeks. They believed that if an animal came out of hibernation on this day and saw its shadow, winter would continue.

For centuries, farmers in France and England looked to a bear; in Germany, they kept their eye on the badger. In the 1800s, German immigrants to Pennsylvania brought the tradition with them. Finding no badgers there, they adopted the groundhog to fit the lore. Pennsylvania's Punxsutawney Phil has predicted spring's arrival since 1887.

Since 1956, albino groundhogs named Wiarton Willie have made annual weather prognostications in Wiarton, Ontario. Several other groundhogs are employed across the nation, including Nova Scotia's Shubenacadie Sam, who, because of location and special training, has the honor of making the first groundhog end-of-winter prediction for North America.

U.S. FEDERAL HOLIDAYS

JAN. 1: New Year's Day

JAN. 15: Martin Luther King Jr.'s Birthday

FEB. 19: Presidents' Day

MAY 27: Memorial Day, observed

JUNE 19: Juneteenth National Independence Day

JULY 4: Independence Day

SEPT. 2: Labor Day

OCT. 14: Columbus Day, observed

NOV. 11: Veterans Day

NOV. 28: Thanksgiving Day

DEC. 25: Christmas Day

Movable Religious Observances

JAN. 28: Septuagesima Sunday

FEB. 13: Shrove Tuesday

FEB. 14: Ash Wednesday

MAR. 10: Ramadan begins at sundown

MAR. 18: Orthodox Lent begins

MAR. 24: Palm Sunday

MAR. 29: Good Friday

MAR. 31: Easter

APR. 22: Passover begins at sundown

MAY 5: Orthodox Easter
Rogation Sunday

MAY 9: Ascension Day

MAY 19: Whitsunday–Pentecost

MAY 26: Trinity Sunday

JUNE 2: Corpus Christi

JUNE 23: Othodox Pentecost

OCT. 2: Rosh Hashanah begins at sundown

OCT. 11: Yom Kippur begins at sundown

DEC. 1: First Sunday of Advent

DEC. 25: Chanukah begins at sundown

CHRONOLOGICAL CYCLES

Dominical Letters **GF**

Epact **19**

Golden Number (Lunar Cycle) **11**

Roman Indiction **2**

Solar Cycle (Julian Calendar) **17**

Year of Julian Period **6737**

–Beth Krommes

ERAS

ERA	YEAR	BEGINS
Byzantine	7533	September 14
Jewish (A.M.)*	5785	October 2
Chinese (Lunar) [Year of the Dragon]	4722	February 10
Roman (A.U.C.)	2777	January 14
Nabonassar	2773	April 17
Japanese	2684	January 1
Grecian (Seleucidae)	2336	September 14 (or October 14)
Indian (Saka)	1946	March 21
Diocletian	1741	September 11
Islamic (Hegira)*	1446	July 7
Bahá'í*	181	March 19

*Year begins at sundown.

GLOSSARY OF ALMANAC ODDITIES

Many readers have expressed puzzlement over the rather obscure entries that appear on our **Right-Hand Calendar Pages, 121–147.** These "oddities" have long been fixtures in the Almanac, and we are pleased to provide some definitions. Once explained, they may not seem so odd after all!

–Beth Krommes

EMBER DAYS: These are the Wednesdays, Fridays, and Saturdays that occur in succession following (1) the First Sunday in Lent; (2) Whitsunday–Pentecost; (3) the Feast of the Holy Cross, September 14; and (4) the Feast of St. Lucia, December 13. The word *ember* is perhaps a corruption of the Latin *quatuor tempora,* "four times." The four periods are observed by some Christian denominations for prayer, fasting, and the ordination of clergy.

Folklore has it that the weather on each of the 3 days foretells the weather for the next 3 months; that is, in September, the first Ember Day, Wednesday, forecasts the weather for October; Friday predicts November; and Saturday foretells December.

DISTAFF DAY (JANUARY 7): This was the day after Epiphany, when women were expected to return to their spinning following the Christmas holiday. A distaff is the staff that women used for holding the flax or wool in spinning. Hence, the term "distaff" refers to women's work or the maternal side of the family.

PLOUGH MONDAY (JANUARY): Traditionally, the first Monday after Epiphany was called Plough Monday because it was the day when men returned to their plough, or daily work, following the Christmas holiday. (Every few years, Plough Monday and Distaff Day fall on the same day.) It was customary at this time for farm laborers to draw a plough through the village, soliciting money for a "plough light,"

which was kept burning in the parish church all year. This traditional verse captures the spirit of it:

Yule is come and Yule is gone,
and we have feasted well;
so Jack must to his flail again
and Jenny to her wheel.

THREE CHILLY SAINTS (MAY): Mamertus, Pancras, and Gervais were three early Christian saints whose feast days, on May 11, 12, and 13, respectively, are traditionally cold; thus they have come to be known as the Three Chilly Saints. An old French saying translates to "St. Mamertus, St. Pancras, and St. Gervais do not pass without a frost."

MIDSUMMER DAY (JUNE 24): To the farmer, this day is the midpoint of the growing season, halfway between planting and harvest. The Anglican Church considered it a "Quarter Day," one of the four major divisions of the liturgical year. It also marks the feast day of St. John the Baptist. (Midsummer Eve is an occasion for festivity and celebrates fertility.)

CORNSCATEOUS AIR (JULY): First used by early almanac makers, this term signifies warm, damp air. Although it signals ideal climatic conditions for growing corn, warm, damp air poses a danger to those affected by asthma and other respiratory problems.

DOG DAYS (JULY 3–AUGUST 11): These 40 days are traditionally the year's hottest and unhealthiest. They once coincided with the year's heliacal (at sunrise) rising of the Dog Star, Sirius. Ancient folks thought that the "combined heat" of Sirius and the Sun caused summer's swelter.

LAMMAS DAY (AUGUST 1): Derived from the Old English *hlaf maesse,* meaning "loaf mass," Lammas Day marked the beginning of the harvest. Traditionally, loaves of bread were baked from the first-ripened grain and brought to the churches to be consecrated. In Scotland, Lammastide fairs became famous as the time when trial marriages could be made. These marriages could end after a year with no strings attached.

CAT NIGHTS COMMENCE (AUGUST 17): This term harks back to the days when people believed in witches. An Irish legend says that a witch could turn into a cat and regain herself eight times, but on the ninth time (August 17), she couldn't change back and thus began her final life permanently as a cat. Hence the saying "A cat has nine lives."

HARVEST HOME (SEPTEMBER): In Britain and other parts of Europe, this marked the conclusion of the harvest and a period of festivals for feasting and thanksgiving. It was also a time to hold elections, pay workers, and collect rents. These festivals usually took place around the autumnal equinox. Certain groups in the United States, e.g., the Pennsylvania Dutch, have kept the tradition alive.

ST. LUKE'S LITTLE SUMMER (OCTOBER): This is a period of warm weather that occurs on or near St. Luke's feast day (usually October 18).

INDIAN SUMMER (NOVEMBER): A period of warm weather following a cold spell or a hard frost, Indian summer can occur between St. Martin's Day (November 11) and November 20. Although there are differing dates for its occurrence, for more than 230 years the Almanac has adhered to the saying "If All Saints' [November 1] brings out winter, St. Martin's brings out Indian summer." The term may have come from early North American indigenous peoples, some of whom believed that the condition was caused by a warm wind sent from the court of their southwestern god, Cautantowwit.

HALCYON DAYS (DECEMBER): This period of about 2 weeks of calm weather often follows the blustery winds at autumn's end. Ancient Greeks and Romans experienced this weather at about the time of the winter solstice (around December 21), when the halcyon, or kingfisher—having charmed the wind and waves so that waters were especially calm at this time—was thought to brood in a nest floating on the sea.

BEWARE THE POGONIP (DECEMBER): The word *pogonip* refers to frozen fog and was coined by North American indigenous peoples to describe the frozen fogs of fine ice needles that occur in the mountain valleys of the western United States and Canada. According to tradition, breathing the fog is injurious to the lungs. ■

-Beth Krommes

Nature's Germ Killer
Stop a virus before it starts

Scientists have discovered a natural way to kill germs fast.

Now thousands of people are using it against viruses and bacteria that cause illness.

Colds, flu, and many other illnesses start when viruses get in your nose and multiply. If you don't stop them early, they spread and cause misery.

Hundreds of studies confirm copper kills germs like viruses, bacteria, and fungus almost instantly, just by touch.

New research: Copper kills bad germs in seconds.

That's why ancient Greeks and Egyptians used copper to purify water and heal wounds. They didn't know about germs. Now we do.

The National Institutes of Health and the American Society for Microbiology vouch for the power of copper to kill germs.

Scientists say copper's high conductance disrupts the electrical balance in a germ cell and destroys it in seconds.

The EPA recommends hospitals use copper for touch surfaces such as faucets and doorknobs. This cuts the spread of MRSA and other illnesses by over half, and saves lives.

The strong scientific evidence gave inventor Doug Cornell an idea. He made a smooth copper probe with a tip to fit in the bottom of the nostril where viruses collect.

When he felt a tickle in his nose like a cold about to start, he rubbed the copper gently in his nose for 60 seconds.

"It worked!" he exclaimed. "The cold never happened." That was 2012.

Now he's gone 11 years without a cold. "I used to get 2-3 bad colds every year. Now I use my CopperZap right away at any sign I am about to get sick."

After the initial success, he asked relatives and friends to try it. They all said it worked, so he patented CopperZap® and put it on the market.

Soon hundreds of people had tried it. 99% said copper worked if they used it right away at the first sign of bad germs, like a tickle in the nose or a scratchy throat.

Now thousands of people use copper against:

Colds and Flu
Covid
Sinus trouble from germs
Cold sores or fever blisters
Canker sores that get infected
Mold allergies
Congestion or stuffiness
Drippy nose
Hay fever worsened by bacteria
Strep throat
Pink Eye and Styes
Skin infections
Infected sores
Cuts or wounds getting infected
Thrush
Warts
Ringworm

Copper kills germs in the nose.
It's fast and easy to use.

Users say:

"It works! I love it!"
"I can't believe how good my nose feels."
"Is it supposed to work that fast?"
"One of the best presents ever."
"Sixteen airline flights, not a sniffle!"
"Cold sores gone!"
"It saved me last holidays. The kids all got sick, but not me."
"I am shocked! My sinus cleared, no more headache, no more congestion."
"Best sleep I've had in years!"

Longtime users say they haven't been sick in years. Less stress, less medical cost, more time to enjoy life.

The handle is curved and textured to increase contact with fingers and hands in case you touch things sick people may have touched.

Scientists placed millions of viruses on copper. "The viruses started to die literally as soon as they touched it," said Dr. Bill Keevil.

The EPA says copper works just as well when tarnished.

Made in America entirely of pure US copper. Comes with Directions. 90-day **Money-back Guarantee**. Price $79.95. Get $10 off each with code **OFMA4**.

See www.CopperZap.com or call toll-free 1-888-411-6114.

Buy once, use forever.
Statements not evaluated by the FDA. Not claimed to diagnose, treat, cure, or prevent any disease.

Copper kills germs picked up on fingers, too.

Thirty days hath September,
April, June, and November.
All the rest have thirty-one,
Excepting February alone,
And that has twenty-eight days clear
And twenty-nine in each leap year.

–NURSERY RHYME

GETTING THE
JUMP ON
LEAP DAY

BY TIM GOODWIN

ILLUSTRATIONS BY TIM ROBINSON

2024 IS A LEAP YEAR!

It is widely assumed that leap year—or, more specifically, Leap Day—appears on the calendar every 4 years and that an extra day is added to February in any year that is divisible by four.

Not exactly true. Leap years are defined by two general rules:

■ A year may be a leap year if it is evenly divisible by four, as is this year.

■ However, century years (those that are divisible by 100, such as 1900 or 2000) can not be leap years unless they are also divisible by 400. So, the years 1700, 1800, and 1900 were not leap years, while the year 2000 was.

The next year that is evenly divisible by four that will not have a Leap Day is the year 2100.

Why Have a Leap Day?

Julius Caesar introduced the Julian calendar in 46 B.C. It was created to replace the Roman calendar, which was initially a complicated lunar arrangement based on Moon phases. The Julian calendar was not perfect, though: It overestimated the length of the year by more than 11 minutes and installed leap years every 4 years, which was too often. By the mid-1500s, the Julian seasons had shifted by about 10 days.

In 1582, Pope Gregory XIII introduced the Gregorian calendar, currently used by much of the world, as a modification to the Julian calendar. Its first iteration contained 10 fewer days in October in order to realign with the solar year. (In 1752, Britain and her colonies adopted the Gregorian calendar, skipping 11 days in September to be in sync.) The Gregorian calendar also instituted the current criteria for adding leap days.

In the Gregorian calendar, a year has 365 days. But Earth's orbit around the Sun takes about 365.2422 days. If we didn't add the extra day (February 29) almost every 4 years, our calendar would once again get out of sync with the astronomical seasons.

A PROPOSAL PROPOSITION

According to legend, in the 5th century, Saint Brigid of Ireland asked Saint Patrick to grant women the right to propose marriage. The two negotiated, and it was agreed that women could propose on Leap Day. Some claim that Brigid then proposed to Patrick, who declined and then gave her a silk gown to soothe her broken heart.

Gifts for rejected proposals by women became the tradition. According to Scottish lore, a rejected proposal would entitle a woman to a kiss, a silk gown, or 12 pairs of gloves—the latter so that the woman could hide the fact that she was not wearing a ring. The legend grew, and the practice spread throughout Europe before eventually arriving in the United States.

(continued)

Leap Day Weather

Look up historical weather events for February 29, and you will find some extreme conditions.

■ In 1956, the coldest temperature ever recorded in the United States on a Leap Day, -66°F, was measured at Hughes, Alaska.

■ The hottest U.S. Leap Day on record occurred in the towns of Encinal, Mission, and Weslaco, Texas, where the temperature reached 100°F in 1940.

■ On February 29, 1944, 33 inches of snow fell in Cisco Grove, California.

■ Hawaii has recorded more than 10 inches of rain on eight different Leap Days, with the most (21 inches) falling in 1984, in Maui.

■ In the early morning hours of February 29, 2012, an E4 tornado, reaching 180 miles per hour, destroyed more than 200 homes and about 25 businesses in the Harrisburg, Illinois, area. Eight people died and more than 100 were injured. The twister was part of the Leap Day Tornado Outbreak, when more than 30 tornadoes developed in Nebraska, Kansas, Missouri, Kentucky, Tennessee, and Illinois.

LEAP DAY BABIES

■ Only one of every 1,461 births occurs on Leap Day.

■ Peter Anthony Keogh was born in Ireland on Leap Day 1940. His son, Peter Eric, entered the world on February 29, 1964, in the United Kingdom. In 1996, Peter Eric's daughter, Bethany, became a Leap Day baby. This is the only documented case of three consecutive generations of one family being born on Leap Day.

■ Karin Henriksen of Norway can lay claim to the title of the only mom on record to bear three children on Leap Days—Heidi in 1960; Olav, 1964; and Leif-Martin, 1968.

■ Folks born on Leap Day are known as 29ers, leaplings, leapers, and leapsters.

■ The Honor Society of Leap Year Day Babies connects leaplings around the world through social media and Leap Day events.

■ During non–leap years, Leap Day birthdays are usually celebrated on February 28 or March 1.

Leap Year Odds and Ends

■ Anthony, New Mexico, and Anthony, Texas, share the title "Leap Year Capital of the World." These communities sit on the border between Texas and New Mexico. In 1988, Anthony (Texas) resident Mary Ann Brown, a leapling herself, led a campaign to encourage the governors of both states to issue proclamations recognizing the title. Since 1988, the communities have celebrated every Leap Year with a festival.

■ *La Bougie du Sapeur,* a French satirical publication that translates to "The Sapper's Candle," has been sold on newsstands across France every February 29 since 1980. It claims to be the least frequently published newspaper in the world because it is printed only during leap years. About 150,000 copies are sold every Leap Day.

■ Rare Disease Day was created on Leap Day in 2008 by the European Organisation for Rare Disease (February 29 being the rarest day). During non-leap years, Rare Disease Day is held on February 28.

■ Non-leap years always begin and end on the same day of the week. The first and last days of leap years are different.

DON'T BE CONFUSED

A leap second has nothing to do with a leap year or Leap Day. In fact, if necessary, a leap second can be added or subtracted at the end of June or December by the International Earth Rotation and Reference Systems Service to adjust Coordinated Universal Time (UTC) to align with the imprecise observed Universal Time (UT1). The first leap second was added on June 30, 1972. To date, no seconds have been subtracted. ■

Tim Goodwin, the Almanac's associate editor, hopes that everyone will consider leaping in the air at least once on Leap Day.

BEHOLD
NATURE'S
GRANDEST
EVENT!

Here's how to make
April 8, 2024, one of the most
memorable days of your life.

BY BOB BERMAN

*I shall only say that
I have passed a
varied and eventful
life, that it has been
my fortune to see
earth, heavens, ocean,
and man in most of
their aspects; but
never have I beheld
any spectacle which so
plainly manifested the
majesty of the Creator
or so forcibly taught
the lesson of humility
to man as a total
eclipse of the Sun.*

–from "The Eclipse," by
James Fenimore Cooper,
American writer (1789–1851)

Photo: Aubrey Gemignani/NASA

159

THE COMPOSITE IMAGE ABOVE SHOWS THE PROGRESSION OF A TOTAL SOLAR ECLIPSE.

Numerous surveys have probed the public's opinion on a very simple issue: What's the most impressive natural spectacle that you've ever seen?

People who have seen several notable events generally agree that a "Great Comet" ranks high, as does a meteor storm, when shooting stars explode across the sky every few seconds. Both are rare events, occurring only once every two, three, or more decades. A major display of the northern lights always makes the list, too.

But the ultimate sky show—the visual experience that's the best of the best—is, hands-down, a total eclipse of the Sun, which happens also to be the only such event that makes many observers weep with emotion.

One reason for this enthusiasm for solar eclipses is that they are brief and rare: Totality persists for just a few minutes (7½ minutes being its absolute—and only occasional—maximum duration), so a badly timed cloud can spoil everything. What's more, any given place on Earth sees a solar totality only once every 360 years, on average.

For example, Los Angeles was last in the path of a total solar eclipse in 1724, and the next one to occur there will not arrive until 3290. On the other hand, Carbondale, Illinois, was in the path of the recent total solar eclipse of 2017 and also happens to lie within the 115-mile-wide path of the 2024 totality. How, you might wonder, did the Carbondale area get so lucky? Blame it on the randomness of the universe.

On a global scale, the random and occasional occurrences of total solar eclipses means that relatively few people have seen one. This—and the fact that we all spend much of our lives going about the business

Photo: Aubrey Gemignani/NASA

of living and may have only a grade school knowledge of eclipses—means that many people are not aware of the vastly different types of eclipses. For instance, a lunar eclipse occurs when the Moon enters Earth's shadow—but which area of shadow? Earth's dark, Moon-obscuring umbra shadow or its outer, barely visible penumbral shadow? Each is a different event, a different experience for an observer.

Consider this: All four lunar eclipses in 2020 were of the penumbral variety, which is quite different from solar totality. This is why, after TV meteorologists and others that year urged people to go outdoors to see an "amazing lunar eclipse," most observers who gazed upward with high expectations were disappointed or perplexed: Nothing appeared to happen. Nobody had told them that during a penumbral eclipse, a full Moon undergoes no discernible change.

In vivid contrast, at the ultimate and opposite point on the eclipse spectacularness spectrum, stands the event that will occur on April 8, 2024—a total solar eclipse. Conveniently, this one will be visible from along a path running from Mexico to Canada. In the United States, optimum viewing opportunities will first occur in south and central Texas before moving up through Arkansas and into the Ohio Valley, traversing Lakes Erie and Ontario, and crossing northern New York and New England. In Canada, the route will include large swaths of New Brunswick and Newfoundland.

Interestingly, this eclipse will unfold only 7 years after the spectacular 2017 U.S. totality. That event made millions of the people who observed it believers in the unique and compelling nature of the experience and

VIEWER, BEWARE!
Some publications and Web sites will say that the eclipse is visible from almost everywhere in eastern Canada and the eastern United States. In a way, this is true. However, outside the narrow, 115-mile-wide path of totality—say, on the northern part of the Island of Montreal, for example—only a partial eclipse will occur. Viewing this will require eye protection for the entire time and will not feature the glorious natural wonders such as prominences, the corona, and stars appearing in the daytime that are visible only where the eclipse is total. Thus, you should consider making every effort possible to travel, if necessary, to be within this grand event's enchanted path.

convinced many of those who saw it as a "partial" eclipse that they had missed the true glories of a full totality.

Speaking of "glories," many people are of the notion that the main attraction of a solar eclipse is an effect called "blackness at noon." The popularity of this belief was made clear by American writer James Fenimore Cooper in his memoir titled "The Eclipse," which was based on his observation of the totality viewable in his hometown of Cooperstown, New York, on June 16, 1806. He writes of being most moved by the darkness at midday. Absent are observations of the features that fascinate many of today's observers, such as "the diamond ring effect" (more on this in a moment) and coronal streamers, largely because the Sun's magnetic field and the streamers were unknown at the time.

A RADIANT "DIAMOND" OF SUNLIGHT IS SEEN IN THE MOMENTS AFTER TOTALITY DURING THE TOTAL SOLAR ECLIPSE ON AUGUST 21, 2017.

Today, those who presume that experiencing natural midday blackness is the most compelling reason to travel to put themselves in the eclipse's path miss a good portion (some would say the best parts) of the show—the unearthly glories that appear only during the event's total portion.

To wit, only in totality is there the opportunity to . . .

■ safely stare at the Sun directly or even through binoculars; with the naked eye, you can actually watch the Moon's 1-kilometer-per-second motion as it orbits Earth! (Direct viewing during the hours-long partial solar eclipse periods requires special filters or goggles to protect eyesight from retinal damage.)

■ see the famous "diamond ring"—the brief, surrealistically intense pinpoint of light just before and immediately after totality that appears wholly different from its appearance in photographs.

■ gaze at long, thin, ethereal "streamers" radiating from the Sun as it hides behind the inky-black Moon. These force-field lines reveal the solar magnetic field, the largest structure in the solar system that is normally invisible.

■ observe pink prominences resembling fiery geysers sprouting from the Sun's edge. These are the features most dramatically enhanced by those who take a minute to use binoculars at around totality's midpoint.

HOW TO PREPARE FOR A *REALLY* BIG SHOW

FOR VIEWING IN THE UNITED STATES:

■ Go to NASA's eclipse Web site: Solarsystem.nasa.gov/eclipses. Click on "Total Solar Eclipse April 8, 2024," click on "Where & When," and study the map showing the path of totality in an area that you can access. The event will be as well seen from U.S. cities as from rural areas. On April 8, more than 3 full minutes of totality will be visible from dozens of major cities, including Dallas, Texas; Hot Springs, Arkansas; Fairfield, Illinois; Evansville and Jasper, Indiana; Sandusky, Ohio; Erie, Pennsylvania; Buffalo, Niagara Falls, Rochester, and Watertown, New York; Burlington, Vermont; Pittsburg, New Hampshire; and Jackman, Maine. For a complete list of towns and cities in the path of totality, the exact local times of the eclipse, and the length of totality at each site, go to Nationaleclipse.com.

FOR VIEWING IN CANADA:

■ Go to the Royal Astronomical Society of Canada's New Brunswick site at RASCNB.ca and click on "2024 Solar Eclipse." Then click on the "interactive map" under "ECLIPSE PATH MAP" to find where the path of totality will be in an area that you can access. The event will be as well seen from Canadian cities as from rural areas. On April 8, certain parts of New Brunswick—in particular, Fredericton, Woodstock, Florenceville-Bristol, and Miramichi—will experience 100% totality, the complete coverage of the Sun. For a complete list of towns and cities in the path of totality, the exact local times of the eclipse, and the length of totality at each site, go to Eclipse2024.com.

FOR VIEWING IN BOTH:

■ Ideal weather conditions would be clear skies. For a real-time, 5-day forecast of conditions based on a specific zip or postal code, go to Almanac.com/Weather or Weather.gov for the U.S. or Almanac.ca/Weather for Canada. ■

Bob Berman, astronomy editor of *The Old Farmer's Almanac,* has led 11 solar eclipse expeditions and is the author of *The Sun's Heartbeat* (Little Brown, 2015).

ADVICE FOR VIEWERS EVERYWHERE

■ Contact a welding supply store and order several shade 12, 13, or 14 filters. Do not accept shade 10; it is more common than the others but not dark enough to keep your eyes safe while viewing the eclipse's partial phases.

■ If hotel accommodations or camping reservations are booked up, remember that you can see the event from the rooftop of a camper or a lawn chair on a highway pull-off or rest area. Study the maps!

■ Review the short-term weather forecast regularly.

■ Never use binoculars to view the Sun except during those few minutes of totality. During the rest of the eclipse—the partial phases—you would suffer permanent eye damage in a mere 1 or 2 seconds.

■ If you experience totality, count yourself among a select lucky few people in the world!

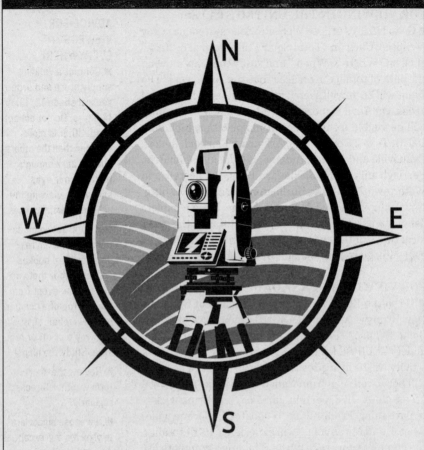

SURVEY *SAYS!*

The location of your property lines
should be more than a matter of guesswork
or memory. Here's how to make
sure that you know exactly what's yours.

BY CARY RIDEOUT

"THIS BE YOURS AND THIS BE MINE, BUT WHERE, OH, WHERE BETWIXT IS THE LINE?"

A neighbor of mine mentioned one April morning that he was having the old homestead surveyed. As with most family acreages, a survey hadn't been done there in over 100 years. The next time I ran into him, I asked how the survey had gone. "Oh, that was an education," he growled. It turned out that the correct boundaries were way off from where his family had believed them to be.

The vague notion of boundaries— which is especially common regarding rural land—is a mess of problems waiting to happen, but these usually can easily be solved with a land survey.

A GOOD DEED, INDEED

Any question of land ownership starts with a deed. This document will state who owns the property, with an explanation of the outline of the boundaries. If the deed isn't in the bureau drawer, you can obtain one easily. Look on the last tax bill that you received for the property identification number. Every piece of ground, no matter its dimensions, has an identity number for recording its ownership with the province or territory. With this number, you can obtain a copy of the deed at the nearest Lands Registry Office. Records in these offices will go back to the first Crown surveys and list all of the times that the property was sold or subdivided.

Old deeds play a valuable role in any land survey, and part of every surveyor's job is to hunt up the oldest survey available. Why? Any information about pre-existing surveys is essential to establishing correct lines of division. Surveyors look for evidence of original boundaries both in documents and on the property when preparing a survey.

A lawyer or professional land surveyor can help with a deed search and, yes, you need both for any land dealings. Deeds

are tricky things, so it's wise to have all documents explained by a professional with land transaction experience. Underground utility lines and Provincial Crown Roads run all over the countryside, and many times a new landowner won't know about them.

LINES AND LANGUAGE MATTER

Another point of confusion in many deeds is the amount of land being stated as so many acres "more or less." Do you have more property than the amount stated on the deed? Chances are, yes; often, original Crown surveys added a few extra acres to the stated amount, mostly in case the Government needed to put in a road at some time. However, more than one landowner has been surprised to

learn that a 100-acre parcel is, sadly, sometimes much less.

Land deeds speak in terms of "compass degrees," "save and except,"

"easements," and "right[s]-of-way," which can be baffling to interpret. An original Crown survey deed may also use words like "chains," "links," "leagues," "rods," and all sorts of medieval-sounding language—more on this in a moment.

In a perfect world, property would be divided into equal identical sections, but it's not—at least not outside of the Prairies. The first Crown surveys had the countryside neatly spaced, sectioned off, and ready for the pioneers. But, over time, these neat blocks of land have changed such that today property maps can look like jigsaw puzzle pieces. To make matters worse, it only takes a couple of years of crowding to confuse the property lines.

In many cases, property has been inherited several times and boundary lines have become sketchy. Say that two farms are separated by a fence and over time the fence has deteriorated. Both farmers know where to stop plowing, right? Sure, until the furrow wanders a little more. Sometimes a row of trees serves as the line, but after a generation or two, the trees may get cut down for firewood. Then what? These kinds of situations can get out of hand.

SURVEYOR AS SLEUTH

Any professional surveyor can tell tales of confusion, conundrums, and consternation. One interesting example of detective work concerned a property's corner marked by "a large tree"— which, of course, was no longer there. Searching data back decades revealed continuous mention of the large tree but no location. The surveyor was at a loss as how to accurately survey the property. Finally, on a hunch, he consulted aerial mapping images from the 1940s and found a shadow exactly where the tree was mentioned. With this he was able to plot a starting point and outline the rest of the section.

Along with this hard evidence, oral history is also useful. For example, a surveyor was working on a parcel of land and couldn't find the correct line that worked with the neighbors' land deed. Gathering adjacent property information often will solve a mystery, but it did

not help this time. Finally, a conversation with a local historian revealed that in the late 1800s, a barn had stood on the edge of the property. The surveyor grabbed a shovel and, after digging down over a meter, found a stone foundation that cleared up the problem.

(continued)

ON YOUR MARK . . .

Despite having GPS technology available to make surveys extremely accurate, surveyors will search out old markers to establish boundaries. Just about every object, from rusty farm machinery to a cow skull, has been used as a property line marker. As noted, early Crown deeds often reference a "large tree." The trouble is that

trees get cut down or fall over in a winter gale. On the big prairie, sod or field stones were piled up to serve as markers. A stone monument is usually an unmistakable indicator. Iron bars often mark corners, and just about every

kind of fence—including the classic split rail, Page wire, or barbed wire—runs along boundary lines. Streams have played a role in land division and are usually divided down the middle. Roads are used as boundaries, but these may be altered or even abandoned.

Today, surveyors mark property lines with orange flagging tape and blaze trees at regular intervals before spraying

OF CHAINS AND RODS

Few terms appear in old deeds as often as the word "chain," which is an actual metal chain 66 English feet long consisting of 100 links, each of 7.92 inches. A chain is equal to 4 rods, each rod being 16.5 English feet. Countless surveys were done with a chain and compass right up to the 1900s, which is why this term is still in many deeds.

Doing a survey with a chain was tough work over rough ground. After a compass bearing was established, a man with a long, colored wooden pole walked ahead to an indicated point and lined up with the surveyor. The chain was then run out and staked at intervals with long metal pins to keep the line straight. Once all 66 feet were out, the chain was checked for straightness, unhooked back at the start, swung around, and the process was repeated with a sharp eye following the compass. The problem herein was that the metal in a chain could stretch or the links work free, and repairs made a difference in the actual measurements. This venerable device, although long since replaced by superior tools, is a "link" to the hard work of those early surveyors.

them with reflective paint. They mark corners with a large wooden post and a metal pin driven in at the base. The pin has a plastic cap with the surveyor's name, number, and year for future reference. Never touch any survey marker no matter how old. It is of value to future surveys and might just save you in a dispute.

WALKING THE LINE

Before hiring a surveyor, thoroughly inspect your acreage for any boundary markers. Late autumn, when there are no leaves or tall grass to obstruct your view and before the snow comes, is a good time. If you are a longtime resident, you probably know roughly where the lines run—but you might be a wee bit off.

Have a copy of the deed, any old land transaction documents, and/or even photos of the property for the surveyor. Walk the property with the surveyor, indicating all line markers of which you know, and mention the neighbors. Speaking of which, be a good

one and let the folks over the fence know what you're doing. No one likes to be surprised by a group of fellows with tripods traipsing through the turnips.

Once the survey is completed, you will have an opportunity to examine it before the final okay. If there are discrepancies, now's the time to have them resolved, but—remember—the surveyor can work only with the information available. Despite family folklore, sometimes you just have to accept the outcome.

Finally, after the survey is completed to your satisfaction, send it to your lawyer to make sure it is recorded promptly! If it's not on the government's books, a new deed is not worth the paper that it's written on, so make certain that it's registered. ■

Used with permission of Small Farm Canada *magazine, online at SmallFarmCanada.ca.*

Cary Rideout is an award-winning freelance writer who has contributed to publications across North America. He shares a fourth-generation holding in Carlow, New Brunswick, with his wife Lorain, where his ties to the land run as true as a boundary barbed wire fence.

MEMORABLE
OLYMPIC
MOMENTS

WHEN IT COMES TO GOLD AND GLORY, OLYMPIC ATHLETES GET THEIR RIGHTFUL SHARE, BUT COULD IT BE THAT THEIR BACKGROUND STORIES ARE THE REAL WINNERS?

BY KRISTIN KRAUSE · ILLUSTRATIONS BY KELLY ALDER

While the Olympic motto of "Faster, Higher, Stronger" promises great athletic accomplishments, the Games' human tales of sportsmanship, sacrifice, and character often remind us that the quadrennial sports extravaganza can mean much more than just going for the gold. In celebration of the 2024 Summer Olympics in Paris, we present some little-known side stories from past Olympiads.

STROKE OF GENIUS

Thirteen-year-old Alfréd Hajós resolved to become a good swimmer after witnessing his father drown in the Danube. Five years later, in 1896, the young Hungarian traveled to Athens to compete in the first modern Olympiad. The swimming competitions were held in the Mediterranean Sea, whose temperature in early April was only 55°F—cold enough to make limbs numb and clumsy from hypothermia. Hajós smeared his body with grease to fend off the cold and fought through waves up to 12 feet high in two events—the 100- and 1,200-meter freestyle contests—on the same day. He won both.

At the 1924 Games in Paris, Hajós won again—a silver medal for architecture. Yes, architecture. From 1912 to 1952, Olympic competitions included fine arts. Medals were awarded for architecture, literature, music, painting, and sculpture.

FAIR PLAY

During the 1936 Berlin Games, two close friends, Shuhei Nishida and Sueo Oe, tied for second place in the pole vault. Officials demanded a tiebreaker to determine the silver and bronze medal winners, but Nishida and Oe declined. Nishida was awarded the silver because he had cleared the height in fewer attempts, but it didn't matter. When the athletes returned to Japan, they had their medals cut in half to create two new ones, each half-silver and half-bronze. These became known as "the Medals of Friendship."

DUCKING OUT

Australian phenom Henry Robert "Bobby" Pearce dominated the 1928 Olympic rowing trials in Amsterdam. However, a complication arose during his quarterfinal race. Hearing shouts from the bank, he turned to see a mother duck and her ducklings crossing the racecourse ahead of him. Pearce stopped to let them pass, winning the adoration of the Dutch spectators. The pause allowed his competitor to take the lead, but Pearce caught up and won the match. After defeating the eventual silver medalist by 9.8 seconds in the finals—a huge margin for the 2,000-meter race—he would go on to win Olympic gold again in Los Angeles in 1936. *(continued)*

GOLDEN GIRL

Europe had not yet recovered from WWII when the Games were held in London in 1948. Food was rationed, and athletes had to bring their own towels. In these "Austerity Games," 30-year-old Fanny Blankers-Koen of Holland, mother of two, won four gold medals in track and field while pregnant with her third child. At this time, married female athletes were rare and mothers unheard of. Newspapers said she was too old to compete, criticized her for leaving her children at home, and dubbed her the "Flying Housewife." Nonetheless, her wins made her the most successful athlete of that Olympiad.

LIKE FATHER, LIKE SON

In 1924, canoeist Bill Havens learned that his wife was due to give birth during the Paris Olympics. Reluctantly, he resigned his place on the United States Olympic team to be present at the birth of his son Frank. The team, which included Bill's brother Bud, paddled to glory without him, winning three gold, one silver, and two bronze medals in six events.

Twenty-eight years later, at the 1952 Olympics in Helsinki, the gold medal in the 10,000-meter single-blade canoeing event was won by Frank Havens. In a telegram to his father (and coach), Frank wrote, "Dear Dad, thanks for waiting around for me to get born in 1924. I'm coming home with the gold medal that you should have won. Your loving son, Frank."

LIFESAVER

At the 1988 Games in Seoul, Canadian sailor Lawrence Lemieux was racing through rough seas, in second place in his race, when he heard cries of distress. The boat of two sailors from Singapore, competing in a different race, had capsized, and the men were in danger of being swept out to sea. Lemieux changed course to come to their aid, knowing that he could get to them more quickly than any rescue boats could. Although he ended up finishing in 21st place after diverting to ensure their safety, his gallantry did not go unnoticed: The International Olympic Committee later awarded him the Pierre de Coubertin medal for sportsmanship.

RUNNING INTO HISTORY

In 1904, St. Louis, Missouri, concurrently hosted both the Olympics and the World's Fair. At the time of this, its third modern iteration, the Olympiad was still relatively unknown, so to increase participation, the organizers allowed anybody to compete. That year's marathon is remembered for a number of interesting moments, including:

■ Len Taunyane and Jan Mashiani, two members of South Africa's Tswana tribe who were in St. Louis to perform in the World's Fair, decided to enter the road race. In so doing, they became the first Black Africans to compete in the Olympics. Running barefoot, they finished ninth and twelfth, respectively, even though Taunyane was chased a mile off course by dogs.

■ Cuba's first Olympian, Félix Carvajal, traveled to New Orleans by boat, then walked and hitchhiked the 670 miles to St. Louis. His running outfit consisted of a beret, a long-sleeve shirt, long pants, and dress shoes. Another entrant cut the trousers off at the knees for him so that he would not overheat. During the race, Carvajal seemed unhurried: He stopped to chat with spectators and, one time, to pick and eat apples from a roadside tree. The fruit upset his stomach, so he lay down and took a nap. When he woke up, he continued running, eventually—remarkably—finishing fourth.

■ The race took place with temperatures in the 90s. Water was available only at the 6- and 12-mile marks of the 24.85-mile course. (The chief organizer of the Games supported research on the effects of dehydration on the body.) American Thomas Hicks begged his handlers for water. Instead, they gave him a mixture of strychnine and raw egg whites (and later, brandy). Strychnine, a form of rat poison, was believed to be a stimulant when taken in small doses. This marked the first recorded use of performance-enhancing drugs in the modern Olympics. (Strychnine is poison. Do not consume, inhale, or inject it into your body.)

■ American Fred Lorz also struggled in the heat, so he rode 11 miles in a car, waving at spectators. After it broke down, he jumped out, finished the race, and was declared the winner by the none-the-wiser officials. Then, as President Theodore Roosevelt's daughter Alice was presenting him the gold medal, he was abruptly disqualified. An hour later, the dehydrated Hicks, half-dead in the arms of his trainers, lurched across the finish line, to be declared the winner. His time of 3:28 remains the slowest winning marathon mark in Olympic history. ■

Kristin Krause is a scientist, teacher, author, and mom who enjoys history's odd moments. She watches the Olympics with her family in Maine.

SIMPLE STEPS TO
SEED-STARTING
SUCCESS

Learning to grow your own seedlings is one of the most valuable gardening skills that you can acquire. By starting with seeds, you can choose from a huge selection of interesting varieties that are not available as seedlings. Growing your own seedlings also allows you to control timing. You can kick-start spring by starting cool-season plants like broccoli and lettuce indoors in late winter. Then switch to starting tomatoes, peppers, and summer crops in midspring. Plan on another flurry of seed-starting activity in summer, as you get ready to stock your fall garden with spinach, kale, and kohlrabi. In addition to having the seedlings that you want when you want them, you will save a ton of money by growing your own.

HOW SEEDS GERMINATE

Seeds are plants in a deep dormant state. When triggered by moisture, temperature, and sometimes light, specialized cells inside the seeds wake up and start to grow. Stored nutrients are sent to the embryo, which holds the basic

WHAT REALLY GOES ON INSIDE
AWAKENING SEEDS AND WHY YOU SHOULD
START YOUR OWN SEEDLINGS INDOORS

BY BARBARA PLEASANT

botanic structures for roots, stem, and leaves. Fast-germinating seeds for vegetables like cucumbers and tomatoes have well-developed embryos, but seeds of the carrot and onion families do not. Their tiny embryos must grow before the seeds can sprout, so they take longer to emerge.

Priming seeds by soaking them in water for a few hours and then drying them on paper towels before planting often improves the germination of older seeds, but too much water, for too long, can be deadly.

Germination requires oxygen because until leaves emerge to synthesize solar energy, seeds combine oxygen with their stored food reserves to grow new cells. When you force out soil oxygen with too much water, seeds struggle or rot.

SPECIAL SOIL FOR STARTERS

As soon as they sprout, seedlings must defend themselves from fungi and bacteria, particularly those that live in soil. To prevent potential problems, buy a fresh bag of organic seed-starting mix every spring and keep it indoors, closed and dry, between uses. Most seed-starting mixes are composed of peat moss, coconut coir, and vermiculite or perlite, materials that are hospitable to plant roots but not to soilborne diseases.

You can make your own seed-starting mix from rich, fluffy compost that has been placed in a heatproof pan, tightly covered, and heated to 150°F in the oven for 30 minutes to kill pathogens and weed seeds, but you should still add perlite or vermiculite to help the

mixture to hold air. Made from naturally occurring minerals, vermiculite alone forms a moist, semi-sterile barrier when spread in a thin layer over germinating seeds.

CHOOSING RELIABLE CONTAINERS

The most common seed-starting containers are plastic cell packs like those used for bedding plants. These clean up quickly in warm, soapy water; can be watered easily from the top or the bottom; and can be reused several times. Three-ounce paper cups with holes punched in the bottom also work well, and you can write the names of the varieties right on the cups. Be careful with peat pellets, which hold too much water and not enough nutrients, and peat pots, which form a dry, acidic barrier that frustrates plant roots.

When you are ready to plant, fill containers halfway with moist seed-starting mix, dribble in a teaspoon or so of water, add enough mix to fill to the top, and then water again. Tamp down the soil with your finger to eliminate air pockets. Plant seeds at their proper depth in the seed-starting mix, spray with water from a pump spray bottle, cover the tops with a thin layer of vermiculite, and spritz again.

Plastic domes are used to retain surface moisture until the seeds germinate, but a damp, folded newspaper placed directly over the planted seeds works just as well. If you are starting only a few seeds, place the planted containers on a plate or in a baking pan that you enclose loosely in a plastic produce bag. Remove the bag when the seedlings start to sprout.

SIMULATING WARM SUN

Once seedlings are equipped with leaves, they switch to light as their primary energy source. To simulate sunshine, grow your veggie seedlings under bright light from a fluorescent or LED light fixture. Inexpensive shop lights from a building supply store, suspended over seedlings, will meet this need. (There is little difference in seedlings' performance under fluorescent and LED lights. Super-efficient broad-spectrum LED plant lights that glow pink seem to have a comforting effect on stressed seedlings, yet they also thrive under fluorescent fixtures, which give off a little heat, like a gentle Sun.)

As soon as little sprouts appear, keep your seedlings under lights for 12 hours a day. Adjust the height of the lights as the seedlings grow. Fluorescent lights should be less than 2 inches from the tops of the plants, while LEDs should be at least 4 inches from the highest leaves. (If you can not raise or lower the lights, raise or lower the containers by putting books or the like under them.)

Seeds germinate best when temperatures range between 75°F during the day and 65°F at night. When growing seedlings in a cool space like a basement, add modest bottom heat to your seedling setup with a seed-heating mat or electric heating pad. You can use food cans or books to hold a tray of seedlings over a heating pad set at its lowest setting.

THINNING AND FEEDING

A week or so after germination, seedlings develop their first true leaf, a sign that roots are also making good progress. This is the best time to thin seedlings by nipping out the weakest ones with little scissors. Or, separate and replant the seedlings into containers filled with regular potting soil, a step which is called "pricking out."

To do this, remove the mass of seedlings from its container and place it on its side. Then use your fingers to lift individual seedlings, touching only their seedling leaves. Gently slip seedlings into their new containers, press lightly to firm soil around the roots, water well, and return the seedlings to the same position under lights where they were before. New growth should resume in a day or two.

As the seedlings grow and roots fill the containers, the plants use up soil-borne nutrients. Keep them well nourished by using a water-soluble plant food mixed at half the rate recommended on the package every other time you water. Make a habit of lifting seedling containers to judge their weight. Very light containers are likely to be too dry, while heavy ones are loaded with water.

Learning to grow your own seedlings takes practice, but the life force locked away in every seed wants you to be successful. After all, only the luckiest seeds will get to be planted and cared for by you! ■

Barbara Pleasant is the author of many best-selling garden books, including *Starter Vegetable Gardens* (Storey Publishing, 2022).

WANT TO GROW A

Say hello to your new old flame!

Plants are seldom collected and cultivated for the purpose of performing party tricks. Yes, many put on a show, with gorgeous blooms, sensuous foliage, and/or seductive scents. But the real showstopper may be the gas plant: It emits a flammable oil that, under the right conditions, can be ignited for a brief but glorious flare-up.

In its extinguished state, this horticultural curiosity—a member of the citrus family native to Europe and Asia—might not immediately spark your interest. The perennial gas plant (*Dictamnus albus,* aka dittany) forms broad and dense clumps of glossy, aromatic, dark-green leaves that emerge from the earth in early spring. Footlong spikes of pure-white flowers develop in early summer. When

rubbed or crushed, the gas plant's leaves release a pleasant, lemony fragrance—but beware and touch with care (wear gloves): The aromatic oil can trigger an allergic reaction or photoreactive burn in some people.

The gas plant grows from 2 to 4 feet tall, needs very little care (just well-draining soil in full sun), and is exceptionally hardy—to Zone 3. Because it is taprooted, it can

SUREFIRE SENSATION?

WHEN CONDITIONS ARE JUST RIGHT, STRIKE A MATCH NEAR THE FLOWER STEM, JUST BELOW THE BLOOMS— AND *POOF!*

179

A GAS PLANT CAN TAKE SEVERAL YEARS TO MATURE, BUT ONCE IT'S ESTABLISHED, IT WILL LAST FOR DECADES.

be tricky to grow in containers and fares poorly if divided. The species can produce pink or purple flowers, but these are less common than white, which are magnificent in an all-white garden or mixed bed.

The flowers are your cue to prepare for the spectacle. Timing is critical: Still, sultry conditions are essential. (Wind would disperse the plant's volatile oils.) When conditions are just right, strike a match near the flower stem, just below the blooms—and *poof!* In only a second or two, a burst of flame travels upward (without harm to the plant), and then disappears! Each flambeau passes out quickly but not so fast that it can not be caught on camera. The flame does not leap to an adjacent stem; you must ignite each one. As you can imagine, the

pyrotechnic effect is especially dramatic after sunset.

Propagation of the gas plant is best achieved with seeds and patience. Fading flowers develop into curious ornamental seedpods, hard and woody to the touch (crafty sorts will note that these could easily be dried for everlasting arrangements). The pods hold beautiful, shiny, black oval seeds, each kept in place by an intriguing spring mechanism. When ripe, the bulging pods split or shoot out the seeds to fall where they may—or into a bag that you arrange on or near the pod. A gas plant can take several years to mature, but once it's established, it will last for decades: "Instances are known where *D. fraxinella* has outlived father, son, and grandson in the same spot without increase," says Henderson's *Handbook of Plants, 1890.* That's a long-running show! ■

–*Cynthia Van Hazinga, with Almanac editors*

WALKING FISH, BEANSTALKS
THAT STING, AND JUMPING WORMS?
YOU'LL NOT FIND THESE IN
A MOVIE OR THE METAVERSE—
THEY'RE RIGHT OUTSIDE.
BY JEFF HELSDON
ILLUSTRATIONS BY KRISTIN KEST

WILD THINGS THAT

NORTHERN SNAKEHEADS

Sharp teeth and an aggressive eating habit earned the northern snakehead the name "frankenfish." As if that weren't bad enough, it also has a lunglike organ that allows it to survive out of water for up to 4 days. Still not alarmed? This freshwater freak can travel *across dry land* by moving its head and back fins in opposite directions.

Native to Siberia, China, and Korea and first reported in California in 1997, the northern snakehead is suspected to have gained a finhold in North America after being released into the wild illegally by people who bought them from pet shops or live fish markets. The first breeding population in the U.S. was found in the Potomac River in Maryland in 2002. Populations are now established in New York, Pennsylvania, Virginia, and Maryland. In Canada, there were

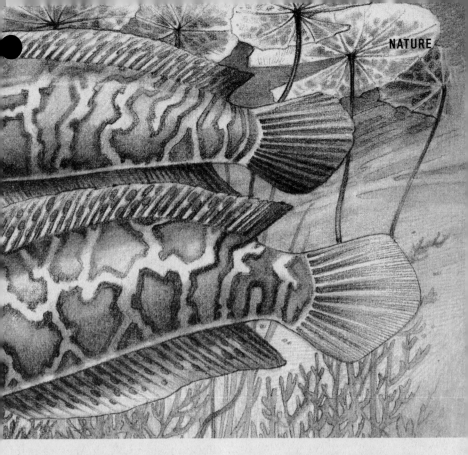

WREAK HAVOC

no known breeding populations as of the summer 2022, despite a few reports of individual fish catches.

The highly adaptable northern snakehead can live in lakes, rivers, wetlands, and smaller streams. It prefers shallow, slow-moving water and has a diverse diet: When young, it preys on plankton, insects, and small fish. As it grows, it begins to also feed on small reptiles and birds and mammals up to a third of its size. Well-fed and unchallenged (it has no natural enemies in North America and can outcompete native fish for both food and habitat), the northern snakehead can mature to 3 feet in length and weigh 19 pounds.

Its torpedo-shape body, scale-clad head, and large single dorsal and anal fins distinguish it from native burbot, bowfin, and eels. Report any suspected encounter with a northern snakehead immediately to a state or local fish and/or wildlife management agency. *(continued)*

GIANT HOGWEED

Giant hogweed, which can reach a height of more than 18 feet, evokes the mythical beanstalk grown from a bean by Jack in the classic children's story, but this monster works only black magic.

On contact with human skin, the clear sap of giant hogweed can burn and sting, causing dermatitis. After exposure to sunlight, the contacted flesh can develop blisters that leave scars for years.

It is no kinder to kindred flora, shading out native plants and in turn degrading wildlife habitat.

This biennial nuisance is a member of the carrot family (Apiaceae), which is a scary clan as it includes both delicious and deadly plants. The giant hogweed takes 2 to 5 years to flower, at which time it can produce up to 120,000 seeds before dying. Its winged seeds are spread by wind and waterways.

Native to Eurasia, giant hogweed was first brought to North America more than 100 years ago as an ornamental for gardens. It has since spread across all Canadian provinces except the Prairies, as well as into U.S. states from New England south to the Carolinas, the U.S. Midwest, and Oregon and Washington.

Manual removal is one method of control—but with a few provisos: Protective clothing should be worn. If the plant is in flower, extra care should be taken to ensure that no seeds fall off. Flowers should be placed in a black garbage bag (sealed closed) for a week to ensure their demise; they should not be burned or composted. Sightings should be reported to local branches of an invasive species network.

JUMPING WORMS

What looks like a common earthworm, thrashes wildly about like a snake and leaps when disturbed, and can shed a portion of its tail to escape?

A jumping worm.

Native to China, Korea, and Japan, the "jumping worm" can be any of several Asian worm species. These creepy crawlers were first introduced to North America in the early 1900s. Spread through mulch and soil on plants, they have begun appearing in forests in more recent years, particularly in the midwestern and northeastern United States.

Jumping worms live in the top layer of soil. Driven by an insatiable hunger, they eat forest leaf litter and remove nutrients from the soil, while leaving behind castings (feces) on the surface of the soil that wash away and/or won't penetrate deep into it where roots can access them. The worms' presence makes soil susceptible to erosion and creates an environment in which many plants and even trees can't live.

When mature, jumping worms can reach 4 to 8 inches in length. A telltale sign that differentiates them from earthworms is a milky white ring (clitellum). One known enemy is Old Man Winter: Jumping worms die during the first frost, but their eggs overwinter in the soil before hatching in April and May. Jumping worms mature in 60 days. Adults reproduce in late summer.

Authorities advise destroying mature jumping worms by drowning them in alcohol, vinegar, or soapy water or putting them into a sealed plastic bag that is then left in the sun. Consult with a state or local natural resources department if you see or catch any jumping worms. ◾

Jeff Helsdon is a freelance writer and photographer based in Ontario. He writes for several publications in the United States and Canada, including *Ontario Out of Doors*.

CURES, CHARMS, OINTMENTS, and PRESCRIBED UNDERTAKINGS

FOR BRIEF RELIEF IN A WORLD OF HURT

ILLUSTRATIONS BY TIM ROBINSON

In ancient Egypt, c. 2500 B.C., the treatment for a wound—a sign that an individual had been visited by evil spirits—involved donkey feces. Records from the period indicate that it worked; modern science (c. 2015) suggests that the manure's efficacy derives from antibacterial agents and probiotics in the animal's digestive system.

Over time, physicians learned of the antibiotic effect of other substances—herbs, minerals, milk, and water—and washed wounds with them. By 400 B.C., Greek physician Hippocrates (c. 460–375 B.C.) had added wine or vinegar to that list of options.

In the centuries since, folk remedies or traditional medicine have proliferated around the globe primarily because they were perceived—or proven—to be effective. You may know a few and may have tried these or others. Nonetheless, we advise that you not try these at home and instead just read on. Whether you call them science or superstition, these medical treatments are amazing.

THE GOAT

UNITED KINGDOM

I n the year 410, cancer patients in the United Kingdom were treated with an ointment of goat's gall bladder and honey, while people experiencing "half-dead disease," aka a stroke, were encouraged to inhale the smoke of a burning pine tree. (In the late 1700s, smoke again found favor as a nostrum, this time when delivered to the rectum. The "smoke enema" was believed to stimulate respiration, especially in a drowning victim; relieve headaches, hernias, and stomach cramps, the latter especially if administered while the patient consumed chicken broth; and cure cholera and typhoid.)

Meanwhile, charmers prescribed cures for warts, a common ailment. One still in use involves rubbing the wart with a piece of raw meat before burying it. The expectation is that as the meat deteriorates, so too will the wart.

By the late 19th century, people in the UK with tumors or an enlarged thyroid gland (goiter) were told that they would be restored to health if they touched a hangman's hand, while those who had been bitten by a mad dog would seek relief by holding the key of a church door. Baldness was reputedly cured by sleeping on stones, and fevers were broken by the consumption of willow tree tea (the latter may indeed have been efficacious, as willow contains salicin, a chemical similar to aspirin).   *(continued)*

UKRAINE

In Ukraine, the way to bring a fever down was to drink tea spiked with honey and alcohol while standing in ankle-deep hot water. A straight shot of hard liquor taken with a raw egg was the solution for an ulcer. A cloth soaked in cognac and warm water and then pressed against the neck was said to eliminate a sore throat, while for a stuffy nose, you were advised to bring a pot of chopped garlic to a boil and then stand over it and inhale the fumes.

INDIA, GHANA, AND THE DOMINICAN REPUBLIC

The antidote for a common cold or cough varies around the world: In India, it's a cup of boiling milk with 1 teaspoonful of turmeric. In Ghana, halves of a peeled onion are placed on either side of a child's bed to absorb toxins from the air. In the Dominican Republic, the fix is a tea made by boiling four halves of passion fruit and two halves of onion in water, straining the liquid, and then sweetening the concoction with honey before imbibing it.

ITALY

Farmers in Italy's South Tyrol district have been easing aches and pains in hay baths for centuries. Legend has it that the practice began some 300 years ago when local farmers fell asleep in a meadow. Upon waking, they found that their discomforts had vanished. The farmers capitalized on this happy accident by inviting people to lie in holes in the ground, after which the farmers covered them with dry hay. Today, visitors to area spas can replicate this experience indoors by lying on an air mattress or water bed for 20 minutes while covered in boiled mountain grass. This, locals say, opens pores and stimulates metabolism—albeit most effectively with a week's worth of treatments.

TURKEY

In Turkey, folks suffering from rheumatism would soak in a barley bath. They might eat hedgehog meat to eliminate eczema, consume one pigeon egg per day for 40 days to cure asthma, lay a round slice of lemon on their forehead to cure a headache, relieve an earache with water dripping from a leek, or inhale the ashes of a burnt eggshell to stanch a nosebleed. *(continued)*

UNITED STATES

I n the United States, people who experienced "jerking fits" (epileptic seizures) were advised to swallow the heart of a rattlesnake. (When worn around the waist, rattlesnake skin was thought to prolong life.) High blood pressure could supposedly be lowered if green Spanish moss was tucked into a person's shoes. An eel skin tied around the head diffused a headache; tied into the hair, it stimulated growth. A toothache would go away if a splinter from a pine tree that had been struck by lightning was used to pick the tooth. In the Ozarks, wounds were disinfected with turpentine or kerosene; chapped skin was moisturized with possum fat, mutton tallow, or beeswax; and congestion broke up when onion and mustard poultices were applied to the chest.

SOUTH AMERICA

I n South America, Incas found a use for every part of the native molle tree (*Schinus molle,* aka Peruvian pepper): The sap had a laxative effect, the resin healed wounds, and teas made from its leaves and bark repaired a panoply of ailments.

CANADA

In Canada, fever, pneumonia, or a cold was treated with a goose fat–and–mustard plaster on the chest. Hot ashes bound in cloth and wrapped around the neck helped to relieve a sore throat. Bleeding wounds were bound in birch bark, and a combination of spruce pitch and grease was applied to skin rashes and burns. Plant parts—roots, stems, leaves, and berries—were used to make teas for a variety of conditions: asthma, diarrhea, headache, muscle or menstrual cramps, sore throat, stomachache— even labor contractions.

SOUTHEAST ASIA

A cure for almost any cold, flu, or headache in Southeast Asia was "coining" (*cao gio,* pronounced "gow yaw"), or catching the wind. This was based on the popular belief that a body's blood contained too much wind, which needed to be released in order for the body to be relieved.

The procedure itself involved applying warm oil to the chest, back, or shoulders and then rubbing a coin over the skin until the pressure caused red marks— which were taken to be the cue for the wind to exit. ■

–Almanac editors

WHEN THE RAT
TRICKED THE CAT

This simple explanation of the Chinese zodiac
provides valuable insight into an important part of Chinese
culture that has thrived for more than two millennia.

BY TEAM CHINEASY

WHAT IS THE CHINESE ZODIAC?

In the traditional Chinese calendar, each year is denoted by one of 12 animals, and the 12 animals together are known as the Chinese zodiac. The animals appear in the following order: Rat, Ox, Tiger, Rabbit, Dragon, Snake, Horse, Goat, Monkey, Rooster, Dog, and Pig. Each animal begins a year, after which the cycle is repeated again and again. 2024 brings us the Year of the Dragon.

ONE POSSIBLE ORIGIN OF THE CHINESE ZODIAC

There are several versions of how these 12 animals were chosen. One popular story involves a race held by the Jade Emperor, one of the most influential gods in the traditional Chinese religion. In ancient China, recording time—years, months, days, or hours—was not an easy task. According to legend, the Jade Emperor decided to use animals to form calendar years, thus developing an easy way to allow Chinese people to keep track of years.

Yet, even the clever Jade Emperor could not decide which animals should be included. As a solution, he declared on his birthday that he would be holding a swimming race on the river for all of the animals. The goal would be to swim across the river, with the first 12 animals to reach the opposite riverbank to be honored accordingly as the zodiac signs.

Water sports wasn't a fair competition for every species. Some animals were not good at swimming at all; among these were close friends the Cat and the Rat. So, these two decided to ask a favor of the Ox, who was known to be kind, gentle, and a sturdy vessel to cross waters. The kind Ox eventually agreed to take the Cat and the Rat across the river.

In the early morning of the day of the competition, the devious Rat deliberately failed to wake up the Cat. Even worse, the Rat lied to the Ox, telling him that the Cat was dropping out of the race. The Rat then urged the Ox to take only itself across the river. The Ox, ever kind and gentle, agreed to carry the Rat. After numerous splashes and struggles in the water by all, 12 animals were finally nearly ready to complete the crossing.

Each in its turn struggled ashore. Just before the finish line, as the Ox approached the riverbank, the sneaky Rat jumped ahead, stealing the title of winner. The rest followed, in this order: Ox, Tiger, Rabbit, Dragon, Snake, Horse, Goat, Monkey, Rooster, Dog, and Pig.

Poor Cat, having missed the race altogether, was bitter. It blamed the Rat for destroying the trust between them and thus started chasing it. This is why and when the vindictive Cat and the guilty Rat became enemies. Although we know that cats had not been introduced into China by the time the zodiac was established, a story ending like this brings a modern twist to this interesting folktale.

HOW THE CHINESE ZODIAC INFLUENCES PEOPLE'S LIVES

For thousands of years, the Chinese zodiac has influenced people on many levels. The earliest literature that mentions the zodiac dates from the Qin dynasty (c. 220 B.C.), with an ancient storyline featuring the Dragon as a Bug.

The Chinese zodiac is often regarded as the Chinese horoscope divided by years rather than months, as in Western astrology. Each zodiac is associated with different personalities. The zodiac is still in use today as a social indicator for people. Some Chinese people believe that their Chinese signs must be compatible in order for them to get along with others. Theories have been developed to predict one's personality, fortune, and significant life decisions, such as career and marriage, based on the characteristics attributed to each animal of the zodiac.

Moreover, many Chinese people firmly believe that their marriage's happiness (or unhappiness) is determined by the perfect match of a couple's zodiac. Most Chinese also believe that children born into a certain zodiac year will have better luck and fortune than others. For example, many families dream of having a Dragon child, as Dragon babies will supposedly have a prosperous career and good fortune.

Although the Chinese zodiac might seem to have had a mysterious beginning, it has asserted a remarkable influence on Chinese people's lives and decisions for more than 2,000 years. It is deeply rooted in Chinese culture. ■

Chineasy (Chineasy .com) is a globally recognized, award-winning brand in the field of language education.

ANIMAL SIGNS OF THE CHINESE ZODIAC

The animal designations of the Chinese zodiac follow a 12-year cycle and are always used in the same sequence. The Chinese year of 354 days begins 3 to 7 weeks into the western 365-day year, so the animal designation changes at that time, rather than on January 1. This year, the Lunar New Year in China starts on February 10.

RAT
Ambitious and sincere, you can be generous with your money. Compatible with the dragon and the monkey. Your opposite is the horse.

1936	1948	1960
1972	1984	1996
2008	2020	2032

OX OR BUFFALO
A leader, you are bright, patient, and cheerful. Compatible with the snake and the rooster. Your opposite is the goat.

1937	1949	1961
1973	1985	1997
2009	2021	2033

TIGER
Forthright and sensitive, you possess great courage. Compatible with the horse and the dog. Your opposite is the monkey.

1938	1950	1962
1974	1986	1998
2010	2022	2034

RABBIT OR HARE
Talented and affectionate, you are a seeker of tranquility. Compatible with the goat and the pig. Your opposite is the rooster.

1939	1951	1963
1975	1987	1999
2011	2023	2035

DRAGON
Robust and passionate, your life is filled with complexity. Compatible with the monkey and the rat. Your opposite is the dog.

1928	1940	1952
1964	1976	1988
2000	2012	2024

SNAKE
Strong-willed and intense, you display great wisdom. Compatible with the rooster and the ox. Your opposite is the pig.

1929	1941	1953
1965	1977	1989
2001	2013	2025

HORSE
Physically attractive and popular, you like the company of others. Compatible with the tiger and the dog. Your opposite is the rat.

1930	1942	1954
1966	1978	1990
2002	2014	2026

GOAT OR SHEEP
Aesthetic and stylish, you enjoy being a private person. Compatible with the pig and the rabbit. Your opposite is the ox.

1931	1943	1955
1967	1979	1991
2003	2015	2027

MONKEY
Persuasive, skillful, and intelligent, you strive to excel. Compatible with the dragon and the rat. Your opposite is the tiger.

1932	1944	1956
1968	1980	1992
2004	2016	2028

ROOSTER OR COCK
Seeking wisdom and truth, you have a pioneering spirit. Compatible with the snake and the ox. Your opposite is the rabbit.

1933	1945	1957
1969	1981	1993
2005	2017	2029

DOG
Generous and loyal, you have the ability to work well with others. Compatible with the horse and the tiger. Your opposite is the dragon.

1934	1946	1958
1970	1982	1994
2006	2018	2030

PIG OR BOAR
Gallant and noble, your friends will remain at your side. Compatible with the rabbit and the goat. Your opposite is the snake.

1935	1947	1959
1971	1983	1995
2007	2019	2031

THE BEST BREAD

BY SUSAN PEERY

This quirky, smelly way of making bread is a true American treasure and produces a loaf that tastes remarkably good. The recipes and techniques (and loaf's common name, "salt-rising bread") harken back to the early 1800s, before commercial yeast or other leavening was available, when settlers moving across the Appalachian Mountains simply had to make do. If they had a potato, some cornmeal, flour, and a way to keep a bread starter warm, they could make loaves of a peculiar taste, texture, and appearance that were almost addictive to their families.

Today, old cookbooks from West Virginia to Minnesota and Montana and onward to California testify to the tenacity of this recipe. Bread gurus James Beard and Bernard Clayton included it (with cautionary advice) in their books. Two women who grew up in the heart of Appalachia, Genevieve "Jenny" Bardwell and Susan Ray Brown, have even written an entire book, *Salt Rising Bread* (St. Lynn's Press, 2016), about this finicky, distinctive bread and its rich folklore.

ABOUT THE NAME

It is not salt that makes the bread rise. (Only a small amount of salt is used.) I found two explanations, both reasonable. One is that bakers would warm a pan of rock salt and nestle a jar of starter into the salt to keep it warm overnight. The second is that the term "salt rising" is a variation of "salt raisin'," which in turn is a corruption of "saleratus," a naturally occurring mineral that was a precursor to baking soda, a pinch of which is found in most salt-rising bread recipes.

ABOUT THE SMELL

The starter for this bread develops a rather alarming odor somewhere between the stenches of sweaty old sneakers and overripe cheese. "Stinky feet" is a common descriptor. The more fermentation you get, the better—and the smellier. One family member described it as "dog breath after the dog has been in the compost pile." The

Photo: baibaz/Getty Images

WHEN EVERYTHING WORKS PERFECTLY, IT TAKES ABOUT 18 HOURS TO GO FROM STARTER TO FINISHED BREAD.

rising dough retains much of the smell. But once the bread is baking, it starts to smell "better," and the bread itself is delicious, with a slight hint of cheese. Aficionados claim that it makes the best toast ever.

WHAT CAUSES THE ODOR?

The microbe that enlivens the starter, *Clostridium perfringens,* is naturally present in the potato and/or cornmeal and is the source of the smell. It multiplies quickly and creates hydrogen gas (just as yeast-generated dough creates carbon dioxide). The scalding-hot liquid used to make the starter wipes out any natural yeasts and leaves only the *Clostridium* microbes to leaven the bread.

YOU WILL NEED . . .

1. Patience. When everything works perfectly, it takes about 18 hours to go from starter to finished bread. One of my efforts took 26 hours. You will know after 5 to 6 hours whether your starter works (i.e., starts to get foamy). At this point, if nothing is bubbling in the jar, give up and start over. It is better to throw out a couple of cups of starter than to prolong the agony and never end up with a loaf of bread. I had one total failure out of five attempts.

2. Heat. The starter and the rising dough need to be held at 100°F or slightly above. This can be hard to achieve. The strategy that worked best for me was to make the starter in the late afternoon, put it in the oven with just the oven light on and a pan of hot (boiling) water on the rack below the starter, and then renew the hot water before going to bed. By bedtime, the starter should have started to foam up. (If not, see Step 1, "Patience.") You may end up devising other ways to maintain a steady 100° to 110°F temperature. Use an oven thermometer to make sure that the oven is warm enough.

SALT-RISING BREAD

This is an adaptation of James Beard's recipe in Beard on Bread *(Knopf, 1995). Keep in mind that the dough is not as elastic as with a yeast-based dough, nor does it rise into a dome shape.*

STARTER:

1 medium white potato, scrubbed and sliced thin
2 tablespoons good-quality cornmeal
1 teaspoon sugar
½ teaspoon salt
1½ cups boiling water

■ Into a large jar, deep ceramic or glass bowl, or heatproof quart jar, put the potato, cornmeal, sugar, and salt. Pour the boiling water into the jar. Cover loosely with a plate and place in the oven inside a larger pan, to catch any drips. Pour more boiling water into a shallow pan set on the rack below the jar of starter. Turn the oven light on. Replace the water in the lower pan with more boiling water, if needed, to keep the starter warm at around 100° to 110°F.

■ After about 12 hours, the starter will have a layer of foam on top as much as an inch thick. This is a good sign. (If no foam appears after about 6 hours, discard and start over.)

■ Pour the jarful of foamy liquid through a strainer into a large mixing bowl or the bowl of a stand mixer. Pour another ½ cup of warm (100° to 110°F or above) water over the potatoes in the strainer and press down on them to extract as much liquid starter as possible into the bowl. Discard potatoes.

DOUGH:

5 cups unbleached, all-purpose flour, divided
½ cup warm (about 100°F) whole milk
1 tablespoon melted butter, plus more to brush on top
1 teaspoon salt
¼ teaspoon baking soda

■ Into the bowl with the starter, put 2 cups of flour, milk, butter, salt, and baking soda. Using a wooden spoon (or dough hook if using a stand mixer), mix well until smooth. Gradually add up to 3 more cups of flour until a soft dough is formed. Turn out onto a floured board and knead until smooth, adding up to ½ cup of flour if needed. Divide the dough and shape into two equal loaves. Place the loaves in well-greased 8x4-inch loaf pans and brush them with melted butter.

■ Cover and let rise in a warm place until the dough has risen to the top of the pans. The dough will be flat, not domed. This may take at least 4 to 5 hours.

■ Bake at 375°F for about 40 minutes, or until loaves are golden and pull away from the pan. The loaves will be flat-topped. Cool slightly before slicing.
Makes 2 loaves. ■

Susan Peery is a regular contributor to Almanac publications.

FOOD

(continued from page 71)

GINGER GREMOLATA BAKED SALMON

GREMOLATA:

½ cup salted, roasted pistachios,
  finely chopped
½ cup fresh cilantro, chopped
¼ cup fresh mint, chopped
3 tablespoons freshly grated ginger
2 tablespoons chopped chives
2 tablespoons agave syrup or honey
1 tablespoon lemon zest
1 tablespoon fresh lemon juice

SALMON:

1 salmon fillet (1 lb.), cut into two pieces
2 tablespoons olive oil
½ teaspoon salt
½ teaspoon freshly ground black pepper

■ *For gremolata:* In a bowl, combine all ingredients. Cover and set aside.

■ *For salmon:* Preheat oven to 425°F. Line a baking sheet with aluminum foil or parchment paper.

■ Pat salmon dry. Brush with olive oil. Place on prepared baking sheet, skin side down. Season with salt and pepper.

■ Bake for 12 to 14 minutes, or until salmon registers an internal temperature of 145°F on a meat thermometer.

■ *To serve:* Stir gremolata, then equally divide over tops of salmon portions.

Makes 4 servings.

–Sharyn LaPointe Hill, Las Cruces, New Mexico

THAI GINGER MEATBALL SALAD

DRESSING:

¼ cup honey
¼ cup vegetable oil
3 tablespoons fresh lime juice
2 tablespoons smooth peanut butter
1½ tablespoons teriyaki sauce
1 tablespoon freshly grated ginger
1 teaspoon sesame oil

MEATBALLS:

1½ pounds ground chicken breast

½ cup chopped fresh cilantro,
  plus more for garnish
2 tablespoons freshly grated ginger
1½ tablespoons teriyaki sauce
2 tablespoons vegetable oil

SALAD:

4 cups coleslaw mix
1 cup matchstick carrots
4 scallions, chopped

■ *For dressing:* In the bowl of a food processor or blender, combine all ingredients. Pulse until well combined. Set aside.

■ *For meatballs:* In a bowl, combine chicken, cilantro, ginger, and teriyaki sauce. Use hands or a small cookie scoop to form mixture into 1- to 1½-inch meatballs.

■ In a large skillet over medium-high heat, warm oil. Working in batches, cook meatballs for 10 to 15 minutes, or until cooked through. Add more oil as needed. Set meatballs aside and keep warm.

■ *For salad:* In a bowl, toss together coleslaw, carrots, scallions, and dressing. Mix until well combined.

■ *To serve:* Divide coleslaw mixture onto individual plates and top with meatballs. Garnish with cilantro.

Makes 4 to 6 servings.

–Arlene Erlbach, Morton Grove, Illinois

GINGER PEACH CRISP WITH GINGER-INFUSED WHIPPED CREAM

WHIPPED CREAM:

1 cup heavy whipping cream
2 tablespoons minced candied ginger
  or 1 tablespoon fresh ginger,
  roughly chopped
2 tablespoons confectioners' sugar

CRISP:

4 to 5 large peaches, peeled, pitted,
  and sliced
1 teaspoon cornstarch
½ cup old-fashioned oats
¼ cup almond flour

tablespoons brown sugar
1 tablespoon minced candied ginger or
   ½ tablespoon freshly grated ginger
1 teaspoon ground cinnamon
⅛ teaspoon ground nutmeg
⅛ teaspoon salt
4 tablespoons (½ stick) cold unsalted
   butter, cut into pieces

■ *For whipped cream:* In a saucepan over medium heat, bring cream and ginger to a simmer. Reduce heat to low and cook for 10 minutes, stirring often. Turn off heat, cover, and allow to cool in the pan. Once cooled, place in the refrigerator until very cold. This may take several hours.

■ *For crisp:* Preheat oven to 350°F. Grease an oven-safe 7x5-inch baking dish or two small cast-iron skillets.

■ Toss peaches with cornstarch. Place them evenly into prepared baking dish.

■ In a bowl, combine oats, flour, brown sugar, ginger, cinnamon, nutmeg, and salt. With a fork or pastry cutter, cut in butter until all ingredients are incorporated and no pockets of dry oats or flour remain. Spread over peaches.

■ Bake for 30 to 35 minutes, or until top is dark golden brown and peach juices are bubbling. Move to a wire rack to cool.

■ *To serve:* While crisp is cooling, strain ginger pieces out of cream. In a bowl, combine cream and confectioners' sugar. Beat until soft peaks form. Top each serving with whipped cream.

Makes 4 servings.

–Kristen Streepey, Geneva, Illinois

GINGER SWIRL BUNS

FILLING:
8 ounces (1 package) cream cheese,
   softened
½ cup confectioners' sugar
2 tablespoons freshly grated ginger

BUNS:

2¼ cups lukewarm (105° to 115°F) water
2 tablespoons molasses
1 package (2¼ teaspoons) active dry yeast
6 cups all-purpose flour, divided
⅓ cup sugar
2 tablespoons canola oil
2¼ teaspoons salt
1 tablespoon freshly grated ginger

FROSTING:
4 ounces (½ package) cream cheese,
   softened
2 tablespoons butter, softened
1¼ cups confectioners' sugar
½ teaspoon vanilla extract

■ *For filling:* Beat together all ingredients until smooth. Store in refrigerator until 30 minutes before using.

■ *For buns:* Line a baking sheet with parchment paper.

■ Into the bowl of a mixer with a dough hook, add water, molasses, and yeast. Allow mixture to bubble. Add 2 cups of flour, sugar, oil, salt, and ginger. Mix well. Add remaining 4 cups of flour, slowly, until dough comes away from sides of bowl. Place in a greased bowl, cover with a cloth. Let rise until doubled. Punch down, cover with a cloth, then let rise again until doubled.

■ On a lightly floured surface, roll dough into a long rectangle. Spread filling to edges of dough, leaving one long edge bare. Roll to bare edge and pinch seam to seal. Cut into 2-inch sections and lay cut side down on prepared baking sheet. Cover with cloth and let rise.

■ Preheat oven to 350°F. Bake for 20 to 25 minutes, or until golden. Cool slightly.

■ *For frosting:* Beat cream cheese and butter until smooth. Slowly add in confectioners' sugar, then vanilla. Beat until smooth. Spread over warm buns.

Makes 12 buns.

–Sandy Metzler, Kelowna, British Columbia ■

A **VERY PRICKLY** PROPOSITION

Meet (safely!) the North American porcupine, a gentle, often misunderstood loner that also happens to be Canada's second-largest rodent (after the beaver).

BY SANDY NEWTON

PORCUPINES ARE CHAMPION . . .

SWIMMERS: Their air-filled, honeycombed (not hollow) quills also aid in flotation.

SNIFFERS: Their weak eyesight is offset by an excellent sense of smell, which is used in identifying trees that bear food (especially on nighttime feeding forays).

VOCALISTS: Porcupines chatter and coo to their offspring—and to themselves. Males scream at each other when competing for the attention of a female.

CLIMBERS: Long claws, soft footpads, and a muscular, prickly tail help porcupines to climb trees for food and shelter. In between climbing up and later backing down tail first, they perch, eat, and even sleep on high, thin branches. Porkies have even been known to snap off a branch and fall to the ground—often sticking themselves with some of their own quills.

The first time you see a spiny porcupine in your path, danger bells may ring. We all know that a porcupine's quills will pierce your skin on contact, but fear not! If you don't actually bump into one, you'll soon discover that this shy, mainly nocturnal rodent is simply a nearsighted, slightly pigeon-toed sweet creature that mutters and chatters its way through life—and it certainly won't hurt *you* if you don't alarm *it*.

UP A TREE IN A WOODS NEAR YOU

From Canada's East Coast to our western shores and north to the tree line, the North American porcupine *(Erethizon dorsatum)*—our only porcupine species—lives pretty much everywhere that there's boreal forest (although not on a few of our large wooded islands, such as Vancouver, Newfoundland, and PEI). This vegetarian is so widespread because its main food sources are leaves and needles, bark, nuts, and berries—and because it can survive considerable cold and snow in its winter den (taking brief trips out to dine). Porcupines climb trees to find and eat most of their meals, so if you think you hear or smell one, look up!

WHY DID THE PORCUPINE GNAW ON THE OUTHOUSE?

A porcupine's summertime leafy diet is low on sodium. Quests for that missing element send them into the territory of their biggest threat: humans. "Porkies" (as some call them) are particularly drawn to salt-infused matter, such as wooden tool handles, salt licks, plywood, leather, road runoff, and, yes, places where urine has soaked into the wood of a privy.

RED TEETH AND A BAD SMELL

The porcupine's four incisors (among 20 teeth

in total) are a distinct red-orange, like those of its beaver cousins. The color comes from iron embedded in the enamel, which covers only the front of these four gnawing teeth (white dentine coats the back). The difference in hardness allows the teeth to be ground into a chisel-like shape that is excellent for gnawing off bark and, coincidentally, through plywood.

Like skunks, porcupines can emit a foul smell from the skin on their lower back (a patch called the "rosette"): Think body odor plus stinky cheese. Their coat is thinnest here, which helps the scent to spread. This off-putting smell plus a porcupine's black-and-white quills are its first line of defense against nosy predators.

WHAT'S THAT FUR, ANYWAY?

A porcupine's coat (or "pelage") has many components. It includes whiskers, bristles on

QUILLWORK

Decorative quillwork is the sacred Indigenous art of using naturally dyed porcupine quills. First Nations like the Mi'kmaq, Ojibwa, and Cree decorated clothing, birch bark boxes, and personal items with quills before glass beads became readily available in the mid-1800s.

Photo: Songbird839/Getty Images

ABOUT THAT AWESOME ARMOR

1. The quills covering a porcupine's back, sides, and tail number approximately 30,000.

2. They embed on contact, break at the root, and stay with the attacker when the porcupine pulls away. (On the porky, quills point in different directions, which means that not all of them pierce an attacker when contact is made.)

3. Tiny, one-directional barbs on the quill tip ease its penetration into the skin, hook it into the flesh beneath, and cause pain if the quill's removal is attempted via the same route through which it entered.

4. Because of the barbs' shape, once they are embedded, every movement by the host causes them to rachet farther and farther into its flesh.

5. Quills regrow in 2 to 9 months. The time needed depends on quill length, where they are on the porcupine's body, and such environmental factors as time of year (quills grow back more slowly in winter, for example).

the underside of the tail, guard hairs almost all over, the quills (which are modified guard hairs), and fur, which is a warm and thick pelt that is molted in spring and regrown in the fall.

NEITHER FLIGHT NOR FIGHT

A porcupine under threat does not run away, although it will climb a tree or seek shelter if a den is close by. If neither refuge is available, it turns its back to the predator, protects its face, erects the sharp spines on its back and tail, makes a chattering sound, stamps its feet, and emits that off-putting scent. The message is clear: Come near at your peril. If a predator persists, the next step is a deft, sharp swipe from the tail. If contact is made, the resulting snout-full of quills is usually enough to send the foe packing.

Porcupine encounters can be deadly for wildlife: The unlucky predator may get a mouthful of quills, be unable to eat, and starve to death—or die if

a barb is embedded in an eye or works its way from piercing the skin into a vital organ.

IT'S NOT TRUE!

Sometimes, the stamping of feet and thumping of tail makes loose quills drop off—and this is probably why some people believe that porkies can shoot their quills. But this is false: Porcupines can not eject these barbs.

AND YET, PORCUPINES STILL GET EATEN

Coyotes, cougars, lynx, bobcats, wolves, wolverines, and even great horned owls all will occasionally prey on porcupines. The most successful porky hunters, however, are fishers. They can follow a porcupine up a tree, but their best strategy is used on the ground: They repeatedly bite at a porcupine's quill-less head until they can grab it and flip the animal over to attack its soft, also quill-less underbelly. *(continued)*

A QUILL QUESTIONNAIRE

■ What color? Quills are dark at the tip with white or yellow shafts, which makes them discernible even at night.

■ How long? This varies: Quills are shorter near the face and longer on the back. The latter can be more than 4 inches (10 centimeters) long. The microscopic barbs cover only about the first 1½ inches (4 cm).

Photo: Gerald Corsi/Getty Images

DID YOU KNOW?

■ Outweighed by their rodent relative the beaver, porcupines can be as heavy as 33 pounds (15 kilograms). Generally, they average around 11 pounds (5 kg) and can grow to as much as 3 feet (90 centimeters) in length. Male porkies are larger than females.

■ Porcupines are slow: Their "running" speed—which is more of a fast waddle—is just over 2 miles per hour (3 kilometers per hour).

■ Porcupines are generally solitary but often share winter dens with other porkies.

■ The porcupine's large natural range in Canada is reflected on our national map, where you can find at least 31 Porcupine Lakes and 19 Porcupine Creeks.

I HATE IT WHEN I DO THAT!

Can porcupines prick themselves? You bet—if they fall out of a tree, for example. But their quills have an antibiotic coating that limits infection. They are also able to remove quills from their own flesh with their front teeth and paws. Importantly, they can hold their quills flat to their backs, minimizing painful mishaps during close but friendly encounters such as mating. Although a porcupine's quills are soft and pliable at birth, they become hard only a few days later.

THE PIG CONNECTION

Although the ancient roots of the word "porcupine" are Latin—*porcus* is pig and *spina* is thorn or spine—the English name arrived via the French *(porc espin)*. Porcupines are definitely rodents, but their pig connection endures in some terminology: Male porcupines are sometimes referred to as boars; females, sows. Babies, however, are porcupettes. And, fittingly, a group of porkies is called a "prickle"! ■

Sandy Newton is a regular contributor to the Almanac. As a dog owner, she is thankful that porcupines are not native to the island of Newfoundland, where she lives.

HOW WE PREDICT THE WEATHER

We derive our weather forecasts from a secret formula that was devised by the founder of this Almanac, Robert B. Thomas, in 1792. Thomas believed that weather on Earth was influenced by sunspots, which are magnetic storms on the surface of the Sun.

Over the years, we have refined and enhanced this formula with state-of-the-art technology and modern scientific calculations. We employ three scientific disciplines to make our long-range predictions: solar science, the study of sunspots and other solar activity; climatology, the study of prevailing weather patterns; and meteorology, the study of the atmosphere. We predict weather trends and events by comparing solar patterns and historical weather conditions with current solar activity.

Our forecasts emphasize temperature and precipitation deviations from averages, or normals. These are based on 30-year statistical averages prepared by government meteorological agencies and updated every 10 years. Our forecasts are based on the tabulations that span the period 1981 through 2010.

The borders of the provincial weather regions **(page 210)** are based primarily on climatology and the movement of weather systems. For example, while both Ottawa and Toronto are in Ontario, we place Ottawa in Region 2 rather than Region 3 (Toronto) because its weather trends more closely resemble those of other locales in Region 2.

We believe that nothing in the universe happens haphazardly, that there is a cause-and-effect pattern to all phenomena.

However, although neither we nor any other forecasters have as yet gained sufficient insight into the mysteries of the universe to predict the weather with total accuracy, our results are almost always very close to our traditional claim of 80%.

WEATHER

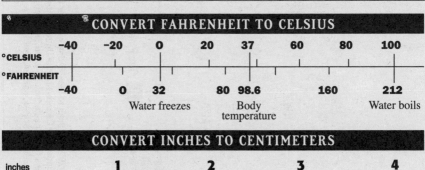

CONVERT FAHRENHEIT TO CELSIUS

°CELSIUS	-40	-20	0	20	37	60	80	100

°FAHRENHEIT	-40	0	32	80	98.6	160	212

Water freezes — Body temperature — Water boils

CONVERT INCHES TO CENTIMETERS

inches: 1 2 3 4

centimeters: 1 2 3 4 5 6 7 8 9 10

WEATHER REGIONS

WEATHER

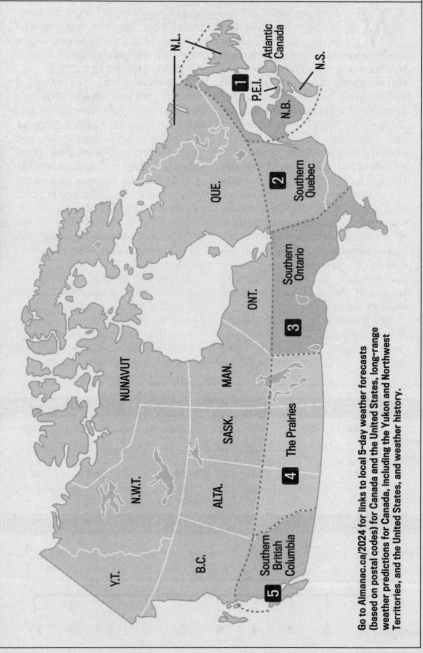

N.L.

Atlantic Canada

N.S.

P.E.I.

N.B.

1

QUE.

2 Southern Quebec

Southern Ontario

ONT.

3

NUNAVUT

MAN.

The Prairies

SASK.

4

N.W.T.

ALTA.

B.C.

Southern British Columbia

Y.T.

5

Go to Almanac.ca/2024 for links to local 5-day weather forecasts (based on postal codes) for Canada and the United States, long-range weather predictions for Canada, including the Yukon and Northwest Territories, and the United States, and weather history.

Illustrations of Canadian map and regional maps 1–5: Rob Schuster

ATLANTIC CANADA

SUMMARY: Winter temperatures will be above normal, with the coldest periods in early to mid-November, early December, and early to mid-February. Precipitation will be above normal, with below-normal snowfall in the east and above-normal snowfall in the west. The snowiest periods will be in December and early to mid-January. **April** and **May** temperatures will be above normal. Precipitation will be less than usual in the north and greater in the south. **Summer** will be warmer and wetter than normal, with the hottest periods in early to mid-June and late July. **September** and **October** will be warmer than normal, with above-normal precipitation. Watch for tropical storms in early September and mid-October.

NOV. 2023: Temp. 1°C (2°C below avg.); precip. 110mm (avg. north, 60mm below south). 1–12 Showers, mixed with snow north; mild, then chilly. 13–16 Sunny, chilly. 17–21 Rain and snow north, sunny south; cold. 22–30 Periods of rain and snow, cold.

DEC. 2023: Temp. -2°C (1°C above avg.); precip. 140mm (10mm above avg.). 1–5 Sunny, then snowstorm; cold. 6–13 Periods of snow and rain, turning mild. 14–16 Snow showers north, snowstorm south; cold. 17–31 Periods of rain and snow, mild.

JAN. 2024: Temp. -3°C (3°C above avg.); precip. 215mm (95mm above avg.). 1–3 Rain and snow, mild. 4–9 Sunny, then rain and snow; chilly. 10–15 Snowy periods, some heavy; cold. 16–28 Periods of rain and snow, quite mild. 29–31 Flurries, turning cold.

FEB. 2024: Temp. -6.5°C (1°C below avg.); precip. 63mm (75mm below avg. north, avg. south). 1–4 Snow showers, cold. 5–13 Flurries, then sunny; bitter cold. 14–17 Sunny north, rain and snow showers south; mild. 18–21 Rain and snow, some heavy; turning mild. 22–29 Sunny, mild.

MAR. 2024: Temp. 0°C (2°C above avg.); precip. 195mm (75mm above avg.). 1–3 Rain and snow, some heavy; mild. 4–14 Periods of rain and snow, mild. 15–21 Sunny, then rainy periods; mild. 22–31 Periods of rain and snow, chilly.

APR. 2024: Temp. 3.5°C (0.5°C below avg.); precip. 130mm (20mm above avg.). 1–6 Periods of rain and snow, chilly. 7–10 Sunny, cool. 11–19 Rain and snow showers, chilly. 20–30 Rainy periods; mild, then cool.

MAY 2024: Temp. 11.5°C (2°C above avg.); precip. 140mm (40mm below avg. north, 100mm above south). 1–6 Periods of rain and snow, chilly north; showers, mild south. 7–10 Showers north, rainy south; warm. 11–17 A few showers, warm. 18–24 Showers north; rainy periods south, some heavy; mild. 25–31 Sunny north, showers south; mild.

JUNE 2024: Temp. 15.5°C (2°C above avg. north, avg. south); precip. 80mm (20mm below avg.). 1–10 Showers, then sunny; turning warm north, mild south. 11–19 Showers, warm. 20–30 Sunny, then rainy periods; turning cool.

JULY 2024: Temp. 20°C (2°C above avg.); precip. 145mm (avg. north, 100mm above south). 1–9 Sunny, then showers; mild. 10–13 Rainy periods, some heavy south; cool. 14–17 Sunny, warm. 18–31 Showers, warm.

AUG. 2024: Temp. 17.5°C (0.5°C below avg.); precip. 140mm (50mm above avg.). 1–6 Showers, cool. 7–10 Rainy periods, some heavy south; cool. 11–19 Sunny, then showers; cool. 20–31 Scattered showers, turning warm.

SEPT. 2024: Temp. 14°C (avg.); precip. 125mm (avg. north, 40mm above south). 1–3 Tropical storm threat. 4–9 Showers, cool. 10–15 Sunny, then showers; turning chilly. 16–18 Rainy, chilly. 19–30 Rainy periods; cool, then mild.

OCT. 2024: Temp. 9°C (0.5°C above avg.); precip. 155mm (35mm above avg.). 1–9 Rainy periods, turning chilly. 10–16 Showers, turning mild. 17–19 Tropical storm threat. 20–29 Rainy periods, turning quite mild. 30–31 Sunny, chilly.

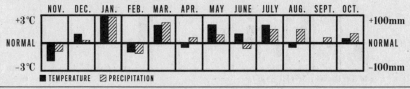

SOUTHERN QUEBEC

Quebec •
Montreal •
Ottawa •

SUMMARY: Winter temperatures will be above normal in the east and below normal in the west, with the coldest periods in mid- to late November, early December, early January, and early February. Precipitation and snowfall will be above normal. The snowiest periods will be in late November, mid- and late December, and early to mid-January. **April** and **May** will be warmer and wetter than normal. **Summer** will be warmer and wetter than normal, with the hottest periods in early and late July. **September** and **October** will be cooler and wetter than normal. Watch for a tropical storm in early September.

NOV. 2023: Temp. –1°C (2°C below avg.); precip. 85mm (avg.). 1–4 Sunny, turning mild. 5–16 Periods of rain and snow, then sunny; turning cold. 17–30 Snowy periods, cold.

DEC. 2023: Temp. –6.5°C (0.5°C below avg.); precip. 80mm (25mm below avg. east, 25mm above west). 1–7 Flurries, very cold. 8–18 Snow showers, then sunny; cold. 19–21 Sunny north, snowstorm south; chilly. 22–24 Sunny; mild east, cold west. 25–31 Periods of rain and snow, turning cold.

JAN. 2024: Temp. –7.5°C (6°C above avg. east, avg. west); precip. 115mm (40mm above avg.). 1–6 Flurries, turning very cold. 7–9 Snowstorm. 10–14 Snow showers, cold. 15–17 Snowstorm. 18–24 Periods of rain and snow, very mild. 25–31 Showers, warm east; snow showers, cold west.

FEB. 2024: Temp. –10.5°C (1.5°C below avg.); precip. 60mm (avg.). 1–12 Snow showers, then sunny; bitter cold. 13–18 Periods of rain and snow, turning mild. 19–29 Rain and snow showers, mild.

MAR. 2024: Temp. –1.5°C (2°C above avg.); precip. 90mm (20mm above avg.). 1–5 Few showers, mild. 6–8 Rain and snow showers, chilly. 9–18 Sunny, turning warm. 19–26 Rain and snow showers, turning mild. 27–31 Rain and snow, chilly.

APR. 2024: Temp. 6.5°C (3°C above avg. east, avg. west); precip. 145mm (120mm above avg. east, 10mm above west). 1–7 Periods of occasionally heavy rain and snow east, sunny west; chilly. 8–15 Sunny, mild east; showers, chilly west. 16–30 Rainy periods; mild east, cool west.

MAY 2024: Temp. 14°C (1°C above avg.); precip. 100mm (10mm above avg.). 1–10 Sunny, then showers; warm, then cool. 11–14 Sunny, warm. 15–24 Rainy periods, cool. 25–31 A few showers, mild.

JUNE 2024: Temp. 19°C (1°C above avg. east, 1°C below west); precip. 140mm (50mm above avg.). 1–4 A few t-storms, warm. 5–12 Rainy periods; cool, then mild. 13–18 Sunny, then showers; cool. 19–30 Showers; mild east, cool west.

JULY 2024: Temp. 23°C (3°C above avg.); precip. 100mm (5mm above avg.). 1–10 Sunny, then scattered t-storms; turning hot. 11–20 Sunny, then isolated t-storms; warm. 21–31 A few t-storms; mild, then hot.

AUG. 2024: Temp. 18.5°C (0.5°C below avg.); precip. 120mm (25mm above avg.). 1–14 Scattered t-storms, cool. 15–25 Rainy periods, turning warm. 26–31 A few showers, warm.

SEPT. 2024: Temp. 14°C (avg.); precip. 130mm (40mm above avg.). 1–6 Scattered showers, cool. 7–9 Tropical storm threat. 10–15 A few showers, turning cool. 16–21 Sunny, mild. 22–30 Showers, mild.

OCT. 2024: Temp. 7.5°C (0.5°C below avg.); precip. 80mm (5mm below avg.). 1–13 Rain and snow showers, cold. 14–18 Rainy periods, warm. 19–22 A few showers, cool. 23–31 Sunny, then showers; mild.

QUÉBEC DU SUD

RÉSUMÉ: L'hiver sera plus chaud que la normale à l'est et plus froid que la normale à l'ouest. Les périodes les plus froides seront mi- à fin novembre, début décembre, début janvier, et début février. Les précipitations et les chutes de neige seront plus fréquentes que la normale. Les périodes les plus neigeuses seront fin novembre, mi- et fin décembre, et début à mi-janvier. **Avril** et **mai** seront plus chauds et pluvieux que la normale. **L'été** sera plus chaud et pluvieux que la normale. Les périodes les plus chaudes seront début et fin juillet. **Septembre** et **octobre** seront plus frais et pluvieux que la normale. Une tempête tropicale pourrait avoir lieu début septembre.

NOV. 2023: Temp. –1°C (2°C au-dessous de la moy.); précip. 85mm (moy.). 1–4 Ensoleillé, devenant doux. 5–16 Périodes pluvieuses et neigeuses, puis ensoleillé; devenant froid. 17–30 Périodes de neige, froid.

DÉC. 2023: Temp. –6,5°C (0,5°C au-dessous de la moy.); précip. 80mm (25mm au-dessous de la moy. à l'est, 25mm au-dessus à l'ouest). 1–7 Rafales, très froid. 8–18 Chutes de neige, puis ensoleillé; froid. 19–21 Ensoleillé au nord, tempêtes de neige au sud; très frais. 22–24 Ensoleillé; doux à l'est, froid à l'ouest. 25–31 Périodes pluvieuses et neigeuses, devenant froid.

JAN. 2024: Temp. –7,5°C (6°C au-dessus de la moy. à l'est, moy. à l'ouest); précip. 115mm (40mm au-dessus de la moy.). 1–6 Rafales, devenant très froid. 7–9 Tempêtes de neige. 10–14 Chutes de neige, froid. 15–17 Tempêtes de neige. 18–24 Périodes pluvieuses et neigeuses, très doux. 25–31 Averses, chaud à l'est; chutes de neige, froid à l'ouest.

FÉVR. 2024: Temp. –10,5°C (1,5°C au-dessous de la moy.); précip. 60mm (moy.). 1–12 Chutes de neige, puis ensoleillé; froid glacial. 13–18 Périodes pluvieuses et neigeuses; devenant doux. 19–29 Averses et chutes de neige, doux.

MARS 2024: Temp. –1,5°C (2°C au-dessus de la moy.); précip. 90mm (20mm au-dessus de la moy.). 1–5 Quelques averses, doux. 6–8 Averses et chutes de neige, très frais. 9–18 Ensoleillé, devenant chaud. 19–26 Averses et chutes de neige, devenant doux. 27–31 Pluie et neige, très frais.

AVR. 2024: Temp. 6,5°C (3°C au-dessus de la moy. à l'est, moy. à l'ouest); précip. 145mm (120mm au-dessus de la moy. à l'est, 10mm au-dessus à l'ouest). 1–7 Périodes occasionnelles de fortes pluies et de neige à l'est, ensoleillé à l'ouest; très frais. 8–15 Ensoleillé, doux à l'est; averses, très frais à l'ouest. 16–30 Périodes pluvieuses; doux à l'est, frais à l'ouest.

MAI 2024: Temp. 14°C (1°C au-dessus de la moy.); précip. 100mm (10mm au-dessus de la moy.). 1–10 Ensoleillé, puis averses; chaud, puis frais. 11–14 Ensoleillé, chaud. 15–24 Périodes pluvieuses, frais. 25–31 Quelques averses, doux.

JUIN 2024: Temp. 19°C (1°C au-dessus de la moy. à l'est, 1°C au-dessous à l'ouest); précip. 140mm (50mm au-dessus de la moy.). 1–4 Quelques orages, chaud. 5–12 Périodes pluvieuses; frais, puis doux. 13–18 Ensoleillé, puis averses; frais. 19–30 Averses; doux à l'est, frais à l'ouest.

JUIL. 2024: Temp. 23°C (3°C au-dessus de la moy.); précip. 100mm (5mm au-dessus de la moy.). 1–10 Ensoleillé, puis orages épars; devenant très chaud. 11–20 Ensoleillé, puis orages isolés; chaud. 21–31 Quelques orages; doux, puis très chaud.

AOÛT 2024: Temp. 18,5°C (0,5°C au-dessous de la moy.); précip. 120mm (25mm au-dessus de la moy.). 1–14 Orages épars, frais. 15–25 Périodes pluvieuses, devenant chaud. 26–31 Quelques averses, chaud.

SEPT. 2024: Temp. 14°C (moy.); précip. 130mm (40mm au-dessus de la moy.). 1–6 Averses éparses, frais. 7–9 Risque de tempête tropicale. 10–15 Quelques averses, devenant frais. 16–21 Ensoleillé, doux. 22–30 Averses, doux.

OCT. 2024: Temp. 7,5°C (0,5°C au-dessous de la moy.); précip. 80mm (5mm au-dessous de la moy.). 1–13 Averses et chutes de neige, froid. 14–18 Périodes pluvieuses; chaud. 19–22 Quelques averses, frais. 23–31 Ensoleillé, puis averses; doux.

WEATHER

SOUTHERN ONTARIO

Thunder Bay

Sudbury

Toronto

SUMMARY: Winter will be colder than normal, with above-normal precipitation and snowfall. The coldest periods will be in late December, early January, and early to mid-February, with the snowiest periods in mid- to late December and early to mid-January. **April** and **May** will be cooler and wetter than normal. **Summer** will be warmer than normal, with rainfall above normal in the east and below normal in the west. The hottest periods will be in early and mid-July. **September** and **October** will be warmer than normal, with rainfall below normal in the north and near average in the south. Watch for a tropical storm in early September.

NOV. 2023: Temp. 0.5°C (3°C below avg. north; avg. south); precip. 80mm (5mm above avg.). 1–7 Sunny, then rain and snow showers; turning chilly. 8–16 Rain and snow, then flurries; cold. 17–27 Snowy periods north, rain and snow showers south; cold. 28–30 Flurries, chilly.

DEC. 2023: Temp. –5°C (1°C below avg.); precip. 70mm (10mm above avg.). 1–5 Flurries, cold. 6–11 Snow showers, mild. 12–16 Snowy north, flurries south; chilly. 17–21 Flurries, cold. 22–25 Snowstorm, cold north; rain and snow showers, mild south. 26–31 Flurries, very cold.

JAN. 2024: Temp. –9°C (2°C below avg.); precip. 70mm (10mm above avg.). 1–12 Snowy periods, very cold. 13–20 Snowy periods, some rain south; turning mild. 21–31 Sunny, then snow showers; turning cold.

FEB. 2024: Temp. –8°C (3°C below avg.); precip. 83mm (40mm above avg. north, 5mm above south). 1–12 Flurries, bitter cold. 13–17 Periods of rain and snow, turning mild. 18–29 Sunny, then periods of rain and snow; cold, then mild.

MAR. 2024: Temp. 0°C (avg.); precip. 95mm (40mm above avg.). 1–10 Periods of rain and snow, turning cold. 11–15 Rain and snow showers, mild. 16–22 Snowy periods, mixed with rain; cold. 23–31 Rain and snow showers, chilly.

APR. 2024: Temp. 6°C (1°C below avg.); precip. 115mm (50mm above avg.). 1–8 Periods of rain and snow, some heavy; cold. 9–14 Sunny, cool. 15–19 Showers, warm. 20–30 Rainy periods, chilly.

MAY 2024: Temp. 12.5°C (avg.); precip. 95mm (20mm above avg.). 1–5 Rainy periods, warm. 6–17 Showers, cool. 18–22 Sunny north, rainy periods south; cool. 23–31 A few showers, cool.

JUNE 2024: Temp. 17°C (0.5°C below avg.); precip. 75mm (30mm above avg. east, 40mm below west). 1–4 Scattered t-storms, warm. 5–11 Sunny, then a few t-storms; turning warm. 12–25 A few showers, cool. 26–30 Sunny, cool.

JULY 2024: Temp. 22.5°C (1.5°C above avg.); precip. 90mm (60mm above avg. east, 40mm below west). 1–8 Rainy periods east, a few showers west; turning very warm. 9–19 Sunny, then a few t-storms; turning very warm. 20–31 Isolated t-storms, warm.

AUG. 2024: Temp. 19.5°C (0.5°C below avg.); precip. 70mm (10mm below avg.). 1–11 Isolated t-storms, then sunny; cool. 12–23 Showers, cool. 24–31 Isolated t-storms, warm.

SEPT. 2024: Temp. 15.5°C (0.5°C above avg.); precip. 85mm (25mm below avg. north, 15mm above south). 1–6 Scattered showers, cool. 7–9 Tropical storm threat. 10–19 A few showers north, sunny south; turning cool. 20–30 Showers; warm, turning cool.

OCT. 2024: Temp. 10°C (avg.); precip. 75mm (15mm above avg. north, 15mm below south). 1–10 Isolated showers, then sunny; chilly. 11–15 Rainy north, a few showers south; turning warm. 16–22 Rain and snow showers, turning chilly. 23–31 A few showers; warm north, cool south.

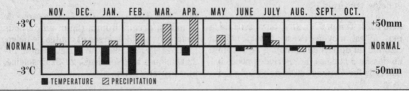

	NOV.	DEC.	JAN.	FEB.	MAR.	APR.	MAY	JUNE	JULY	AUG.	SEPT.	OCT.
+3°C / +50mm												
NORMAL												
-3°C / –50mm												

■ TEMPERATURE ▨ PRECIPITATION

WEATHER

THE PRAIRIES

SUMMARY: Winter will be colder than normal, with above-normal precipitation and snowfall. The coldest periods will be in mid-November, late December, early and late January, and early and mid-February. The snowiest periods will be in early November, early February, and late March. **April** and **May** will be cooler and wetter than normal, with a snowstorm in early April. **Summer** will be warmer and drier than normal, with the hottest periods in mid-July and mid-August. **September** and **October** will also be warmer and drier than normal.

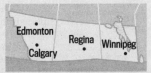

NOV. 2023: Temp. –6°C (3°C below avg.); precip. 35mm (20mm above avg.). 1–2 Sunny, warm. 3–9 Snowstorm east, flurries west; cold. 10–15 Snow showers, frigid. 16–22 A few snow showers; cold east, mild west. 23–30 Flurries, quite cold.

DEC. 2023: Temp. –11°C (2°C below avg.); precip. 25mm (20mm above avg. east, avg. west). 1–2 Sunny, bitter cold. 3–10 Flurries, then sunny; mild. 11–16 Flurries, turning mild. 17–25 Snow showers, turning very cold. 26–31 Sunny, frigid.

JAN. 2024: Temp. –17°C (4°C below avg.); precip. 25mm (5mm above avg.). 1–10 Flurries, bitter cold. 11–18 Sunny, mild. 19–31 A few snow showers, turning frigid.

FEB. 2024: Temp. –15°C (4°C below avg.); precip. 40mm (25mm above avg.). 1–11 Snowy periods, then sunny; frigid. 12–15 Flurries, cold. 16–23 Snowy periods, bitter cold. 24–29 Sunny, turning mild.

MAR. 2024: Temp. –5.5°C (4°C below avg. east, 1°C above west); precip. 30mm (20mm above avg. east, avg. west). 1–4 Snow showers, cold east; sunny, mild west. 5–15 Flurries, mild. 16–24 Sunny, then snowy periods; mild, then cold. 25–31 Snow showers, bitter cold.

APR. 2024: Temp. 2°C (3°C below avg.); precip. 65mm (50mm above avg. east, 20mm above west). 1–3 Snow showers, cold east; sunny, mild west. 4–6 Snowstorm. 7–9 Flurries, cold. 10–15 Periods of rain and snow,

cold. 16–23 Rain and snow east, sunny west; chilly. 24–30 Rain and snow showers, cold.

MAY 2024: Temp. 10°C (1°C below avg.); precip. 40mm (10mm below avg.). 1–15 Isolated showers, then rainy periods; chilly. 16–22 Sunny, mild. 23–31 Showers, cool.

JUNE 2024: Temp. 16°C (0.5°C above avg.); precip. 65mm (40mm below avg. east, 10mm above west). 1–7 A few showers, turning warm. 8–18 Isolated showers east, rainy periods west; turning cool. 19–27 Scattered t-storms, mild. 28–30 Sunny east, showers west; warm.

JULY 2024: Temp. 20°C (1.5°C above avg.); precip. 50mm (40mm below avg. east, 10mm below west). 1–9 A few showers, turning cool. 10–16 Isolated t-storms, hot. 17–22 Sunny east, a few t-storms west; warm. 23–31 A few t-storms, turning cool.

AUG. 2024: Temp. 17.5°C (0.5°C above avg.); precip. 30mm (30mm below avg.). 1–5 A few showers, cool. 6–15 Sunny east, isolated t-storms west; turning hot. 16–31 Isolated t-storms; cool, then warm.

SEPT. 2024: Temp. 14°C (3°C above avg.); precip. 35mm (10mm below avg.). 1–11 Rainy periods, then sunny; turning very warm. 12–16 Showers, cool. 17–22 Isolated showers, very warm. 23–30 Sunny, warm.

OCT. 2024: Temp. 8°C (2°C above avg.); precip. 20mm (5mm below avg.). 1–9 A few showers, quite warm. 10–24 Isolated showers; cool, then mild. 25–31 Sunny, chilly.

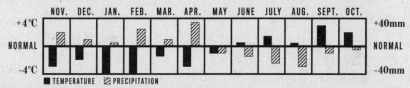

SOUTHERN BRITISH COLUMBIA

WEATHER

Prince George

Vancouver
Cranbrook

SUMMARY: Winter will be colder than normal, with the coldest periods in late December, early and late January, and early February. Precipitation will be below normal, with snowfall above normal in the north and below normal in the south. The snowiest periods will be in early December and early February. **April** and **May** will bring cooler-than-normal temperatures, with precipitation above normal in the east and below normal in the west. **Summer** will be warm, with the warmest periods in early July and late August. Rainfall will be above normal in the east and below normal in the west. **September** and **October** will be warmer than normal, with rainfall above normal in the east and below normal in the west.

NOV. 2023: Temp. 2°C (3°C below avg.); precip. 100mm (50mm below avg.). 1–8 Rainy, then sunny; chilly. 9–12 Rain and snow north, showers south; chilly. 13–20 Sunny, then rain and snow showers; cold. 21–27 Rainy periods coast, snow showers inland; chilly. 28–30 Sunny, cold.

DEC. 2023: Temp. –2°C (4°C below avg.); precip. 113mm (avg. east, 75mm below west). 1–11 Showers coast, snowy periods inland; cold. 12–20 Rain and snow showers, chilly. 21–31 Sunny coast, snow showers inland; bitter cold.

JAN. 2024: Temp. –3°C (4°C below avg.); precip. 180mm (10mm above avg. east, 50mm below west). 1–10 Sunny, frigid north; periods of rain and snow, cold south. 11–17 Showers coast, snow showers inland; mild. 18–26 Sunny coast, flurries inland; quite cold. 27–31 Periods of rain and snow, turning mild.

FEB. 2024: Temp. –1.5°C (4°C below avg. north, 1°C above south); precip. 170mm (30mm above avg.). 1–7 Snowy periods north, some heavy, frigid; rainy periods south, mild. 8–16 Rain and snow showers, cold. 17–29 Periods of rain and snow, turning mild.

MAR. 2024: Temp. 4.5°C (0.5°C above avg.); precip. 90mm (avg. east, 60mm below west). 1–4 Sunny, mild. 5–7 Sunny coast, rain and snow inland; cool. 8–12 Showers, mild. 13–21 Sunny, cool. 22–31 A few showers, chilly.

APR. 2024: Temp. 7.5°C (0.5°C below avg.); precip. 100mm (avg.). 1–12 Showers, chilly. 13–25 Sunny, turning warm. 26–30 Rainy periods, turning cool.

MAY 2024: Temp. 12°C (avg.); precip. 90mm (20mm above avg. east, 20mm below west). 1–15 Sunny east, isolated showers west; chilly. 16–22 Isolated showers coast, rainy periods inland; mild. 23–31 Sunny, then showers; turning cool.

JUNE 2024: Temp. 15°C (1°C above avg. east, 1°C below west); precip. 75mm (10mm above avg. east, 20mm below west). 1–9 Sunny, cool coast; showers, mild inland. 10–17 Scattered showers, cool. 18–23 Sunny, warm. 24–30 A few showers, cool.

JULY 2024: Temp. 18°C (1°C above avg.); precip. 35mm (15mm below avg.). 1–6 A few showers, cool. 7–13 Sunny, very warm. 14–20 Sunny coast, a few t-storms inland; warm. 21–31 A few showers north, sunny south; turning cool.

AUG. 2024: Temp. 18.5°C (1.5°C above avg.); precip. 75mm (25mm above avg.). 1–7 Sunny, warm. 8–17 Scattered showers; cool, then warm. 18–23 Sunny, very warm. 24–31 Rainy periods, turning cool.

SEPT. 2024: Temp. 16°C (2°C above avg.); precip. 65mm (25mm above avg. east, 15mm below west). 1–4 Showers, cool. 5–16 Isolated showers north, sunny south; turning warm. 17–19 Sunny, warm. 20–30 Rainy periods, then isolated showers; warm.

OCT. 2024: Temp. 10°C (1°C above avg.); precip. 100mm (avg.). 1–6 Sunny, turning warm. 7–22 Rainy periods; cool, then warm. 23–31 Sunny, then a few showers; chilly.

	NOV.	DEC.	JAN.	FEB.	MAR.	APR.	MAY	JUNE	JULY	AUG.	SEPT.	OCT.	

■ TEMPERATURE ▨ PRECIPITATION

WEATHER PHOBIAS

FEAR OF	PHOBIA
Clouds	Nephophobia
Cold	Cheimatophobia Frigophobia Psychrophobia
Dampness, moisture	Hygrophobia
Daylight, sunshine	Heliophobia Phengophobia
Extreme cold, frost, ice	Cryophobia Pagophobia
Floods	Antlophobia
Fog	Homichlophobia Nebulaphobia
Heat	Thermophobia
Hurricanes, tornadoes	Lilapsophobia
Lightning, thunder	Astraphobia Brontophobia Keraunophobia
Northern lights, southern lights	Auroraphobia
Rain	Ombrophobia Pluviophobia
Snow	Chionophobia
Thunder	Ceraunophobia Tonitrophobia
Wind	Ancraophobia Anemophobia

Local 5-day weather forecasts for postal codes in the United States and Canada, as well as long-range weather predictions and weather history, are available via Almanac.ca/2024.

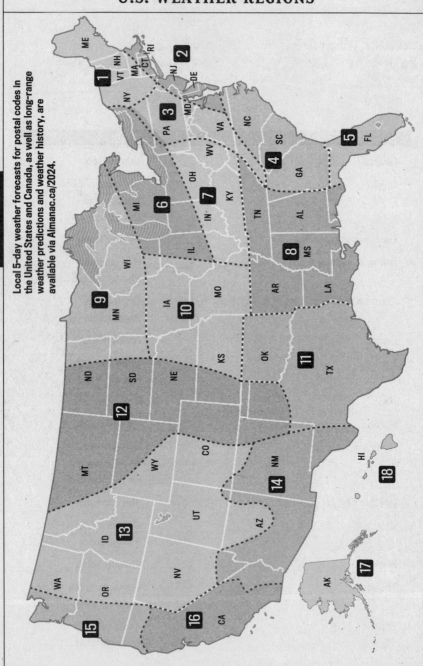

Illustration of U.S. map: Rob Schuster

U.S. REGIONAL WEATHER FORECASTS, 2023–24

1. NORTHEAST

SUMMARY: Winter temperatures will be above normal, as will be precipitation and snowfall. The coldest periods will occur in mid- to late November, early to mid-January, and early to mid-February, while the snowiest stretches will arrive in mid- to late November, mid-December, and early to mid-January. **April** and **May** will be warmer and wetter than normal. **Summer** temperatures will be above normal, with rainfall below normal. The hottest periods will be in early June and mid-July. **September** and **October** temperatures will average near normal, while rainfall will be below normal.

2. ATLANTIC CORRIDOR

SUMMARY: Winter temperatures, precipitation, and snowfall will all be above normal. The coldest spell will run from late January into mid-February, while the snowiest periods will occur in late December, late January, and mid-February. **April** and **May** will be warmer and wetter than normal. **Summer** will be hotter than average, while rainfall will be below normal in the north and above normal in the south. The hottest periods will be in early July, late July into early August, and late August. Watch for a tropical storm in late August. **September** and **October** will be slightly cooler than normal, with near-normal precipitation.

3. APPALACHIANS

SUMMARY: Winter temperatures will be below normal, with above-normal precipitation and snowfall. The coldest period will run from early January through mid-February, while the snowiest spells will occur in late December, mid- to late January, and early to mid-February. **April** and **May** temperatures will be near normal, with rainfall slightly above normal. **Summer** temperatures will average below normal, as will precipitation. The hottest periods will arrive in early July and early and late August. **September** and **October** temperatures will be below average, while precipitation will be greater than normal.

4. SOUTHEAST

SUMMARY: Winter temperatures will be above normal, as will be precipitation and snowfall. The coldest periods will arrive in late December and early and mid-February, with the best chances for snow occurring in late January and mid-February. **April** and **May** will be warmer and wetter than normal. **Summer** temperatures will be cooler than normal, with the hottest periods in late June, early July, and late July into mid-August. Rainfall will be above normal in the east and below normal in the west. Watch for a hurricane in late August. **September** and **October** will be slightly cooler than

WEATHER

WEATHER

normal, with normal precipitation.

5. FLORIDA

SUMMARY: Winter will be warmer than normal, with the coldest temperatures in late December, late January, and early February. Winter rainfall will be above normal in the north and below normal in the south. **April** and **May** will be warmer and wetter than normal. **Summer** will bring above-normal temperatures and below-normal rainfall. The hottest periods will be in late June and early July. Watch for a hurricane in late August. **September** and **October** will be slightly cooler and drier than normal.

6. LOWER LAKES

SUMMARY: Winter will be colder than normal, with the coldest periods in early and late December and from January through mid-February. Precipitation and snowfall will average above normal, with the snowiest periods occurring from late December through most of January and in mid-February. **April** and **May** temperatures will be above normal, while precipitation will be slightly below normal. **Summer** temperatures will be warmer than normal in the east and cooler than normal in the west, with the hottest periods in early and mid-July. Rainfall will be above normal. **September** and **October** will be cooler than

normal, with precipitation above normal in the east and below normal in the west.

7. OHIO VALLEY

SUMMARY: Winter will be colder than normal, with above-normal precipitation and snowfall. The coldest spells will occur in late December, early January, and late January through mid-February. The snowiest periods will be in late December through mid-January and late January through mid-February. **April** and **May** temperatures will be warmer than normal in the east and cooler than normal in the west. Precipitation will average slightly below normal. **Summer** will be cooler than normal, with rainfall below average in the east and above average in the west. The hottest periods will be late July and early August. **September** and **October** will be cooler than normal, with above-normal precipitation.

8. DEEP SOUTH

SUMMARY: Winter will be colder than normal in the north and warmer than normal in the south, with the coldest periods in late December, early January, late January, and early February. Precipitation and chances for snow will be above normal, with the best threats for snow in the north in mid- and late January and mid-

WEATHER

February. **April** and **May** will be warmer and wetter than normal. **Summer** will be hotter and drier than normal, with the hottest periods in late June, late July, and much of August. Watch for a hurricane in early July and a tropical storm in mid-July. **September** and **October** temperatures will average near normal, with rainfall above normal in the north and below normal in the south. Watch for a hurricane in early September.

9. UPPER MIDWEST

SUMMARY: Winter temperatures will be below normal, with the coldest periods in mid- to late November, most of December, early and late January, and early February. Precipitation and snowfall will be above normal. The snowiest periods will be in late November, mid- to late December, mid-January, and early February. **April** and **May** temperatures will be below normal, while precipitation will be below normal in the east and near normal in the west. **Summer** will be warmer than normal, with rainfall above normal in the east and below normal in the west. The hottest periods will be in early, mid-, and late July, interspersed with cool spells. **September** and **October** will have near-normal temperatures and below-normal precipitation.

10. HEARTLAND

SUMMARY: Winter will be colder than normal, with the coldest periods in early and late December, early and late January, and early February. Precipitation and snowfall will be slightly above normal. The snowiest periods will be in late December and early to mid-January. **April** and **May** will be warmer than normal, with near-normal precipitation. **Summer** will be hotter and drier than normal, with the hottest periods in early and late July and early and mid-August. **September** and **October** will be warmer than normal, with below-average precipitation.

11. TEXAS–OKLAHOMA

SUMMARY: Winter will be colder than normal north and warmer south. It will be coldest in early and late December, early and late January, and mid-February. Precipitation and snow will be above normal. Best snow chances (north) will occur in late December and late January. **April** and **May** will be cool north and warm south, with more rain than usual. **Summer** will be cooler than normal north, hotter south, and hottest in late June, late July, and mid-August. Rainfall will be above normal, with tropical storms possible in mid-July and late August. **September** and **October** will be warmer than

U.S. REGIONAL WEATHER FORECASTS, 2023–24

WEATHER

normal, with less rain than normal north and more south. Expect a tropical storm in mid-September.

12. HIGH PLAINS

SUMMARY: Winter will be colder than normal, with the coldest periods in late November, late December, and early to mid-January, as well as early February in the north only. Precipitation and snowfall will be slightly above normal, with the snowiest periods in late November, mid-December, and mid-January. **April** and **May** will be cooler and drier than normal in the north and warmer and wetter in the south. **Summer** will be hot, with the hottest periods in late June, mid-July, and late August. Rainfall will be below normal in the north and above normal in the south. **September** and **October** will be warmer and drier than normal.

13. INTERMOUNTAIN

SUMMARY: Winter will be colder than normal, with the coldest periods in early and late November, late December, and late January. Precipitation will be below normal in the north and above normal in the south. Snowfall will be above normal, with the snowiest periods in mid- to late November, early and late January, and mid-February. **April** and **May** will be warmer than normal, with near-normal precipitation. **Summer**

will be hotter than normal, with the hottest periods in mid- to late July and late August. Rainfall will be above normal in the north and below normal in the south. **September** and **October** will be quite warm, with below-normal rainfall.

14. DESERT SOUTHWEST

SUMMARY: Winter will be colder than normal, with the coldest periods in late November, early and late December, and late January. Precipitation will be above normal, as will be snowfall in most areas that normally receive snow, with the snowiest periods in mid- to late January and mid-February. **April** and **May** will bring temperatures near normal in the east and above normal in the west. Precipitation will be above normal. **Summer** will be hot, with rainfall below normal in the east and above normal in the west. The hottest periods will occur in early and mid-June as well as early and late July. **September** and **October** will be warmer and drier than normal.

15. PACIFIC NORTHWEST

SUMMARY: Winter temperatures will be colder than normal, with below-normal precipitation and snowfall. The coldest periods will be in mid-November, late December, and mid-January. The snowiest periods will occur in mid- to late December and

U.S. REGIONAL WEATHER FORECASTS, 2023–24

mid-January. **April** and **May** will be warmer than normal, with near-normal rainfall. **Summer** temperatures will be below normal in the north and above normal in the south, with the hottest periods in early to mid-July. Precipitation will be slightly above normal. **September** and **October** will be warmer than normal, with rainfall near normal in the north and above normal in the south.

16. PACIFIC SOUTHWEST

SUMMARY: Winter will be cooler and wetter than normal, with above-normal mountain snows. The coldest temperatures will occur in early and late November, early and late December, and late January. The stormiest periods will be in early and late January, early to mid-February, and mid-March. **April** and **May** will be warmer and drier than normal. **Summer** temperatures will be above normal, with slightly above-normal rainfall. The hottest periods will be in early June and early and late July. **September** and **October** will be warmer and wetter than normal.

17. ALASKA

SUMMARY: Winter temperatures will be milder than normal, with the coldest periods in mid-December, late January, and early to mid-February.

Precipitation will be slightly below normal, while snowfall will be slightly above normal. The snowiest periods will be in late November, mid-December, mid- to late January, and early March. **April** and **May** will be warmer than normal, with above-normal precipitation. **Summer** will be warmer than normal, with precipitation above normal in the north and below normal in the south. The hottest periods will be in early and mid-August. **September** and **October** will be milder than normal, with above-normal precipitation.

18. HAWAII

SUMMARY: Winter will be cooler than normal, with the coolest periods in mid-December through early January and early February. Rainfall will be above normal, with the stormiest periods in early November in the east and early January and mid-February throughout. **April** and **May** will be warmer than normal in the east and cooler than normal in the west. Rainfall will be below normal. **Summer** will be cooler and drier than normal, with the hottest periods in mid-July and late August. **September** and **October** will be warmer than normal, with the hottest periods in early and late September and early October. Rainfall will be below normal. ■

SECRETS OF THE ZODIAC

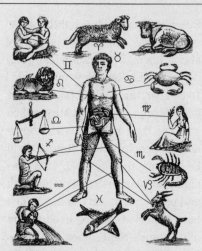

ASTROLOGY VS. ASTRONOMY

Astrology is a tool we use to plan events according to the placements of the Sun, the Moon, and the planets in the 12 signs of the zodiac. In astrology, the planetary movements do not cause events; rather, they explain the path, or "flow," that events tend to follow. *The Moon's astrological place is given on the next page.* **Astronomy** is the study of the actual placement of the known planets and constellations. The Moon's astronomical place is given in the **Left-Hand Calendar Pages, 120–146.** *(The placement of the planets in the signs of the zodiac is not the same astrologically and astronomically.)*

The dates in the **Best Days** table, **pages 226–227,** are based on the astrological passage of the Moon.

WHEN MERCURY IS RETROGRADE

Sometimes the other planets appear to be traveling backward through the zodiac; this is an illusion. We call this illusion *retrograde motion.*

Mercury's retrograde periods can cause our plans to go awry. However, intuition is high during these periods and coincidences can be extraordinary.

When Mercury is retrograde, stay flexible, allow more time for travel, and don't sign contracts. Review projects and plans but wait until Mercury is direct again to make final decisions.

Mercury will be retrograde from December 13, 2023–January 1, 2024, and during April 1–24, August 4–27, and November 25–December 15, 2024.

–Celeste Longacre

The Man of the Signs

Ancient astrologers believed that each astrological sign influenced a specific part of the body. The first sign of the zodiac—Aries—was attributed to the head, with the rest of the signs moving down the body, ending with Pisces at the feet.

♈ Aries, head	**ARI**	*Mar. 21–Apr. 20*
♉ Taurus, neck	**TAU**	*Apr. 21–May 20*
♊ Gemini, arms	**GEM**	*May 21–June 20*
♋ Cancer, breast	**CAN**	*June 21–July 22*
♌ Leo, heart	**LEO**	*July 23–Aug. 22*
♍ Virgo, belly	**VIR**	*Aug. 23–Sept. 22*
♎ Libra, reins	**LIB**	*Sept. 23–Oct. 22*
♏ Scorpio, secrets	**SCO**	*Oct. 23–Nov. 22*
♐ Sagittarius, thighs	**SAG**	*Nov. 23–Dec. 21*
♑ Capricorn, knees	**CAP**	*Dec. 22–Jan. 19*
♒ Aquarius, legs	**AQU**	*Jan. 20–Feb. 19*
♓ Pisces, feet	**PSC**	*Feb. 20–Mar. 20*

GARDENING BY THE MOON'S SIGN

USE CHART ON NEXT PAGE TO FIND THE BEST DATES FOR THE FOLLOWING GARDEN TASKS . . .

PLANT, TRANSPLANT, AND GRAFT: Cancer, Scorpio, Pisces, or Taurus

HARVEST: Aries, Leo, Sagittarius, Gemini, or Aquarius

BUILD/FIX FENCES OR GARDEN BEDS: Capricorn

CONTROL INSECT PESTS, PLOW, AND WEED: Aries, Gemini, Leo, Sagittarius, or Aquarius

PRUNE: Aries, Leo, or Sagittarius. During a waxing Moon, pruning encourages growth; during a waning Moon, it discourages it.

SETTING EGGS BY THE MOON'S SIGN

Chicks take about 21 days to hatch. Those born under a waxing Moon in Cancer, Scorpio, or Pisces are healthier and mature faster. To ensure that chicks are born during these times, "set eggs" (place eggs in an incubator or under a hen) 21 days before the desired hatching dates.

EXAMPLE:
The Moon is new on April 8 and full on April 23 (EDT). Between these dates, the Moon is in the sign of Cancer on April 14 and 15. To have chicks born on April 14, count back 21 days; set eggs on March 24.

Below are the best days to set eggs in 2024, using only the fruitful dates between the new and full Moons and counting back 21 days:

JAN.: 2, 3, 20, 21, 29, 30   **APR.:** 2, 20, 21, 30   **JULY:** 21, 22   **OCT.:** 11, 12, 20, 21
FEB.: 18, 25–27   **MAY:** 1, 17–19, 27, 28   **AUG.:** 17, 18, 26, 27   **NOV.:** 16, 17
MAR.: 24, 25   **JUNE:** 14, 15, 23–25   **SEPT.:** 13–15, 23, 24   **DEC.:** 13–15, 22, 23

The Moon's Astrological Place, 2023–24

	NOV.	DEC.	JAN.	FEB.	MAR.	APR.	MAY	JUNE	JULY	AUG.	SEPT.	OCT.	NOV.	DEC.
1	GEM	LEO	VIR	LIB	SCO	CAP	AQU	ARI	TAU	CAN	LEO	VIR	SCO	SAG
2	CAN	LEO	VIR	SCO	SAG	CAP	AQU	ARI	GEM	CAN	VIR	LIB	SCO	SAG
3	CAN	LEO	LIB	SCO	SAG	AQU	PSC	TAU	GEM	LEO	VIR	LIB	SAG	CAP
4	LEO	VIR	LIB	SAG	SAG	AQU	PSC	TAU	GEM	LEO	LIB	SCO	SAG	CAP
5	LEO	VIR	SCO	SAG	CAP	PSC	ARI	GEM	CAN	LEO	LIB	SCO	CAP	AQU
6	LEO	LIB	SCO	CAP	CAP	PSC	ARI	GEM	CAN	VIR	LIB	SCO	CAP	AQU
7	VIR	LIB	SCO	CAP	AQU	ARI	TAU	CAN	LEO	VIR	SCO	SAG	CAP	PSC
8	VIR	LIB	SAG	AQU	AQU	ARI	TAU	CAN	LEO	LIB	SCO	SAG	AQU	PSC
9	LIB	SCO	SAG	AQU	PSC	TAU	GEM	CAN	VIR	LIB	SAG	CAP	AQU	ARI
10	LIB	SCO	CAP	PSC	PSC	TAU	GEM	LEO	VIR	LIB	SAG	CAP	PSC	ARI
11	LIB	SAG	CAP	PSC	ARI	GEM	CAN	LEO	VIR	SCO	SAG	AQU	PSC	TAU
12	SCO	SAG	AQU	ARI	ARI	GEM	CAN	VIR	LIB	SCO	CAP	AQU	ARI	TAU
13	SCO	CAP	AQU	ARI	TAU	GEM	LEO	VIR	LIB	SAG	CAP	AQU	ARI	TAU
14	SAG	CAP	PSC	TAU	TAU	CAN	LEO	VIR	SCO	SAG	AQU	PSC	TAU	GEM
15	SAG	CAP	PSC	TAU	GEM	CAN	LEO	LIB	SCO	SAG	AQU	PSC	TAU	GEM
16	CAP	AQU	ARI	TAU	GEM	LEO	VIR	LIB	SCO	CAP	PSC	ARI	GEM	CAN
17	CAP	AQU	ARI	GEM	CAN	LEO	VIR	SCO	SAG	CAP	PSC	ARI	GEM	CAN
18	AQU	PSC	TAU	GEM	CAN	VIR	LIB	SCO	SAG	AQU	ARI	TAU	CAN	LEO
19	AQU	PSC	TAU	CAN	CAN	VIR	LIB	SAG	CAP	AQU	ARI	TAU	CAN	LEO
20	PSC	ARI	GEM	CAN	LEO	VIR	LIB	SAG	CAP	PSC	TAU	GEM	LEO	VIR
21	PSC	ARI	GEM	LEO	LEO	LIB	SCO	SAG	AQU	PSC	TAU	GEM	LEO	VIR
22	PSC	TAU	GEM	LEO	VIR	LIB	SCO	CAP	AQU	ARI	GEM	CAN	LEO	VIR
23	ARI	TAU	CAN	LEO	VIR	SCO	SAG	CAP	PSC	ARI	GEM	CAN	VIR	LIB
24	ARI	GEM	CAN	VIR	VIR	SCO	SAG	AQU	PSC	TAU	CAN	LEO	VIR	LIB
25	TAU	GEM	LEO	VIR	LIB	SCO	CAP	AQU	ARI	TAU	CAN	LEO	LIB	SCO
26	TAU	CAN	LEO	LIB	LIB	SAG	CAP	PSC	ARI	GEM	CAN	VIR	LIB	SCO
27	GEM	CAN	LEO	LIB	SCO	SAG	CAP	PSC	ARI	GEM	LEO	VIR	LIB	SCO
28	GEM	CAN	VIR	LIB	SCO	CAP	AQU	ARI	TAU	CAN	LEO	VIR	SCO	SAG
29	CAN	LEO	VIR	SCO	SCO	CAP	AQU	ARI	TAU	CAN	VIR	LIB	SCO	SAG
30	CAN	LEO	LIB	—	SAG	AQU	PSC	TAU	GEM	LEO	VIR	LIB	SAG	CAP
31	—	VIR	LIB	—	SAG	—	PSC	—	GEM	LEO	—	SCO	—	CAP

BEST DAYS FOR 2024

This chart is based on the Moon's sign and shows the best days
each month for certain activities. –*Celeste Longacre*

	JAN.	FEB.	MAR.	APR.	MAY	JUNE	JULY	AUG.	SEPT.	OCT.	NOV.	DEC.
Quit smoking	2, 7	4, 29	6, 29	7, 28	5, 24	1, 28	25, 30	22, 26	22, 30	19, 29	16, 25	22, 27
Bake	23, 24	19, 20	17–19	14, 15	11, 12	7–9	5, 6	1, 2, 28, 29	24–26	22, 23	18, 19	16, 17
Brew	5–7	2, 3, 29	1, 27–29	23–25	21, 22	17, 18	14–16	11, 12	7, 8	4–6, 31	1, 2, 28, 29	25–27
Dry fruit, vegetables, or meat	8, 9, 26, 27	4, 5	2–4, 30, 31	26, 27	5, 6	1, 2, 28, 29	25–27	3, 22, 23	1, 27, 28	24, 25	20–22	18, 19
Make jams or jellies	14, 15	10, 11	9, 10	5, 6	3, 4, 30, 31	26, 27	23, 24	20, 21	16, 17	14, 15	10, 11	7, 8
Can, pickle, or make sauerkraut	5–7	2, 3, 29	1, 27–29	5, 6, 24, 25	3, 4, 30, 31	26, 27	23, 24	1, 2, 28, 29	24–26	22, 23	28, 29	25–27
Begin diet to lose weight	2, 7	4, 29	6, 29	7, 28	5, 24	1, 28	25, 30	22, 26	22, 30	19, 29	16, 25	22, 27
Begin diet to gain weight	15, 20	12, 16	15, 24	11, 21	13, 18	15, 19	12, 17	8, 13	4, 9	7, 16	3, 12	9, 12
Cut hair to encourage growth	18, 19	14–16	13, 14	9, 10	18–20	14–16	12, 13	8–10	4, 5	13–15	10, 11, 14	11–13
Cut hair to discourage growth	3, 4, 30, 31	1, 26–28	26	5, 6	3, 4	3, 4, 30	28, 29	24, 25	20, 21	29, 30	25–27	23, 24
Perm hair	12, 13	8, 9	7, 8	3, 4, 30	1, 2, 28, 29	24, 25	21, 22	18, 19	14, 15	11–13	8, 9	5, 6
Color hair	18, 19	14–16	13, 14	9, 10	7, 8	3, 4, 30	1, 28, 29	24, 25	20, 21	18, 19	14, 15	11–13
Straighten hair	8, 9	4, 5	2–4, 30, 31	26, 27	23, 24	19–21	17, 18	13–15	9–11	7, 8	3, 4, 30	1, 2, 28, 29
Have dental care	1, 2, 28, 29	24, 25	22–24	18–20	16, 17	12–14	9–11	6, 7	2, 3, 29, 30	1, 26–28	23, 24	20–22
Start projects	12	10	11	9	8	7	6	5	3	3	2	2, 31
End projects	24	23	24	22	22	20	20	18	16	16	14	14
Demolish	5–7	2, 3, 29	1, 27–29	23–25	21, 22	17, 18	14–16	11, 12	7, 8	4–6, 31	1, 2, 28, 29	25–27
Lay shingles	25–27	21–23	20, 21	16, 17	13–15	10, 11	7, 8	3–5, 30, 31	1, 27, 28	24, 25	20–22	18, 19
Paint	3, 4, 30, 31	14–16	13, 14	9, 10	7, 8	15, 16	12, 13	8–10	4–6	2, 3, 29, 30	25–27	23, 24
Wash windows	16, 17	12, 13	11, 12	7, 8	5, 6	1, 2, 28, 29	25–27	22, 23	18, 19	16, 17	12, 13	9, 10
Wash floors	14, 15	10, 11	9, 10	5, 6	3, 4, 30, 31	26, 27	23, 24	20, 21	16, 17	14, 15	10, 11	7, 8
Go camping	8, 9	4, 5	2–4, 30, 31	26, 27	23, 24	19–21	17, 18	13–15	9–11	7, 8	3, 4, 30	1, 2, 28, 29

See what to do when via Almanac.ca/2024.

	JAN.	FEB.	MAR.	APR.	MAY	JUNE	JULY	AUG.	SEPT.	OCT.	NOV.	DEC.
Entertain	25–27	21–23	20, 21	16, 17	13–15	10, 11	7, 8	3–5, 30, 31	1, 27, 28	24, 25	20–22	18, 19
Travel for pleasure	25–27	21–23	20, 21	16, 17	13–15	10, 11	7, 8	3–5, 30, 31	1, 27, 28	24, 25	20–22	18, 19
Get married	3, 4, 30, 31	1, 26–28	25, 26	21, 22	18–20	15, 16	12, 13	8–10	4–6	2, 3, 29, 30	25–27	23, 24
Ask for a loan	5–7	2, 3, 29	1, 27, 28	5, 6	5, 6	3, 4, 30	1, 28, 29	24, 25	20, 21	18, 19, 31	28, 29	25–27
Buy a home	18, 19	14–16	13, 14	23	8, 21, 22	17, 18	14–16	11, 12	7, 8	4–6	1, 2	11–13
Move (house/household)	20–22	17, 18	15, 16	11–13	9, 10	5, 6	2–4, 30, 31	26, 27	22, 23	20, 21	16, 17	14, 15
Advertise to sell	18, 19	14–16	13, 14	9, 10	7, 8, 21, 22	17, 18	14–16	11, 12	7, 8	4–6	1, 2	11–13
Mow to promote growth	14, 15	10, 11	17–19	14, 15	11, 12	17, 18	14–16	11, 12	7, 8	4–6	1, 2	7, 8
Mow to slow growth	5–7	2, 3, 29	1, 27–29	24, 25	3, 4, 30, 31	26, 27	23, 24	28, 29	24, 25	22, 23	28, 29	25–27
Plant aboveground crops	14, 15, 23, 24	10, 11	13, 14	14, 15	11, 12	17, 18	14–16	11, 12	7, 8	4–6	1, 2, 10, 11	7, 8
Plant belowground crops	5–7	2, 3, 29	1, 27–29	5, 6	3, 4, 30, 31	26, 27	23, 24	1, 2, 28, 29	24–26	1, 26–28	18, 19, 28, 29	25–27
Destroy pests and weeds	16, 17	12, 13	11, 12	7, 8	5, 6	1, 2, 28, 29	25–27	22, 23	18, 19	16, 17	12, 13	9, 10
Graft or pollinate	23, 24	19, 20	17–19	14, 15	11, 12	7–9	5, 6	1, 2, 28, 29	24–26	22, 23	18, 19	16, 17
Prune to encourage growth	16, 17	12, 13	11, 12	16, 17	13–15	10, 11	7, 8	13–15	9–11	7, 8	3, 4	9, 10
Prune to discourage growth	26, 27	4, 5	2–4, 30, 31	26, 27	5, 6	1, 2, 28, 29	25–27	3, 30, 31	1, 27, 28	24, 25	20–22	28, 29
Pick fruit	1, 2, 28, 29	24, 25	22–24	18–20	16, 17	12–14	9–11	6, 7	2, 3, 29, 30	1, 26–28	23, 24	20–22
Harvest aboveground crops	18, 19	14–16	22–24	9, 10	16, 17	12–14	9–11	6, 7	12, 13	9, 10	5–7	11–13
Harvest belowground crops	1, 2, 28, 29	6, 7, 25	5, 6	1, 2, 28, 29	25–27	3, 4, 30	1, 28, 29	24, 25	29, 30	26–28	23, 24	21, 22
Cut hay	16, 17	12, 13	11, 12	7, 8	5, 6	1, 2, 28, 29	25–27	22, 23	18, 19	16, 17	12, 13	9, 10
Begin logging, set posts, pour concrete	10, 11	6, 7	5, 6	1, 2, 28, 29	25–27	22, 23	19, 20	16, 17	12, 13	9, 10	5–7	3, 4, 30, 31
Purchase animals	23, 24	19, 20	17–19	14, 15	11, 12	7–9	5, 6	1, 2, 28, 29	24–26	22, 23	18, 19	16, 17
Breed animals	5–7	2, 3, 29	1, 27–29	23–25	21, 22	17, 18	14–16	11, 12	7, 8	4–6, 31	1, 2, 28, 29	25–27
Wean	2, 7	4, 29	6, 29	7, 28	5, 24	1, 28	25, 30	22, 26	22, 30	19, 29	16, 25	22, 27
Castrate animals	12, 13	8, 9	7, 8	3, 4, 30	1, 2, 28, 29	24, 25	21, 22	18, 19	14, 15	11–13	8, 9	5, 6
Slaughter livestock	5–7	2, 3, 29	1, 27–29	23–25	21, 22	17, 18	14–16	11, 12	7, 8	4–6, 31	1, 2, 28, 29	25–27

BEST FISHING DAYS AND TIMES

The best times to fish are when the fish are naturally most active. The Sun, Moon, tides, and weather all influence fish activity. For example, fish tend to feed more at sunrise and sunset, and also during a full Moon (when tides are higher than average). However, most of us go fishing simply when we can get the time off. But there are best times, according to fishing lore:

■ One hour before and one hour after high tides, and one hour before and one hour after low tides. The times of high tides for Halifax are given on **pages 120–146;** also see **pages 238–239.** (Inland, the times for high tides correspond with the times when the Moon is due south. Low tides are halfway between high tides.)

GET TIDE TIMES AND HEIGHTS NEAREST TO YOUR LOCATION VIA ALMANAC.CA/2024.

■ During the "morning rise" (after sunup for a spell) and the "evening rise" (just before sundown and the hour or so after).

■ During the rise and set of the Moon.

■ Just before the arrival of a storm, although the falling barometric pressure will eventually slow down their feeding. Angling can also be good when the pressure is either steady or on the rise 1 to 2 days after a storm. High pressure accompanying clear weather can bring on sluggishness and reduced activity.

■ When there is a hatch of flies—caddis flies or mayflies, commonly.

■ When the breeze is from a westerly quarter, rather than from the north or east.

■ When the water is still or slightly rippled, rather than during a wind.

THE BEST FISHING DAYS FOR 2024, WHEN THE MOON IS BETWEEN NEW AND FULL

January 11–25
February 9–24
March 10–25
April 8–23
May 7–23
June 6–21
July 5–21
August 4–19
September 2–17
October 2–17
November 1–15
December 1–15, 30, 31

Dates based on Eastern Time.

HOW TO ESTIMATE THE WEIGHT OF A FISH

Measure the fish from the tip of its nose to the tip of its tail. Then measure its girth at the thickest portion of its midsection.

The weight of a fat-bodied fish (bass, salmon) = (length x girth x girth)/800

SALMON

The weight of a slender fish (trout, northern pike) = (length x girth x girth)/900

EXAMPLE: If a trout is 20 inches long and has a 12-inch girth, its estimated weight is (20 x 12 x 12)/900 = 2,880/900 = 3.2 pounds

TROUT

CATFISH

GESTATION AND MATING TABLES

	PROPER AGE OR WEIGHT FOR FIRST MATING	PERIOD OF FERTILITY (YRS.)	NUMBER OF FEMALES FOR ONE MALE	PERIOD OF GESTATION (DAYS) AVERAGE	RANGE
CATTLE: Cow	15–18 mos.[1]	10–14		283	279–290[2] 262–300[3]
Bull	1 yr., well matured	10–12	50[4] / thousands[5]		
GOAT: Doe	10 mos. or 85–90 lbs.	6		150	145–155
Buck	well matured	5	30		
HORSE: Mare	3 yrs.	10–12		336	310–370
Stallion	3 yrs.	12–15	40–45[4] / record 252[5]		
PIG: Sow	5–6 mos. or 250 lbs.	6		115	110–120
Boar	250–300 lbs.	6	50[6] / 35–40[7]		
RABBIT: Doe	6 mos.	5–6		31	30–32
Buck	6 mos.	5–6	30		
SHEEP: Ewe	1 yr. or 90 lbs.	6		147 / 151[8]	142–154
Ram	12–14 mos., well matured	7	50–75[6] / 35–40[7]		
CAT: Queen	12 mos.	6		63	60–68
Tom	12 mos.	6	6–8		
DOG: Bitch	16–18 mos.	8		63	58–67
Male	12–16 mos.	8	8–10		

[1]Holstein and beef: 750 lbs.; Jersey: 500 lbs. [2]Beef; 8–10 days shorter for Angus. [3]Dairy. [4]Natural. [5]Artificial. [6]Hand-mated. [7]Pasture. [8]For fine wool breeds.

INCUBATION PERIOD OF POULTRY (DAYS)

Chicken	21
Duck	26–32
Goose	30–34
Guinea	26–28
Turkey	28

AVERAGE LIFE SPAN OF ANIMALS IN CAPTIVITY (YEARS)

Cat (domestic)	14	Goose (domestic)	20
Chicken (domestic)	8	Horse	22
Dog (domestic)	13	Pig	12
Duck (domestic)	10	Rabbit	6
Goat (domestic)	14	Turkey (domestic)	10

	ESTRAL/ESTROUS CYCLE (INCLUDING HEAT PERIOD) AVERAGE	RANGE	LENGTH OF ESTRUS (HEAT) AVERAGE	RANGE	USUAL TIME OF OVULATION	WHEN CYCLE RECURS IF NOT BRED
Cow	21 days	18–24 days	18 hours	10–24 hours	10–12 hours after end of estrus	21 days
Doe goat	21 days	18–24 days	2–3 days	1–4 days	Near end of estrus	21 days
Mare	21 days	10–37 days	5–6 days	2–11 days	24–48 hours before end of estrus	21 days
Sow	21 days	18–24 days	2–3 days	1–5 days	30–36 hours after start of estrus	21 days
Ewe	16½ days	14–19 days	30 hours	24–32 hours	12–24 hours before end of estrus	16½ days
Queen cat		15–21 days	3–4 days, if mated	9–10 days, in absence of male	24–56 hours after coitus	Pseudo-pregnancy
Bitch	24 days	16–30 days	7 days	5–9 days	1–3 days after first acceptance	Pseudo-pregnancy

PLANTING BY THE MOON'S PHASE

ACCORDING TO THIS AGE-OLD PRACTICE, CYCLES OF THE MOON AFFECT PLANT GROWTH.

Plant annual flowers and vegetables that bear crops above ground during the light, or waxing, of the Moon: from the day the Moon is new to the day it is full.

Plant flowering bulbs, biennial and perennial flowers, and vegetables that bear crops below ground during the dark, or waning, of the Moon: from the day after it is full to the day before it is new again.

The Planting Dates columns give the safe periods for planting in areas that receive frost. (See **page 232** for frost dates in your area.) The Moon Favorable columns give the best planting days within the Planting Dates based on the Moon's phases for 2024. (See **pages 120–146** for the exact days of the new and full Moons.)

The dates listed in this table are meant as general guidelines only. For seed-sowing dates based on frost dates in your local area, go to **Almanac.ca/2024.**

Aboveground crops are marked *.
(E) means early; (L) means late.

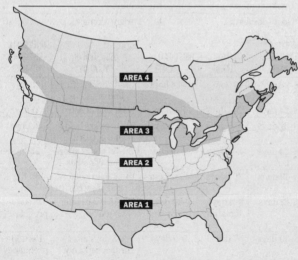

* Barley	
* Beans	(E)
	(L)
Beets	(E)
	(L)
* Broccoli plants	(E)
	(L)
* Brussels sprouts	
* Cabbage plants	
Carrots	(E)
	(L)
* Cauliflower plants	(E)
	(L)
* Celery plants	(E)
	(L)
* Collards	(E)
	(L)
* Corn, sweet	(E)
	(L)
* Cucumbers	
* Eggplant plants	
* Endive	(E)
	(L)
* Kale	(E)
	(L)
Leek plants	
* Lettuce	
* Muskmelons	
* Okra	
Onion sets	
* Parsley	
Parsnips	
* Peas	(E)
	(L)
* Pepper plants	
Potatoes	
* Pumpkins	
Radishes	(E)
	(L)
* Spinach	(E)
	(L)
* Squashes	
Sweet potatoes	
* Swiss chard	
* Tomato plants	
Turnips	(E)
	(L)
* Watermelons	
* Wheat, spring	
* Wheat, winter	

AREA 1		AREA 2		AREA 3		AREA 4	
PLANTING DATES	MOON FAVORABLE	PLANTING DATES	MOON FAVORABLE	PLANTING DATES	MOON FAVORABLE	PLANTING DATES	MOON FAVORABLE
2/15-3/7	2/15-24	3/15-4/7	3/15-25	5/15-6/21	5/15-23, 6/6-21	6/1-30	6/6-21
3/15-4/7	3/15-25	4/15-30	4/15-23	5/7-6/21	5/7-23, 6/6-21	5/30-6/15	6/6-15
8/7-31	8/7-19	7/1-21	7/5-21	6/15-7/15	6/15-21, 7/5-15	–	–
2/7-29	2/7-8, 2/25-29	3/15-4/3	3/26-4/3	4/25-5/15	4/25-5/6	5/25-6/10	5/25-6/5
9/1-30	9/1, 9/18-30	8/15-31	8/20-31	7/15-8/15	7/22-8/3	6/15-7/8	6/22-7/4
2/15-3/15	2/15-24, 3/10-15	3/7-31	3/10-25	5/15-31	5/15-23	6/1-25	6/6-21
9/7-30	9/7-17	8/1-20	8/4-19	6/15-7/7	6/15-21, 7/5-7	–	–
2/11-3/20	2/11-24, 3/10-20	3/7-4/15	3/10-25, 4/8-15	5/15-31	5/15-23	6/1-25	6/6-21
2/11-3/20	2/11-24, 3/10-20	3/7-4/15	3/10-25, 4/8-15	5/15-31	5/15-23	6/1-25	6/6-21
2/15-3/7	2/25-3/7	3/7-31	3/7-9, 3/26-31	5/15-31	5/24-31	5/25-6/10	5/25-6/5
8/1-9/7	8/1-3, 8/20-9/1	7/7-31	7/22-31	6/15-7/21	6/22-7/4	6/15-7/8	6/22-7/4
2/15-3/7	2/15-24	3/15-4/7	3/15-25	5/15-31	5/15-23	6/1-25	6/6-21
8/7-31	8/7-19	7/1-21	7/5-21, 8/4-7	6/15-7/21	6/15-21, 7/5-21	–	–
2/15-29	2/15-24	3/7-31	3/10-25	5/15-6/30	5/15-23, 6/6-21	6/1-30	6/6-21
9/15-30	9/15-17	8/15-9/7	8/15-19, 9/2-7	7/15-8/15	7/15-21, 8/4-15	–	–
2/11-3/20	2/11-24, 3/10-20	3/7-4/7	3/10-25	5/15-31	5/15-23	6/1-25	6/6-21
9/7-30	9/7-17	8/15-31	8/15-19	7/1-8/7	7/5-21, 8/4-7	–	–
3/15-31	3/15-25	4/1-17	4/8-17	5/10-6/15	5/10-23, 6/6-15	5/30-6/20	6/6-20
8/7-31	8/7-19	7/7-21	7/7-21	6/15-30	6/15-21	–	–
3/7-4/15	3/10-25, 4/8-15	4/7-5/15	4/8-23, 5/7-15	5/7-6/20	5/7-23, 6/6-20	5/30-6/15	6/6-15
3/7-4/15	3/10-25, 4/8-15	4/7-5/15	4/8-23, 5/7-15	6/1-30	6/6-21	6/15-30	6/15-21
2/15-3/20	2/15-24, 3/10-20	4/7-5/15	4/8-23, 5/7-15	5/15-31	5/15-23	6/1-25	6/6-21
8/15-9/7	8/15-19, 9/2-7	7/15-8/15	7/15-21, 8/4-15	6/7-30	6/7-21	–	–
2/11-3/20	2/11-24, 3/10-20	3/7-4/7	3/10-25	5/15-31	5/15-23	6/1-15	6/6-15
9/7-30	9/7-17	8/15-31	8/15-19	7/1-8/7	7/5-21, 8/4-7	6/25-7/15	7/5-15
2/15-4/15	2/25-3/9, 3/26-4/7	3/7-4/7	3/7-9, 3/26-4/7	5/15-31	5/24-31	6/1-25	6/1-5, 6/22-25
2/15-3/7	2/15-24	3/1-31	3/10-25	5/15-6/30	5/15-23, 6/6-21	6/1-30	6/6-21
3/15-4/7	3/15-25	4/15-5/7	4/15-23, 5/7	5/15-6/30	5/15-23, 6/6-21	6/1-30	6/6-21
4/15-6/1	4/15-23, 5/7-23	5/25-6/15	6/6-15	6/15-7/10	6/15-21, 7/5-10	6/15-7/7	6/15-21, 7/5-7
2/1-29	2/1-8, 2/25-29	3/1-31	3/1-9, 3/26-31	5/15-6/7	5/24-6/5	6/1-25	6/1-5, 6/22-25
2/20-3/15	2/20-24, 3/10-15	3/1-31	3/10-25	5/15-31	5/15-23	6/1-15	6/6-15
1/15-2/4	1/26-2/4	3/7-31	3/7-9, 3/26-31	4/1-30	4/1-7, 4/24-30	5/10-31	5/24-31
1/15-2/7	1/15-25	3/7-31	3/10-25	4/15-5/7	4/15-23, 5/7	5/15-31	5/15-23
9/15-30	9/15-17	8/7-31	8/7-19	7/15-31	7/15-21	7/10-25	7/10-21
3/1-20	3/10-20	4/1-30	4/8-23	5/15-6/30	5/15-23, 6/6-21	6/1-30	6/6-21
2/10-29	2/25-29	4/1-30	4/1-7, 4/24-30	5/1-31	5/1-6, 5/24-31	6/1-25	6/1-5, 6/22-25
3/7-20	3/10-20	4/23-5/15	4/23, 5/7-15	5/15-31	5/15-23	6/1-30	6/6-21
1/21-3/1	1/26-2/8, 2/25-3/1	3/7-31	3/7-9, 3/26-31	4/15-30	4/24-30	5/15-6/5	5/24-6/5
10/1-21	10/1, 10/18-21	9/7-30	9/18-30	8/15-31	8/20-31	7/10-31	7/22-31
2/7-3/15	2/9-24, 3/10-15	3/15-4/20	3/15-25, 4/8-20	5/15-31	5/15-23	6/1-25	6/6-21
10/1-21	10/2-17	8/1-9/15	8/4-19, 9/2-15	7/17-9/7	7/17-21, 8/4-19, 9/2-7	7/20-8/5	7/20-21, 8/4-5
3/15-4/15	3/15-25, 4/8-15	4/15-30	4/15-23	5/15-6/15	5/15-23, 6/6-15	6/1-30	6/6-21
3/23-4/7	3/26-4/7	4/21-5/9	4/24-5/6	5/15-6/15	5/24-6/5	5/15-31	5/15-23
2/7-3/15	2/9-24, 3/10-15	3/15-4/15	3/15-25, 4/8-15	5/1-31	5/7-23	5/15-31	5/15-23
3/7-21	3/10-21	4/7-30	4/8-23	5/15-31	5/15-23	6/1-15	6/6-15
1/20-2/15	1/26-2/8	3/15-31	3/26-31	4/7-30	4/7, 4/24-30	5/10-31	5/24-31
9/1-10/15	9/1, 9/18-10/1	8/1-20	8/1-3, 8/20	7/1-8/15	7/1-4, 7/22-8/3	–	–
3/15-4/7	3/15-25	4/15-5/7	4/15-23, 5/7	5/15-6/30	5/15-23, 6/6-21	6/1-30	6/6-21
2/15-29	2/15-24	3/1-20	3/10-20	4/7-30	4/8-23	5/15-6/10	5/15-23, 6/6-10
10/15-12/7	10/15-17, 11/1-15, 12/1-7	9/15-10/20	9/15-17, 10/2-17	8/11-9/15	8/11-19, 9/2-15	8/5-30	8/5-19

FROSTS AND GROWING SEASONS

Dates given are normal averages for a light freeze; local weather and topography may cause considerable variations. The possibility of frost occurring after the spring dates and before the fall dates is 33 percent. The classification of freeze temperatures is usually based on their effect on plants. **Light freeze:** –2° to 0°C (29° to 32°F)—tender plants killed. **Moderate freeze:** –4° to –2°C (25° to 28°F)—widely destructive to most plants. **Severe freeze:** –4°C (24°F and colder)—heavy damage to most plants. –dates courtesy Environment Canada

PROV.	CITY	GROWING SEASON (DAYS)	LAST SPRING FROST	FIRST FALL FROST	PROV.	CITY	GROWING SEASON (DAYS)	LAST SPRING FROST	FIRST FALL FROST
AB	Athabasca	103	May 28	Sept. 9	NT	Fort Simpson	81	May 31	Aug. 21
AB	Calgary	99	May 29	Sept. 6	NT	Norman Wells	91	May 29	Aug. 29
AB	Edmonton	123	May 15	Sept. 16	NT	Yellowknife	102	May 31	Sept. 11
AB	Grande Prairie	106	May 22	Sept. 6	ON	Barrie	147	May 12	Oct. 7
AB	Lethbridge	113	May 22	Sept. 13	ON	Brantford	151	May 5	Oct. 4
AB	Medicine Hat	118	May 18	Sept. 14	ON	Hamilton	160	May 3	Oct. 11
AB	Peace River	96	May 28	Sept. 2	ON	Kapuskasing	75	June 18	Sept. 2
AB	Red Deer	108	May 24	Sept. 10	ON	Kingston	161	Apr. 28	Oct. 7
BC	Abbotsford	168	Apr. 30	Oct. 16	ON	London	142	May 13	Oct. 3
BC	Castlegar	141	May 8	Sept. 27	ON	Ottawa	135	May 13	Sept. 26
BC	Chilliwack	191	Apr. 19	Oct. 28	ON	Owen Sound	147	May 14	Oct. 9
BC	Coombs	139	May 13	Sept. 30	ON	Peterborough	137	May 12	Sept. 27
BC	Dawson Creek	76	June 8	Aug. 24	ON	Sudbury	124	May 21	Sept. 23
BC	Kamloops	152	May 3	Oct. 3	ON	Timmins	86	June 13	Sept. 8
BC	Kelowna	150	May 8	Oct. 6	ON	Toronto	161	May 4	Oct. 13
BC	Nanaimo	163	May 4	Oct. 15	ON	Wawa	97	June 6	Sept. 12
BC	Prince George	120	May 20	Sept. 18	ON	Windsor	172	Apr. 28	Oct. 18
BC	Prince Rupert	145	May 14	Oct. 7	PE	Alberton	122	May 31	Oct. 1
BC	Vancouver	180	Apr. 21	Oct. 19	PE	Charlottetown	142	May 22	Oct. 12
BC	Victoria	208	Apr. 14	Nov. 9	PE	Summerside	154	May 13	Oct. 15
MB	Brandon	92	June 6	Sept. 7	QC	Baie-Comeau	103	June 2	Sept. 14
MB	Lynn Lake	87	June 10	Sept. 6	QC	La Tuque	101	June 5	Sept. 15
MB	The Pas	106	May 31	Sept. 15	QC	Magog	129	May 19	Sept. 26
MB	Thompson	58	June 18	Aug. 16	QC	Montréal	152	May 6	Oct. 6
MB	Winnipeg	116	May 21	Sept. 15	QC	Québec	129	May 17	Sept. 24
NB	Bathurst	101	June 4	Sept. 14	QC	Rimouski	140	May 18	Oct. 6
NB	Fredericton	125	May 22	Sept. 25	QC	Roberval	117	May 25	Sept. 20
NB	Miramichi	115	May 27	Sept. 20	QC	Thetford Mines	128	May 20	Sept. 26
NB	Moncton	103	June 3	Sept. 15	QC	Trois-Rivières	128	May 19	Sept. 25
NB	Saint John	165	Apr. 30	Oct. 13	SK	Moose Jaw	110	May 24	Sept. 12
NL	Corner Brook	129	May 27	Oct. 4	SK	North Battleford	108	May 26	Sept. 12
NL	Gander	120	June 7	Oct. 6	SK	Prince Albert	88	June 7	Sept. 4
NL	Grand Falls	105	June 8	Sept. 22	SK	Regina	91	June 1	Sept. 1
NL	St. John's	124	June 6	Oct. 9	SK	Saskatoon	126	May 15	Sept. 19
NS	Halifax	164	May 8	Oct. 20	SK	Weyburn	107	May 26	Sept. 11
NS	Kentville	122	May 26	Sept. 26	SK	Yorkton	106	May 26	Sept. 10
NS	Sydney	135	May 27	Oct. 10	YT	Dawson	62	June 9	Aug. 11
NS	Truro	103	June 7	Sept. 19	YT	Watson Lake	83	June 6	Aug. 29
NS	Yarmouth	162	May 4	Oct. 14	YT	Whitehorse	72	June 12	Aug. 24

GROW UP!

Do you, too, have a weakness for vigorous climbing annuals? Every year, I seek out varieties known for their rampant growth—'Kentucky Wonder' pole beans, 'Scarlet Runner' beans, 'Tall Telephone' ('Alderman') peas. I've even grown to love lima beans, so that I can justify a row of 'Christmas' limas. And I can't resist the ornamental hyacinth bean, which I once saw

PEA STAKES

■ This is an old-time method for supporting climbing peas, beans, and flowers. Best of all, it's free. Cut branches about 4 feet long from trees or shrubs on your property. (Estimate the height of your plants and add an extra 8 to 12 inches to compensate for the part of the branch that goes into the ground.) Leave the twigs on to give your plants lots of places to grab hold. With a hatchet, sharpen the thick ends of the branches and drive them into the ground. Or, if you can, just push them in next to your plants.

TWINE TRELLIS

■ Set two posts 8 feet apart with a crossbar running along the top. Tie a taut string between the two posts at ground level, then weave a grid of untreated biodegradable twine between the two posts and between the crossbar and the ground-level string. Let your plants ramble at will on this web. When the season is over, cut down the plants and twine and toss them into the compost pile.

INVERTED-V FRAME

■ Use 12 slender bamboo poles or branches at least 6 feet long and a 13th pole that is 12 feet long. Push the 12 poles into the ground in pairs, with about 3 feet between their bottom ends and at a slant so that the tops meet, as shown. Leave about 2 feet between the pairs. Lash the top of each inverted "V" to the 13th pole, placed horizontally. Plant two or three seeds around each pole. This makes a wonderful tunnel for small children to crawl through.

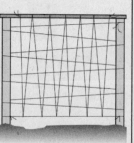

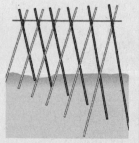

Illustrations: Margo Letourneau

on an arbor at Monticello, or blue morning glories and moonflowers. Vertical garden plants need a good place to climb. I prefer to get the support into place and then plant my peas or flowers. For beans, however, I often wait until the first two leaves have opened and then position the stakes. Here are a few ideas for supports that you can put together yourself. —*Jessica Barlow*

TEPEE

■ To secure plants growing in a circle, push eight to ten bamboo poles (each about 5 to 6 feet long) into the ground following the circle of plants. Slant the poles in toward the center of the circle and tie them together at the top to form a tepee. Run a circle of twine or wire around the bottom of the poles, attach strings to the twine or wire between the poles, and run the strings to the top of the tepee for additional climbing space.

CHICKEN-WIRE FENCE

■ Buy 48- or 60-inch-wide chicken wire with a 2-inch mesh, and support it by nailing or fastening it to posts driven into the ground about 6 feet apart. Try the metal fence posts sold at lumberyards and also at hardware stores. The wedge-shape plate attached to the bottom of the post makes it easy to pound into cold ground, and the posts have little "fingers" that hold the chicken wire in place. When your harvest is over, peel off the vines and roll up the wire for another year.

WALL SUPPORT

■ If you want plants to cover a shed or garage wall, attach two 1x4s (approximately 6 feet long) horizontally to the wall about 8 to 10 feet apart. Screw hooks at 10-inch intervals along the two boards and run string vertically between the hooks. Plant a seed near each string.

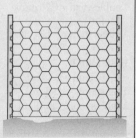

TABLE OF MEASURES

LINEAR
1 hand = 4 inches
1 link = 7.92 inches
1 span = 9 inches
1 foot = 12 inches
1 yard = 3 feet
1 rod = 5½ yards
1 mile = 320 rods = 1,760
  yards = 5,280 feet
1 international nautical
  mile = 6,076.1155 feet
1 knot = 1 nautical mile
  per hour
1 fathom = 2 yards = 6 feet
1 furlong = ⅛ mile =
  660 feet = 220 yards
1 league = 3 miles =
  24 furlongs
1 chain = 100 links =
  22 yards

SQUARE
1 square foot =
  144 square inches
1 square yard =
  9 square feet
1 square rod =
  30¼ square yards =
  272¼ square feet =
  625 square links

1 square chain =
  16 square rods
1 acre = 10 square chains
  = 160 square rods =
  43,560 square feet
1 square mile =
  640 acres = 102,400
  square rods

CUBIC
1 cubic foot = 1,728 cubic
  inches
1 cubic yard = 27 cubic
  feet
1 cord = 128 cubic feet
1 U.S. liquid gallon =
  4 quarts = 231 cubic
  inches
1 imperial gallon =
  1.20 U.S. gallons =
  0.16 cubic foot
1 board foot = 144 cubic
  inches

DRY
2 pints = 1 quart
4 quarts = 1 gallon
2 gallons = 1 peck
4 pecks = 1 bushel

LIQUID
4 gills = 1 pint
63 gallons = 1 hogshead
2 hogsheads =
  1 pipe or butt
2 pipes = 1 tun

KITCHEN
3 teaspoons = 1 tablespoon
16 tablespoons = 1 cup
1 cup = 8 ounces
2 cups = 1 pint
2 pints = 1 quart
4 quarts = 1 gallon

AVOIRDUPOIS
(for general use)
1 ounce = 16 drams
1 pound = 16 ounces
1 short hundredweight =
  100 pounds
1 ton = 2,000 pounds
1 long ton = 2,240 pounds

APOTHECARIES'
(for pharmaceutical use)
1 scruple = 20 grains
1 dram = 3 scruples
1 ounce = 8 drams
1 pound = 12 ounces

METRIC CONVERSIONS

LINEAR
1 inch = 2.54 centimeters
1 centimeter = 0.39 inch
1 meter = 39.37 inches
1 yard = 0.914 meter
1 mile = 1.61 kilometers
1 kilometer = 0.62 mile

SQUARE
1 square inch =
  6.45 square centimeters
1 square yard =
  0.84 square meter
square mile =
  ___ kilometers

1 square kilometer =
  0.386 square mile
1 acre = 0.40 hectare
1 hectare = 2.47 acres

CUBIC
1 cubic yard = 0.76 cubic
  meter
1 cubic meter = 1.31 cubic
  yards

HOUSEHOLD
½ teaspoon = 2.46 mL
1 teaspoon = 4.93 mL
1 tablespoon = 14.79 mL
¼ cup = 59.15 mL

⅓ cup = 78.86 mL
½ cup = 118.29 mL
¾ cup = 177.44 mL
1 cup = 236.59 mL
1 liter = 1.057 U.S. liquid
  quarts
1 U.S. liquid quart =
  0.946 liter
1 U.S. liquid gallon =
  3.78 liters
1 gram = 0.035 ounce
1 ounce = 28.349 grams
1 kilogram = 2.2 pounds
1 pound = 0.45 kilogram

TO CONVE...

FAHRENHEIT: $°C = (°F - 32)/1.8$; $°F = (°C × 1.8) + 32$

...hing at Almanac.ca.

TIDAL GLOSSARY

APOGEAN TIDE: A monthly tide of decreased range that occurs when the Moon is at apogee (farthest from Earth).

CURRENT: Generally, a horizontal movement of water. Currents may be classified as tidal and nontidal. Tidal currents are caused by gravitational interactions between the Sun, Moon, and Earth and are part of the same general movement of the sea that is manifested in the vertical rise and fall, called tide. Nontidal currents include the permanent currents in the general circulatory systems of the sea as well as temporary currents arising from more pronounced meteorological variability.

DIURNAL TIDE: A tide with one high water and one low water in a tidal day of approximately 24 hours.

MEAN LOWER LOW WATER: The arithmetic mean of the lesser of a daily pair of low waters, observed over a specific 19-year cycle called the National Tidal Datum Epoch.

NEAP TIDE: A tide of decreased range that occurs twice a month, when the Moon is in quadrature (during its first and last quarters, when the Sun and the Moon are at right angles to each other relative to Earth).

PERIGEAN TIDE: A monthly tide of increased range that occurs when the Moon is at perigee (closest to Earth).

RED TIDE: Toxic algal blooms caused by several genera of dinoflagellates that usually turn the sea red or brown. These pose a serious threat to marine life and may be harmful to humans.

RIP CURRENT: A potentially dangerous, narrow, intense, surf-zone current flowing outward from shore.

SEMIDIURNAL TIDE: A tide with one high water and one low water every half-day. East Coast tides, for example, are semidiurnal, with two highs and two lows during a tidal day of approximately 24 hours.

SLACK WATER (SLACK): The state of a tidal current when its speed is near zero, especially the moment when a reversing current changes direction and its speed is zero.

SPRING TIDE: A tide of increased range that occurs at times of syzygy each month. Named not for the season of spring but from the German *springen* ("to leap up"), a spring tide also brings a lower low water.

STORM SURGE: The local change in the elevation of the ocean along a shore due to a storm, measured by subtracting the astronomic tidal elevation from the total elevation. It typically has a duration of a few hours and is potentially catastrophic, especially on low-lying coasts with gently sloping offshore topography.

SYZYGY: The nearly straight-line configuration that occurs twice a month, when the Sun and the Moon are in conjunction (on the same side of Earth, at the new Moon) and when they are in opposition (on opposite sides of Earth, at the full Moon). In both cases, the gravitational effects of the Sun and the Moon reinforce each other, and tidal range is increased.

TIDAL BORE: A tide-induced wave that propagates up a relatively shallow and sloping estuary or river with a steep wave front.

TSUNAMI: Sometimes mistakenly called a "tidal wave," a tsunami is a series of long-period waves caused by an underwater earthquake or volcanic eruption. In open ocean, the waves are small and travel at high speed; as they near shore, some may build to more than 30 feet high, becoming a threat to life and property.

VANISHING TIDE: A mixed tide of considerable inequality in the two highs and two lows, so that the lower high (or higher low) may appear to vanish. ∎

HIGH TIDE TIMES AND HEIGHTS

This table lists the biweekly times and heights of high tide at Churchill, Manitoba, and Vancouver, British Columbia. (A dash indicates that high tide occurs on or after midnight and is recorded on the next day.) Tide times for other days can be interpolated; low tides occur about 6 hours before and after high tides. In addition, the **Calendar Pages, 120–147,** list times and some heights of high tides at Halifax, Nova Scotia. This table is *not* meant to be used for navigation. To get predicted tide times and heights for other selected locations, go to **Almanac.ca/2024.**

Standard time shown, except for Daylight Saving Time between 2:00 A.M., Mar. 10, and 2:00 A.M., Nov. 3.

	CHURCHILL					VANCOUVER			
DATE	CST/CDT	HEIGHT (FT.)	CST/CDT	HEIGHT (FT.)	DATE	PST/PDT	HEIGHT (FT.)	PST/PDT	HEIGHT (FT.)
TUES., JAN. 2	11:51	13.1	**11:57**	12.5	TUES., JAN. 2	10:14	15.5	**9:40**	10.2
SAT., JAN. 6	2:35	11.4	**3:00**	12.0	SAT., JAN. 6	3:20	12.0	**12:02**	14.5
TUES., JAN. 9	5:50	12.3	**6:00**	12.7	TUES., JAN. 9	5:36	15.2	**2:11**	14.8
SAT., JAN. 13	9:08	14.4	**9:14**	14.6	SAT., JAN. 13	8:03	16.3	**5:59**	14.3
TUES., JAN. 16	11:26	14.8	**11:40**	14.2	TUES., JAN. 16	9:44	16.5	**9:33**	11.7
SAT., JAN. 20	2:27	12.5	**2:52**	12.7	SAT., JAN. 20	2:52	13.3	**11:56**	14.7
TUES., JAN. 23	6:07	12.3	**6:17**	12.5	TUES., JAN. 23	5:30	15.6	**2:35**	13.7
SAT., JAN. 27	9:08	13.5	**9:09**	13.4	SAT., JAN. 27	7:42	15.6	**5:51**	13.1
TUES., JAN. 30	10:41	13.5	**10:46**	13.1	TUES., JAN. 30	8:49	15.3	**8:24**	11.6
SAT., FEB. 3	12:37	12.0	**12:57**	12.3	SAT., FEB. 3	12:47	11.6	**10:18**	14.3
TUES., FEB. 6	3:47	11.2	**4:08**	11.5	TUES., FEB. 6	4:31	14.6	**12:46**	14.1
SAT., FEB. 10	8:01	13.9	**8:10**	14.2	SAT., FEB. 10	6:48	15.9	**5:15**	14.6
TUES., FEB. 13	10:16	15.1	**10:32**	14.8	TUES., FEB. 13	8:18	16.2	**8:28**	13.0
SAT., FEB. 17	12:51	13.0	**1:11**	12.9	SAT., FEB. 17	1:03	13.2	**10:19**	14.2
TUES., FEB. 20	4:28	11.2	**4:51**	11.2	TUES., FEB. 20	4:23	15.0	**1:38**	12.6
SAT., FEB. 24	8:14	12.9	**8:18**	12.9	SAT., FEB. 24	6:29	15.0	**5:18**	13.1
TUES., FEB. 27	9:39	13.5	**9:47**	13.3	TUES., FEB. 27	7:29	14.7	**7:37**	12.7
SAT., MAR. 2	11:31	12.8	**11:55**	12.3	SAT., MAR. 2	8:44	13.9		
TUES., MAR. 5	1:43	11.3	**2:03**	11.2	TUES., MAR. 5	2:53	14.0	**11:05**	13.0
SAT., MAR. 9	6:48	13.1	**7:02**	13.5	SAT., MAR. 9	5:28	15.4	**4:27**	14.1
TUES., MAR. 12	10:07	15.1	**10:25**	15.0	TUES., MAR. 12	7:54	15.8	**8:34**	14.0
SAT., MAR. 16	12:36	13.8	**12:49**	13.6	SAT., MAR. 16	12:10	13.9	**9:48**	13.6
TUES., MAR. 19	3:24	11.1	**3:50**	10.8	TUES., MAR. 19	3:53	14.4	**1:23**	11.4
SAT., MAR. 23	8:08	12.4	**8:18**	12.3	SAT., MAR. 23	6:09	14.4	**5:43**	12.6
TUES., MAR. 26	9:37	13.4	**9:50**	13.3	TUES., MAR. 26	7:08	14.1	**7:56**	13.4
SAT., MAR. 30	11:29	13.3	**11:54**	13.0	SAT., MAR. 30	8:19	13.5	**11:26**	13.8
TUES., APR. 2	1:17	12.1	**1:29**	11.9	TUES., APR. 2	1:48	14.1	**10:04**	12.3
SAT., APR. 6	6:24	12.5	**6:46**	12.7	SAT., APR. 6	5:02	15.0	**4:35**	13.0
TUES., APR. 9	8:55	14.8	**9:18**	14.8	TUES., APR. 9	6:29	15.4	**7:45**	14.5
SAT., APR. 13	11:40	14.2	—	—	SAT., APR. 13	8:24	13.4	**11:50**	14.8
TUES., APR. 16	1:51	12.1	**2:05**	11.5	TUES., APR. 16	2:00	14.4	**11:21**	10.6
SAT., APR. 20	6:39	11.8	**7:00**	11.7	SAT., APR. 20	4:40	14.0	**5:04**	11.8
TUES., APR. 23	8:31	13.1	**8:51**	13.0	TUES., APR. 23	5:44	13.7	**7:19**	13.6
SAT., APR. 27	10:35	13.6	**11:05**	13.5	SAT., APR. 27	7:02	13.5	**10:23**	14.8
TUES., APR. 30	12:22	12.9	**12:28**	12.7	TUES., APR. 30	12:13	14.8	**8:53**	12.1
SAT., MAY 4	4:50	12.4	**5:19**	12.3	SAT., MAY 4	3:30	14.9	**3:39**	11.8
TUES., MAY 7	7:42	14.3	**8:10**	14.2	TUES., MAY 7	5:01	15.1	**7:00**	14.6
SAT., MAY 11	10:37	14.4	**11:14**	14.2	SAT., MAY 11	7:09	13.5	**10:34**	15.4
TUES., MAY 14	12:45	13.1	**12:53**	12.5	TUES., MAY 14	12:15	14.9	**9:31**	10.7
SAT., MAY 18	4:43	11.7	**5:16**	11.3	SAT., MAY 18	2:56	14.0	**4:11**	11.0
TUES., MAY 21	7:17	12.7	**7:46**	12.6	TUES., MAY 21	4:12	13.6	**6:41**	13.5
SAT., MAY 25	9:44	13.7	**10:18**	13.7	SAT., MAY 25	5:53	13.8	**9:31**	15.2
TUES., MAY 28	11:44	13.4	—	—	TUES., MAY 28	8:08	12.5	**11:47**	15.3
SAT., JUNE 1	3:20	13.0	**3:48**	12.5	SAT., JUNE 1	1:53	15.1	**2:31**	11.0
TUES., JUNE 4	6:23	13.8	**7:00**	13.6	TUES., JUNE 4	3:31	14.8	**6:14**	14.4
SAT., JUNE 8	9:40	14.3	**10:21**	14.3	SAT., JUNE 8	6:02	13.8	**9:29**	15.6

Bold = P.M.   Light = A.M.

DATE	CST/CDT	HEIGHT (FT.)	CST/CDT	HEIGHT (FT.)	DATE	PST/PDT	HEIGHT (FT.)	PST/PDT	HEIGHT (FT.)
TUES., JUNE 11	11:56	13.4	—	—	TUES., JUNE 11	8:22	11.5	11:28	15.1
SAT., JUNE 15	2:53	12.4	3:18	11.6	SAT., JUNE 15	1:03	14.3	2:45	10.2
TUES., JUNE 18	5:40	12.3	6:20	12.0	TUES., JUNE 18	2:28	13.6	5:55	13.2
SAT., JUNE 22	8:48	13.5	9:26	13.7	SAT., JUNE 22	4:48	14.2	8:36	15.2
TUES., JUNE 25	10:58	14.1	11:37	14.3	TUES., JUNE 25	7:24	13.3	10:31	15.5
SAT., JUNE 29	2:03	14.0	2:25	13.4	SAT., JUNE 29	12:17	15.4	1:03	10.9
TUES., JULY 2	4:56	13.5	5:39	13.1	TUES., JULY 2	1:59	14.6	5:24	14.2
SAT., JULY 6	8:48	13.9	9:30	14.2	SAT., JULY 6	5:04	13.8	8:26	15.4
TUES., JULY 9	11:01	14.0	11:34	14.2	TUES., JULY 9	7:29	12.4	10:06	15.1
SAT., JULY 13	1:25	13.4	1:40	12.6	SAT., JULY 13	12:02	10.2	11:46	14.2
TUES., JULY 16	3:42	12.3	4:22	11.7	TUES., JULY 16	12:38	13.7	4:59	12.6
SAT., JULY 20	7:40	12.9	8:24	13.4	SAT., JULY 20	3:43	14.2	7:33	14.9
TUES., JULY 23	10:02	14.5	10:39	14.9	TUES., JULY 23	6:39	14.0	9:14	15.4
SAT., JULY 27	12:53	15.1	1:12	14.4	SAT., JULY 27	11:32	11.5	11:17	15.3
TUES., JULY 30	3:22	13.6	4:05	12.9	TUES., JULY 30	12:28	14.3	4:23	13.8
SAT., AUG. 3	7:55	13.4	8:39	13.8	SAT., AUG. 3	4:16	13.4	7:23	15.0
TUES., AUG. 6	10:08	14.1	10:37	14.4	TUES., AUG. 6	6:46	12.9	8:48	14.9
SAT., AUG. 10	12:13	14.1	12:26	13.5	SAT., AUG. 10	10:20	11.2	10:11	14.1
TUES., AUG. 13	1:55	12.8	2:26	12.1	TUES., AUG. 13	3:24	12.2	11:30	13.3
SAT., AUG. 17	6:15	12.1	7:07	12.7	SAT., AUG. 17	2:33	13.5	6:21	14.6
TUES., AUG. 20	8:59	14.5	9:35	15.0	TUES., AUG. 20	5:52	14.2	7:54	15.2
SAT., AUG. 24	12:04	15.3	—	—	SAT., AUG. 24	10:17	12.7	9:48	15.1
TUES., AUG. 27	1:56	14.1	2:33	13.3	TUES., AUG. 27	2:52	13.6	11:45	13.2
SAT., AUG. 31	6:49	12.7	7:36	13.3	SAT., AUG. 31	3:31	12.6	6:13	14.7
TUES., SEPT. 3	9:15	14.0	9:39	14.4	TUES., SEPT. 3	6:09	12.9	7:29	14.5
SAT., SEPT. 7	11:22	14.1	11:36	14.3	SAT., SEPT. 7	9:18	12.5	8:43	13.7
TUES., SEPT. 10	12:34	13.4	1:01	12.9	TUES., SEPT. 10	12:37	12.6	9:44	13.0
SAT., SEPT. 14	4:23	11.6	5:25	12.0	SAT., SEPT. 14	1:12	12.5	4:57	14.4
TUES., SEPT. 17	7:51	14.0	8:25	14.8	TUES., SEPT. 17	5:03	13.7	6:30	15.0
SAT., SEPT. 21	10:57	15.9	11:15	16.1	SAT., SEPT. 21	9:16	14.1	8:21	15.0
TUES., SEPT. 24	12:40	14.8	1:15	14.2	TUES., SEPT. 24	12:59	14.1	10:09	12.7
SAT., SEPT. 28	5:14	12.1	6:08	12.7	SAT., SEPT. 28	2:38	11.5	4:51	14.5
TUES., OCT. 1	8:13	13.7	8:34	14.2	TUES., OCT. 1	5:34	12.7	6:07	14.2
SAT., OCT. 5	10:22	14.3	10:31	14.5	SAT., OCT. 5	8:32	13.7	7:16	13.5
TUES., OCT. 8	11:57	13.7	11:58	13.5	TUES., OCT. 8	11:08	13.9	8:13	12.8
SAT., OCT. 12	2:29	11.9	3:31	12.0	SAT., OCT. 12	3:18	14.5	—	—
TUES., OCT. 15	6:31	13.3	7:05	14.2	TUES., OCT. 15	4:13	12.8	5:03	15.0
SAT., OCT. 19	9:48	15.9	10:03	16.1	SAT., OCT. 19	8:24	15.2	6:54	15.1
TUES., OCT. 22	12:06	14.9	—	—	TUES., OCT. 22	11:26	15.3	8:39	12.7
SAT., OCT. 26	3:21	12.1	4:11	12.5	SAT., OCT. 26	1:16	10.5	3:12	14.6
TUES., OCT. 29	6:54	12.8	7:16	13.5	TUES., OCT. 29	4:59	12.2	4:39	14.1
SAT., NOV. 2	9:23	14.1	9:29	14.3	SAT., NOV. 2	7:55	14.5	5:51	13.7
TUES., NOV. 5	10:02	14.1	10:01	13.9	TUES., NOV. 5	9:07	15.1	6:01	13.2
SAT., NOV. 9	12:07	12.6	1:00	12.7	SAT., NOV. 9	12:32	15.1	10:42	10.7
TUES., NOV. 12	3:56	12.6	4:33	13.5	TUES., NOV. 12	2:18	11.7	2:30	15.2
SAT., NOV. 16	7:40	15.2	7:53	15.5	SAT., NOV. 16	6:37	15.8	4:30	15.3
TUES., NOV. 19	10:02	15.2	10:09	14.9	TUES., NOV. 19	9:12	16.2	6:26	13.2
SAT., NOV. 23	12:43	12.7	1:25	12.9	SAT., NOV. 23	12:20	15.2	—	—
TUES., NOV. 26	4:06	11.9	4:32	12.6	TUES., NOV. 26	3:11	11.4	1:57	14.3
SAT., NOV. 30	7:22	13.4	7:26	13.7	SAT., NOV. 30	6:19	14.9	3:29	14.0
TUES., DEC. 3	9:10	14.0	9:10	14.0	TUES., DEC. 3	8:15	15.8	5:04	13.9
SAT., DEC. 7	11:54	13.5	—	—	SAT., DEC. 7	10:59	15.9	9:12	11.0
TUES., DEC. 10	2:11	12.6	2:50	13.3	TUES., DEC. 10	1:03	11.0	12:49	15.6
SAT., DEC. 14	6:30	14.1	6:42	14.5	SAT., DEC. 14	5:49	15.9	3:11	15.3
TUES., DEC. 17	9:03	14.8	9:08	14.7	TUES., DEC. 17	8:07	16.5	5:28	13.9
SAT., DEC. 21	12:01	13.6	—	—	SAT., DEC. 21	10:35	15.8	9:35	10.3
TUES., DEC. 24	1:55	11.8	2:24	12.3	TUES., DEC. 24	1:45	10.6	12:02	14.7
SAT., DEC. 28	6:02	12.2	6:09	12.5	SAT., DEC. 28	5:37	14.7	2:05	14.1
TUES., DEC. 31	8:13	13.5	8:13	13.6	TUES., DEC. 31	7:21	15.8	4:18	14.4

TIME CORRECTIONS

Astronomical data for Ottawa (45°25' N, 75°42' W) are given on **pages 104, 106, 108–109,** and **120–146.** Use the Key Letters shown on those pages with this table to find the number of minutes that you must add to or subtract from Ottawa time to get the approximate time for your locale. Time zone codes represent standard time. Newfoundland is –1½, Atlantic is –1, Eastern is 0, Central is 1, Mountain is 2, Pacific is 3. For more information on the use of Key Letters, see **How to Use This Almanac, page 116.**

GET EXACT TIMES EASILY: Download astronomical times calculated for your postal code and presented as Left-Hand Calendar Pages via **Almanac.ca/2024.**

PROVINCE	CITY	NORTH LATITUDE °	'	WEST LONGITUDE °	'	TIME ZONE CODE	KEY LETTERS (MINUTES) A	B	C	D	E
AB	Athabasca	54	43	113	17	2	–18	+9	+28	+51	+71
AB	Banff	51	10	115	34	2	+12	+27	+38	+51	+62
AB	Calgary	51	5	114	5	2	+6	+21	+32	+45	+56
AB	Edmonton	53	33	113	28	2	–10	+13	+29	+48	+65
AB	Fort McMurray	56	45	111	27	2	–41	–3	+21	+49	+75
AB	Fort Vermilion	58	24	116	0	2	–38	+9	+38	+73	+105
AB	Grande-Prairie	55	10	118	48	2	0	+30	+50	+74	+95
AB	Lethbridge	49	42	112	50	2	+8	+19	+27	+37	+45
AB	Medicine Hat	50	3	110	40	2	–1	+10	+19	+29	+38
AB	Peace River	56	14	117	17	2	–14	+21	+44	+71	+96
AB	Red Deer	52	16	113	48	2	–1	+17	+31	+46	+60
BC	Dawson Creek	55	46	120	14	2	+1	+34	+56	+81	+105
BC	Fort Nelson	58	49	122	39	3	–75	–26	+5	+41	+75
BC	Kamloops	50	40	120	20	3	–26	–12	–2	+9	+19
BC	Nelson	49	30	117	17	3	–32	–21	–14	–5	+2
BC	Port Alice	50	23	127	27	3	+3	+16	+26	+37	+46
BC	Prince George	53	55	122	45	3	–35	–10	+6	+26	+44
BC	Prince Rupert	54	19	130	19	3	–8	+18	+36	+58	+77
BC	Telegraph Creek	57	55	131	10	3	–32	+11	+39	+72	+102
BC	Trail	49	6	117	42	3	–28	–19	–12	–4	+2
BC	Vancouver	49	16	123	7	3	–7	+1	+9	+17	+24
BC	Victoria	48	25	123	21	3	–2	+4	+10	+16	+22
MB	Brandon	49	50	99	57	1	+16	+28	+36	+46	+54
MB	Churchill	58	46	94	10	1	–68	–19	+11	+47	+80
MB	Flin Flon	54	46	101	53	1	–4	+23	+43	+65	+85
MB	Gillam	56	21	94	43	1	–45	–9	+14	+41	+66
MB	Gimli	50	38	96	59	1	0	+14	+24	+35	+45
MB	Gypsumville	51	47	98	38	1	0	+18	+30	+45	+57
MB	Norway House	53	59	97	50	1	–15	+9	+27	+47	+65
MB	Portage-la-Prairie	49	59	98	18	1	+9	+21	+29	+39	+48
MB	The Pas	53	50	101	15	1	–1	+23	+40	+60	+78
MB	Winnipeg	49	53	97	9	1	+5	+16	+25	+34	+43
NB	Bathurst	47	36	65	39	–1	+10	+15	+19	+24	+28
NB	Chatham	47	2	65	28	–1	+11	+16	+19	+22	+25
NB	Fredericton	45	58	66	39	–1	+21	+22	+23	+25	+26
NB	Moncton	46	6	64	47	–1	+13	+15	+16	+17	+19
NB	Saint John	45	16	66	3	–1	+21	+21	+21	+21	+21
NL	Corner Brook	48	57	57	57	–1½	+3	+12	+18	+26	+32
NL	Gander	48	57	54	37	–1½	–10	–1	+5	+13	+19
NL	Goose Bay	53	20	60	25	–1	–11	+12	+27	+46	+62
NL	Grand Falls	48	56	55	40	–1½	–6	+3	+9	+17	+23

PROVINCE/STATE	CITY	NORTH LATITUDE °	'	WEST LONGITUDE °	'	TIME ZONE CODE	A	B	C	D	E
NL	St. John's	47	34	52	43	−1½	−11	−5	−1	+2	+6
NL	Stephenville	48	33	58	35	−1½	+7	+15	+21	+28	+33
NS	Halifax	44	39	63	36	−1	+14	+12	+11	+10	+9
NS	Sydney	46	9	60	11	−1	−5	−3	−1	0	0
NS	Yarmouth	43	50	66	7	−1	+27	+24	+21	+19	+16
ON	Fort Severn	56	0	87	38	0	−10	+23	+46	+72	+96
ON	Hamilton	43	15	79	51	0	+24	+20	+16	+13	+9
ON	Kapuskasing	49	25	82	26	0	+8	+19	+26	+35	+42
ON	Kingston	44	15	76	30	0	+7	+5	+3	+1	0
ON	London	42	59	81	14	0	+31	+26	+22	+18	+14
ON	Pembroke	45	49	77	7	0	+3	+4	+5	+6	+7
ON	Peterborough	44	18	78	19	0	+14	+12	+10	+8	+7
ON	Port Arthur	48	30	89	17	0	+40	+48	+53	+60	+66
ON	Sault Sainte Marie	46	31	84	20	0	+29	+32	+34	+36	+38
ON	Sioux Lookout	50	6	91	55	1	−16	−4	+4	+14	+23
ON	Sudbury	46	30	81	0	0	+16	+19	+21	+23	+25
ON	Thunder Bay	48	23	89	15	0	+40	+48	+53	+60	+65
ON	Timmins	48	28	81	20	0	+8	+16	+22	+28	+34
ON	Toronto	43	39	79	23	0	+21	+17	+15	+11	+9
ON	Waterloo	43	28	80	31	0	+26	+22	+19	+16	+13
ON	Windsor	42	18	83	1	0	+40	+34	+29	+24	+19
PE	Charlottetown	46	14	63	8	−1	+6	+8	+9	+11	+13
QC	Chicoutimi	48	26	71	4	0	−32	−24	−18	−12	−6
QC	Fort George	53	50	79	0	0	−30	−4	+12	+31	+49
QC	Gaspé	48	50	64	29	0	−60	−51	−45	−37	−31
QC	Montréal	45	31	73	34	0	−9	−8	−8	−8	−7
QC	Québec	46	49	71	11	0	−24	−20	−18	−15	−12
QC	Schefferville	54	48	66	50	0	−85	−56	−36	−14	+5
QC	Sept-Îles	50	12	66	23	0	−59	−46	−37	−27	−18
QC	Sherbrooke	45	25	71	54	0	−15	−15	−15	−14	−14
QC	Trois-Rivières	46	21	72	33	0	−16	−14	−12	−10	−8
QC	Val-d'Or	48	7	77	47	0	−3	+3	+8	+13	+18
SK	Estevan	49	7	103	5	1	+32	+42	+49	+57	+63
SK	Moose Jaw	50	37	105	32	1	+34	+48	+58	+70	+79
SK	North Battleford	52	47	108	17	2	−26	−5	+9	+26	+41
SK	Prince Albert	53	12	105	46	1	+21	+43	+59	+77	+93
SK	Regina	50	25	104	39	1	+32	+45	+55	+66	+75
SK	Saskatoon	52	7	106	38	1	+31	+49	+62	+77	+91
SK	Swift Current	50	17	107	50	1	+45	+58	+67	+78	+87
SK	Uranium City	59	34	108	36	2	−79	−24	+9	+47	+84
SK	Yorkton	51	13	102	28	1	+19	+35	+46	+59	+70

SELECTED U.S. CITIES

AL	Decatur	34	36	86	59	1	+20	+1	−13	−31	−45
AL	Mobile	30	42	88	3	1	+35	+10	−9	−32	−50
AR	Little Rock	34	45	92	17	1	+41	+22	+7	−10	−23
CA	Palm Springs	33	49	116	32	3	+21	0	−16	−35	−50
CA	Redding	40	35	122	24	3	+24	+14	+7	−1	−7
CO	Grand Junction	39	4	108	33	2	+33	+21	+11	+1	−7
CT	New Haven	41	18	72	56	0	+4	−4	−10	−17	−23
DE	Wilmington	39	45	75	33	0	+19	+8	0	−9	−17
GA	Macon	32	50	83	38	0	+72	+49	+32	+12	−2
IA	Dubuque	42	30	90	41	1	+10	+4	0	−4	−9
ID	Boise	43	37	116	12	2	+48	+44	+42	+38	+36
ID	Pocatello	42	52	112	27	2	+36	+31	+27	+22	+19
IL	Chicago–Oak Park	41	52	87	38	1	0	−6	−11	−18	−23

(continued)

STATE	CITY	NORTH LATITUDE °	NORTH LATITUDE '	WEST LONGITUDE °	WEST LONGITUDE '	TIME ZONE CODE	KEY LETTERS (MINUTES) A	B	C	D	E
IL	Springfield	39	48	89	39	1	+15	+4	−3	−13	−21
IN	Fort Wayne	41	4	85	9	0	+53	+44	+38	+30	+24
IN	South Bend	41	41	86	15	0	+55	+48	+42	+36	+30
IN	Terre Haute	39	28	87	24	0	+67	+56	+47	+37	+28
KS	Oakley	39	8	100	51	1	+62	+50	+41	+30	+21
KS	Topeka	39	3	95	40	1	+42	+29	+20	+9	0
LA	Lake Charles	30	14	93	13	1	+57	+31	+11	−12	−30
LA	Shreveport	32	31	93	45	1	+53	+30	+13	−7	−23
MA	Boston	42	22	71	3	0	−6	−13	−17	−23	−27
MD	Hagerstown	39	39	77	43	0	+28	+17	+8	−1	−9
MD	Salisbury	38	22	75	36	0	+24	+10	0	−11	−21
MI	Cheboygan	45	39	84	29	0	+33	+34	+35	+35	+36
MI	Ironwood	46	27	90	9	1	−6	−4	−2	0	+1
MI	Jackson	42	15	84	24	0	+46	+40	+35	+29	+24
MN	Bemidji	47	28	94	53	1	+7	+12	+16	+20	+24
MO	St. Joseph	39	46	94	50	1	+36	+25	+17	+7	0
MO	Springfield	37	13	93	18	1	+38	+22	+11	−2	−13
MS	Biloxi	30	24	88	53	1	+39	+13	−5	−29	−47
MS	Tupelo	34	16	88	34	1	+28	+7	−7	−25	−39
MT	Glasgow	48	12	106	38	2	−8	−1	+3	+9	+14
MT	Miles City	46	25	105	51	2	−3	−1	0	+2	+4
NC	Raleigh	35	47	78	38	0	+44	+26	+12	−3	−15
NC	Wilmington	34	14	77	55	0	+45	+25	+9	−8	−22
ND	Minot	48	14	101	18	1	+29	+36	+42	+48	+53
ND	Williston	48	9	103	37	1	+39	+46	+51	+57	+62
NE	Lincoln	40	49	96	41	1	+40	+31	+24	+16	+9
NE	North Platte	41	8	100	46	1	+55	+47	+40	+33	+27
NJ	Trenton	40	13	74	46	0	+14	+4	−3	−12	−19
NM	Las Cruces	32	19	106	47	2	+46	+23	+5	−15	−31
NV	Elko	40	50	115	46	3	−3	−12	−19	−27	−33
NY	Binghamton	42	6	75	55	0	+13	+6	+1	−4	−9
NY	Ogdensburg	44	42	75	30	0	+1	0	0	−1	−2
OH	Columbus	39	57	83	1	0	+48	+38	+29	+20	+12
OH	Toledo	41	39	83	33	0	+45	+37	+31	+25	+19
OK	Tulsa	36	9	95	60	1	+52	+35	+22	+6	−5
OR	Pendleton	45	40	118	47	3	−8	−8	−7	−7	−6
OR	Salem	44	57	123	1	3	+10	+9	+9	+8	+8
PA	Reading	40	20	75	56	0	+19	+9	+1	−7	−14
PA	Scranton-Wilkes-Barre	41	25	75	40	0	+14	+6	0	−6	−12
SC	Columbia	34	0	81	2	0	+58	+38	+22	+4	−10
SC	Spartanburg	34	56	81	57	0	+59	+40	+26	+8	−4
SD	Sioux Falls	43	33	96	44	1	+31	+27	+24	+21	+18
TN	Knoxville	35	58	83	55	0	+64	+47	+33	+18	+5
TX	Amarillo	35	12	101	50	1	+78	+59	+45	+28	+15
TX	El Paso	31	45	106	29	2	+46	+22	+4	−17	−33
TX	San Antonio	29	25	98	30	1	+80	+53	+32	+8	−11
UT	Moab	38	35	109	33	2	+39	+26	+16	+4	−4
UT	Ogden	41	13	111	58	2	+40	+31	+25	+18	+12
VA	Norfolk	36	51	76	17	0	+31	+15	+3	−11	−22
VA	Roanoke	37	16	79	57	0	+44	+29	+17	+4	−6
VA	Winchester	39	11	78	10	0	+31	+19	+10	0	−8
WA	Bellingham	48	45	122	29	3	−7	0	+6	+13	+19
WI	Oshkosh	44	1	88	33	1	−3	−6	−8	−10	−12
WI	Wausau	44	58	89	38	1	−2	−3	−4	−4	−5
WV	Charleston	38	21	81	38	0	+48	+34	+24	+12	+2
WY	Sheridan	44	48	106	58	2	+7	+5	+5	+4	+3

Get local rise, set, and tide times via Almanac.ca/2024.

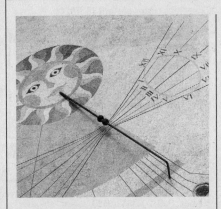

ATOMIC TIME (TA) SCALE: A time scale based on atomic or molecular resonance phenomena. Elapsed time is measured by counting cycles of a frequency locked to an atomic or molecular transition.

DATE: A unique instant defined in a specified time scale. NOTE: The date can be conventionally expressed in years, months, days, hours, minutes and seconds, and fractions thereof.

GREENWICH MEAN TIME (GMT): A 24-hour system based on mean solar time plus 12 hours at Greenwich, England. Greenwich Mean Time can be considered approximately equivalent to Coordinated Universal Time (UTC), which is broadcast from all standard time-and-frequency radio stations. However, GMT is now obsolete and has been replaced by UTC.

INTERNATIONAL ATOMIC TIME (TAI): An atomic time scale based on data from a worldwide set of atomic clocks. It is the internationally agreed-upon time reference conforming to the definition of the second, the fundamental unit of atomic time in the International System of Units (SI).

LEAP SECOND: A second used to adjust UTC to be within 0.9 sec of UT1 (a time scale based on Earth's varying rotation rate). An inserted "positive" second or omitted "negative" second may be applied at the end of June or December of each year.

MEAN SOLAR TIME: Apparent solar time corrected for the effects of orbital eccentricity and the tilt of Earth's axis relative to the ecliptic plane; in other words, corrected by the equation of time, which is defined as the hour angle of the true Sun minus the hour angle of the mean Sun.

SECOND: The basic unit of time or time interval in the International System of Units (SI), which is equal to 9,192,631,770 periods of radiation corresponding to the transition between the two hyperfine levels of the ground state of cesium-133 as defined at the 1967 Conférence Générale des Poids et Mesures.

SIDEREAL TIME: The measure of time defined by the apparent diurnal motion of the vernal equinox; hence, a measure of the rotation of Earth with respect to the reference frame that is related to the stars rather than the Sun. A mean solar day is about 4 minutes longer than a sidereal day.

–(U.S.) National Institute of Standards and Technology (NIST)

GENERAL STORE CLASSIFIEDS

For advertising information and rates, go to Almanac.ca/Advertising
or call RJ Media at 212-986-0016. The 2025 edition closes on April 30, 2024.

ASTROLOGY

REV. BUSH—I remove all ritual work, clear all negative energy. Heal all sickness. Call: 252-458-6864.

REV. BLACK, VOODOO HEALER. Removes evil influences, bad luck, sickness that doctors can't cure. Call: 252-366-4078.

SOPHIA GREEN. Don't tell me, I'll tell you! Helps all problems—Reunites lovers. Guaranteed! Call: 956-878-7053.

ATTENTION: SISTER LIGHT
Spartanburg, South Carolina
One FREE READING when you call.
I will help you with all problems.
Call: 864-576-9397

FREE READING
PSYCHIC SPIRITUALIST ROSELLA
Solves ALL problems. I don't judge.
Specializing: Divorce, Fear, Court Cases,
Spiritual Soul Cleansing.
Don't worry about tomorrow!
Call: 586-215-3838

PSYCHIC HANNAH • NEW YORK PSYCHIC
30 years' experience. Calls out your enemies.
Image Candles—Lucky Charms.
One Free Question!
Call: 347-448-6189

REVEREND EVETTE
Answers ALL questions. Solves life's problems. Need Help Desperately?
CALL IMMEDIATELY!
Does what others claim! 100% Guaranteed!
P.O. Box 80322, Chattanooga, TN, 37414
Call: 423-894-6699

BUSINESS OPPORTUNITIES

$800 WEEKLY POTENTIAL! Process HUD/FHA refunds from home. Free information available. Call: 860-357-1599.

CATALOGS & BOOKS

Catalog $4.00. Lyra Cartoons,
Juvenile Books, Armadillo Squirrel Kits,
Famous Doll Monster Poster from
the Top Archives
Armadillo Astronomy Theory.
3 Eastern Lane,
West Gardiner, Maine 04345

CLAIRVOYANT

CLAIRVOYANT PROPHETIC PSYCHIC. Intuitive, Love, Body, Ancestral Readings. Gives answers! Dreams, Colors, Numbers, Names. Call: 904-862-9520.

HEALTH

MACULAR DEGENERATION?

Restore
Lost Vision!

No need to travel.

Call for free booklet:
888-838-3937

Also helps RP, Stargardt

JEWELRY

WWW.AZUREGREEN.NET Jewelry, Amulets, Incense, Oils, Statuary, Gifts, Herbs, Candles, Gemstones. 8,000 Items. Wholesale inquiries welcome.

PERSONALS

ASIAN WOMEN! Overseas Penpals. Romance! Free brochure (send SASE). P.I.C., Box 4601-OFA, Thousand Oaks, CA 91359. Call today: 805-492-8040. www.pacisl.com

PSYCHIC READINGS

ANGEL PSYCHIC
MEDIUM CLAIRVOYANT
Spiritual - Positive Energy
*Accurate *Honest *Healing
Call: 323-466-3684
www.TruePsychicReader.com

2023 ESSAY CONTEST WINNERS

"A Funny Thing That Happened to Me"

We received hundreds of amusing anecdotes and stories.
Thank you to all of you who submitted entries.

First Prize: $300

I saw an advertisement in a magazine for an exercise machine featuring a beautiful and shapely woman: "Buy this machine now, and be more beautiful like her!"

On the day it arrived, my husband set it up downstairs. After a short while, frustration set in. The space was narrow, and it was impossible to avoid hitting the walls each time I exercised. So, I decided to store the machine in the laundry room. I soon discovered that it was a convenient thing to hang the ironed shirts on.

One day, my husband says, he told me that he had put the machine in the garage. I must have been preoccupied, as I never heard him.

That week, I looked around the local thrift shop and spotted an exercise machine for 20 dollars. A thought came to mind: This would be perfect to use in the laundry room instead of mine.

At home and excited, I waited for my husband's reaction to my idea.

"No, no! That *is* your machine. I took it there when I cleaned out all of the junk from the garage."

My body went limp, as I was feeling betrayed. Mostly I felt disappointment, as I wondered, "Where will I hang the ironed shirts now?"

–Carlene Peters, Barrie, Ontario

Second Prize: $200

My husband and I arrived by ferry in Skagway, Alaska.

We were going to hike the Chilicoot Trail, the old gold rush trail of 1898. When we arrived at the trailhead, there was a notice that a sow (mother) bear and her cub had been spotted on the trail. On the ship, we had seen a film about protecting ourselves from bears. This was tucked into the back of my mind as we set off.

The trail was relatively quiet, and we met only one other couple, with whom we kept playing leapfrog. We were ahead of them when we rounded a corner and saw a small, cinnamon-color, black bear leisurely turning over rocks and eating grubs. At her side, supposedly hidden away from us by the mom, was a little ball of fluff—her cub.

We walked backward, always keeping her in sight. My husband laughed at me as I got onto the ground in a crouching position to protect myself.

Without telling me, he watched the bear and cub wander into the forest. The couple behind us missed the bears but saw me on the ground. The lady bent down beside me and asked, "Have you lost a contact lens?"

–Joanne Hebert,
Canton-de-Hatley, Quebec

Third Prize: $100

I scanned over the recipe card as I scooped out the batter for the last cookie ball onto the pan. The balls looked a little bit runny, but then again I had never made shortbread cookies before. I popped the pan into the oven and set the timer for 20 minutes. A couple of minutes later, I peeked into the oven and found the cookies looking like they were—wait, what?—melting?

As I tried to think of what I could have possibly done wrong, my eyes fell on a bowl sitting on the counter—a bowl of flour and baking powder. I slapped my forehead. How could I have forgotten the flour?!

I quickly took the pan out and salvaged the mostly butter-and-sugar mixture, then re-scooped the dough out, put the pan back into the oven, and set the timer again. The *good* news is that you couldn't taste the mistake that I had made!

–Arden Gallant, Wheatley River,
Prince Edward Island

Honorable Mention

I was about 25 miles away from my house out at Boundary Bay, walking my dogs with my partner. It was very hot out, so on our way home, we stopped for an icy-cold drink. Hours later, after we had gotten home, I was preparing for the next day and realized my wallet was missing. I was panicked. The last place I used it was 25 miles away. I drove all the way out there—no wallet. I arrived back home and went to sit on my back porch, feeling devastated. What did I sit on? My wallet!

–Ingrid Myers, Vancouver, British Columbia

One day, I biked down to my oral surgeon to get the annual computerized CAT scan X-ray of the inside of my skull. My oral surgeon looked at the resulting image and remarked, "Nope. There's nothing inside there."

I really wish that he had phrased his diagnosis differently instead of making me think that he hadn't been able to recognize even two functioning brain cells. *–D. Breneol, Fredericton, New Brunswick* ∎

ANNOUNCING THE 2024 ESSAY CONTEST TOPIC:
THE BEST MONEY I EVER SPENT
SEE CONTEST RULES ON PAGE 251.

MADDENING MIND-MANGLERS

TENNESSEE TEASERS FOR '24

In the following lists, which does not belong?

1. hail, ice, icicle, rain, snow, water

_____

2. bow, dessert, invalid, row, tear, wind, wound

_____

3. badminton, pickleball, racquetball, squash, tennis

_____

4. 7, 17, 27, 37, 47, 67, 97

_____

–*Morris Bowles, Cane Ridge, Tennessee*

5. BALL AND BAT

A baseball and baseball bat cost a total of $1.20. The bat cost a dollar more than the ball. How much did the ball cost?

_____

6. STORE-BOUGHT LOSS

A man went into a store and bought $70 worth of goods with a counterfeit $100 bill. The clerk gave him $30 change in good money. How much did the store lose?

_____

7. FROM THE 1824 *OLD FARMER'S ALMANAC:*

Tho' highly I'm priz'd,
Yet I own a mean birth,
For at my beginning
I was formed from the earth.

So strange my appearance,
You'll believe me a noddy;
Tho' my mouth's very large,
I've neither head nor body.

I have breath without life
And my nature is so frail;
I inhale at my mouth
And exhale at my tail.

I'm esteem'd by the rich;
By the poor I'm admir'd,
Who are fond of the air
Which I have once expir'd.

Let me live with whom I will,
My food is still the same.
Tell me, for you know me,
What is my real name?

_____

Do you have a favorite puzzler for "Maddening Mind-Manglers" that you'd like to share? Send it to us at Mind-Manglers, The Old Farmer's Almanac, P.O. Box 520, Dublin, NH 03444, or via Almanac.ca/Contact, Subject: Mind-Manglers.

ANSWERS

1. icicle (only one not also a verb).
2. dessert (only one with just one pronunciation and spelling).
3. pickleball (only one played with a solid paddle). **4.** 27 (only one not a prime number). **5.** 10 cents. **6.** $200 ($70 in goods, $30 in good cash, left with $100 in worthless cash). **7.** In the early days of the Almanac, answers to one year's puzzles were published in the following year's edition. Readers would mail their answers to the editor, who would list the initials and hometowns of the correct guessers as part of the next Anecdotes & Pleasantries section. It was the fashion in those days for the answers to such cryptic rhyming riddles to themselves be presented in the same form, giving the editor just enough information to be able to understand that the solver did indeed have the correct answer. Readers could submit their response as a simple word or two, or they could go for greater glory by submitting a rhyming answer in hope of seeing it published. In the *1825 Old Farmer's Almanac,* the editor printed the initials of eight readers who had submitted simple correct answers to our #7. He also published two correct rhyming answers that can serve here as further clues for our riddle: **a.** *Priz'd I am by young and old, / In some the ruling passion. / Preceding both in hot or cold / Ere dandies came in fashion.* **b.** *Priz'd as you be, / I hate to see / Pug sucking thee / Eternally.* The answer? A tobacco pipe.

ESSAY AND RECIPE CONTEST RULES

Cash prizes (first, $300; second, $200; third, $100) will be awarded for the best essays in 200 or fewer words on the subject "The Best Money I Ever Spent" and the best "Favorite Holiday Dish" recipes. Entries must be yours, original, and unpublished. Amateur cooks only, please. One recipe per person. All entries become the property of Yankee Publishing, which reserves all rights to the material. The deadline for entries is January 31, 2024. Enter at Almanac .ca/EssayContest or at Almanac.ca/ RecipeContest or label "Essay Contest" or "Recipe Contest" and mail to The Old Farmer's Almanac, P.O. Box 520, Dublin, NH 03444. Include your name, mailing address, and email address. Winners will appear in *The 2025 Old Farmer's Almanac* and on Almanac.ca. ■

ANECDOTES & PLEASANTRIES

A sampling from the thousands of letters, clippings, articles, and emails sent to us during the past year by our Almanac family in the United States and Canada.

ILLUSTRATIONS BY TIM ROBINSON

MIRTHFUL MAGIC, OR HOW TO TURN A DULL PARTY INTO A MERRY ONE

When young people, and often old ones also, first arrive at a party, they are apt to feel a little stiff and awkward, and to stand about in corners, as if oppressed with the responsibility of their best gloves and clothes, and the giver of the entertainment seeks in vain to enliven and stir them up. For her aid we propose to give a few simple recipes which will answer the purpose, and give them a good laugh, after which they will be ready for the harder games which will follow. First she may ask them to join in the game of "Satisfaction."

Every person in the room is invited to stand up, and all join hands in a ring, in the center of which the leader stands, holding a cane in her hand, with which she points to each one in turn, and asks this question, after requesting silence and careful attention, "Are you satisfied?" Each replies in turn as he or she pleases, many probably saying "No," and others "Yes." The leader then says, "All who are satisfied may sit down. The others may stand up until they are satisfied."

–*G. B. Bartlett,* Harper's Young People— An Illustrated Weekly, *July 6, 1880*

THE EASTERNMOST POINT IN THE U.S. IS IN MAINE. *WRONG!*

How far apart are the western- and easternmost points in the United States? Would you say 3,000 miles? 5,000? *How about 63 miles?*

That's right. It turns out that Alaska is home to both the westernmost place—Amatignak Island, at 51°16'7"N latitude, 179°8'55"W longitude—and easternmost point—Semisopochnoi Island, at 51°57'42"N, 179°46'23"E.

How can this be? It's all about the longitude meridian at 180° E/W that separates the Eastern and Western Hemispheres. Whereas Amatignak is 51 minutes, 5 seconds to the east of it—or very, very far west in the Western Hemisphere— Semisopochnoi is only 13 minutes, 37 seconds to the west of it—or very, very far east in the Eastern Hemisphere. Across the water, though, they are separated by only about 63 miles.

–A. Y., Fairbanks, Alaska

BIG TECH GOES INTO THE GARDEN

Apparently failing a basic spelling lesson, one popular social networking app flagged a garden club for its continued use of the word "hoe," which it said violated community standards. Even after the parties agreed that this word did not represent a person, this dastardly group later had its Comments function disabled because it was possibly inciting violence or hate—all due to pest postings that included such evil bug directives as "kill them all" and "drown them in soapy water."

–B. R., East Greenbush, New York

Breaking Bovine Bulletins

• Cattle cooped up in barns were fitted with virtual reality headsets that simulated the experience of being outside in beautiful green pastures. In one study, the mellowed-out moo-ers on VR produced 23% more milk. –G. H., Saskatoon, Saskatchewan

• In search of cost savings, scientists replaced normal cattle feed with hemp left over from industrial processing. Guess what? The hemped-up bovines acted sillier, yawned and drooled more, and engaged in "excessive tongue play." The question, though, was whether drinking milk from these cows would get you stoned. The answer was yes, so that was that—unfortunately for the cows.

–N. M., Stevens Point, Wisconsin

(continued)

WHEN THAT SHADOW THE GROUNDHOG SEES IS, UH, REALLY, *REALLY* DARK

R.I.P. Fred la Marmotte, age 9, former furry prognosticator at Val d'Espoir, Quebec, who was found deceased hours before scheduled to make a recent observation. Apparently he had chucked his last wood some months before, which was no doubt a relief to any onlookers fearing that he had taken a sneak peek the day before and died of fright right then and there. But what about the prediction? *Pas de problème!* A youngster in the crowd wearing a groundhog hat was handed a stuffed marmot, which then somehow made the call. *Miracle des miracles!*

–P. W., Lévis, Quebec

How to Hypnotize Your Foot

1. Sit in a chair.
2. Looking down at your feet, say, "Toes goes. Toes goes. Toes goes."
3. Lift your right foot off the floor and make clockwise circles with it.
4. Quickly say again, "Toes goes. Toes goes. Toes goes."
5. As your foot is still circling, draw the number 6 in the air with your right hand.
6. You have now hypnotized your foot into changing direction. *–T. T., Salt Lake City, Utah*

HANDY TIPS TO MAKE YOU A BETTER PERSON— OR SOMETHING LIKE THAT

• You—yes, *you!*—need a better password. Even if you have one of 6 or fewer characters consisting of numbers, upper- and lowercase letters, *and* symbols, a hacker using sheer, brute-force computer power can figure it out instantly; if it's 9 characters, in 2 days. The good news is that if it's 12 characters, it's safe for 3,000 years.

–S. C., Lloydminster, Alberta

• Can't tell after a power outage whether your freezer has partially or totally thawed while "dark"? Keep a cup of frozen water in it with a quarter on top. If it has sunk all the way to the bottom of your refrozen cup, you've had a total thaw. *–T. S., Barre, Vermont*

• For better sleep, say the experts, put your Christmas tree in your bedroom, as it will bring both the calming effects of nature and the comforting fuzzy-wuzzies of nostalgia to your dreamland vibe. Furthermore, say we, it will serve as a random alarm when the cat knocks it over on you.

–A. K., Columbus, Ohio

Scientific Studies of the Year

DISCO BALL SCALLOPS: Marine scientists in the UK wanted to find an easier way to catch crabs, so they tried outfitting pots with colored lights to attract them. To their surprise, the pots filled with scallops, not crabs. Subsequently, researchers set out 1,886 test traps, half with colored lights and half without, to see if the illuminated pots did indeed attract scallops. Did they ever! Scallops showed up by the hundreds (518) in the lit pots and virtually not at all (2) in the unlit ones, which makes scallops the ultimate marine party animal.

–P. R., Truro, Nova Scotia

BIRD FEEDER PECKING ORDER: Somehow analyzing almost 100,000 reports from citizen scientists, ornithologists created a power ranking of the Top 100 seedy characters at parks and home feeders. Ranked as the #1 most aggressive gobbler was the wild turkey. Among more common backyard diners, the "top dog" bird was #5, the American crow, which was roughly followed by a bunch of woodpeckers and then jays (aka a "descent" of the former and "party" of the latter). The weakest, meekest, and most bullied wannabe diners bringing up the tail end of the list were sparrows, finches, hummingbirds, and, at #100, the brown creeper. (Just for the record, the Almanac's #1-ranked bird feeder boss is the squirrel.) *–A. B., Palo Alto, California*

NESSIE AND CLIMATE CHANGE: Experts are now saying that climate change and rising temperatures may create changes in the diet—whatever it might be—of Scotland's Loch Ness Monster that could cause it to leave the lake in search of food. You have been warned.

–L. D., Shoreham, New York

LUCKIEST AND UNLUCKIEST STATES: After looking at data about Powerball winners, emergency room admissions, federally declared disasters, and fatal traffic accidents, researchers determined that the five luckiest states are, in order, Minnesota, Rhode Island, Wisconsin, Maryland, and Delaware. The unluckiest state was found to be Arkansas, with Oklahoma, Louisiana, Texas, and Florida not far behind—or ahead, as the case may be.

–D. A., Eden Prairie, Minnesota

MOST POPULAR PIE IN AMERICA: Apple, right? Nuts to you! Pecan pie takes the cake (best liked in 15 states), with apple pie right behind (14). Key lime was next (4), with coconut cream and pumpkin (3 each) also on the menu.

–G. P., Fayetteville, Arkansas

Send your contribution for *The 2025 Old Farmer's Almanac* by January 31, 2024, to "A & P," The Old Farmer's Almanac, P.O. Box 520, Dublin, NH 03444, or via Almanac.ca/Contact.

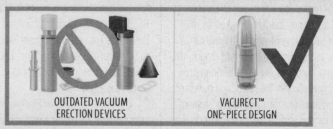